Yvonne Earl
-YPU
April 9,

WORKING WITH TROUBLED ADOLESCENTS

A HANDBOOK

Working With Troubled Adolescents

A Handbook

Editor

John C. Coleman

Sussex Youth Trust
Brighton, Sussex, U.K.

1987

ACADEMIC PRESS

Harcourt Brace Jovanovich, Publishers

London   Orlando   San Diego   New York   Austin
Boston   Sydney   Tokyo   Toronto

ACADEMIC PRESS INC. (LONDON) LTD.
24/28 Oval Road,
London NW1 7DX

United States Edition published by
ACADEMIC PRESS INC.
Orlando, Florida 32887

British Library Cataloguing in Publication Data

Working with troubled adolescents: a handbook.
1. Adolescent psychotherapy
I. Coleman, John
616.89'14   RJ503

ISBN 0-12-179720-1

Typeset by Colset Private Limited, Singapore.
Printed by St Edmundsbury Press
Bury St Edmunds, England.

Contributors

Dr G.R. Adams, *Professor of Psychology, Dept. of Family & Human Devp., Utah State University, Logan, Utah 84322, U.S.A.*

Dr P.R. Adams, *Dept. of Psychology, Utah State University, Logan, Utah 84322-2800, U.S.A.*

Dr P. Ainsworth, *Lecturer in Child and Adolescent Psychiatry, University of Manchester, Booth Hall Children's Hospital, Charlestown Road, Blackley, Manchester M9 2AA, U.K.*

Dr E. Badger, *Associate Professor of Paediatrics, Univ. of Cincinnati Medical Center, Dept. of Paediatrics, Newborn Division, 231 Bethesda Avenue (ML541), Cincinnati, Ohio 45267-0541, U.S.A.*

Dr B. Bates, *Sen. Lecturer in Psychology, Dept. of Developmental Psychology, University of Sussex, Falmer, Brighton BN1 9QN, U.K.*

Dr D. Berkowitz, *Consulting Psychiatrist, 125 Brackett Road, Newton, Massachusetts 02158, U.S.A.*

Dr B. Brown, *District Psychologist, St Pancras Hospital, 4 St Pancras Way, London NW1 0PE, U.K.*

Ms R. Bryant-Waugh, *Clinical Psychologist, Dept. of Developmental Psychology, University of Sussex, Falmer, Brighton BN1 9QN, U.K.*

Dr R.R. Buss, *Assistant Professor of Psychology, Dept. of Psychology, Louisiana State University, Baton Rouge, Louisiana 70803-5501, U.S.A.*

Dr J. Coleman, *Psychologist, Sussex Youth Trust, 23 New Road, Brighton, Sussex BN1 1WZ, U.K.*

Professor R.D. Enright, *Prof. of Educational Psychology, Educational Sciences Building, 1025 West Johnson Street, Madison, Wisconsin 53706, U.S.A.*

Dr R.H. Fulmer, *Consulting Clinical Psychologist, Box 2468 Central Mail Room, Columbia College, Columbia University, New York, NY 10027, U.S.A.*

Dr E. Garralda, *Senior Lecturer in Child and Adolescent Psychiatry, University of Manchester, Booth Hall Children's Hospital, Charlestown Road, Blackley, Manchester M9 2AA, U.K.*

CONTRIBUTORS

Dr P. Holmes, *Consultant Psychiatrist, Battersea Child Guidance Unit, 6 Cambridge Road, London SW11 4RS, U.K.*

Mr D.W. Jones, *Project Leader, Sixteen Plus Project, 36 Grove Road, Hounslow, Middlesex, U.K.*

Dr M.J. Kerfoot, *Lecturer/Principal Psych. Soc. Worker, University of Manchester, Academic Psychiatry Unit, Booth Hall Children's Hospital, Charlestown Road, Blackley, Manchester M9 2AA, U.K.*

Dr A.S. Kerslake, *Lecturer in Social Work, University of Bath, School of Humanities, Claverton Down, Bath BA2 7AY, U.K.*

Dr W.R. Lindsay, *Tayside Area Clinical Psychology Department, Strathmartine Hospital, Dundee DD3 0PG, Scotland, U.K.*

Dr E.K. McAdam, *Child and Family Centre, Bethel Child and Family Centre, Bethel Street, Norwich NR2 1NR, U.K.*

Dr J.A. Medalie, *Senior Clinical Psychologist, Columbia College Counselling Service, Box 2468 Central Mailing Room, Columbia University, New York, N.Y. 10027 U.S.A.*

Dr D. Steinberg, *Consultant Psychiatrist, Bethlem Royal Hospital, Monks Orchard Road, Beckenham, Kent BR3 3BX, U.K.*

Dr D. Will, *Consultant Psychiatrist, Young People's Psychiatric Department, Royal Infirmary, Dundee DD1 9ND, Scotland, U.K.*

Preface

When I first became editor of the *Journal of Adolescence* I was struck by the wealth of interesting and useful material contained in the back issues. I was impressed with the way the first editor, Dr John Evans, had encouraged clinicians from a variety of backgrounds to submit papers of high quality which nonetheless gave the reader a sense of "work in progress". Much of this "work in progress" related to treatment issues which were frequently matters for discussion in settings I knew well, such as adolescent units, special schools, social work departments or therapeutic communities. Issues of sexual abuse, family resistance, suicidal gestures, self-concept development, social skills training, eating disorders, the problems of group leadership, what to do with the younger adolescent and so on seemed to be perennial concerns of professionals working with troubled young people. In thinking about this, and about the value of material which is not always polished and completed but conveys a sense of enquiry and discovery, I considered the possibility of editing a book of articles from the *Journal of Adolescence*.

The goal has been to put together a book which will be helpful to practitioners. It is not intended as an introduction to adolescent psychiatry (in recent years both Evans (1982) and Steinberg (1983) have published excellent examples of such texts), nor is it a review of adolescent development. It has no particular theoretical bias, and it does not, of course, cover the whole field of the treatment of young people. It has been shaped almost entirely by the material submitted to the *Journal of Adolescence* over the last five years and, given that constraint, I believe the range of material to be extensive. All except one of the contributions are based on articles which were first published in the Journal. In most cases, authors have substantially revised their papers, although some have written commentaries or postscripts to bring the material up to date. I should like to express my gratitude to all who have given their time and energy to this project, and who have worked with me to produce what we hope will be a useful and stimulating book.

John Coleman

Acknowledgements

This book is based on articles which have appeared over the last six years in the *Journal of Adolescence*. The Editor acknowledges the assistance and support of the Association for the Psychiatric Study of Adolescents, of Academic Press and of all the authors involved in the preparation of this volume.

Contents

Part I
Treatment approaches

Part II
Problem-oriented approaches

Part I
Treatment approaches

Part I
Treatment approaches

1. Introduction and theoretical overview

JOHN COLEMAN

To introduce this volume I will briefly review some of the major theoretical approaches which underlie the therapeutic interventions described here, and comment on the particular developmental issues pertinent to the adolescent stage which, I believe, make teenagers an especially demanding and challenging group with whom to work. Theory, as I shall be pointing out, has a number of roles to play; one is to provide a framework within which it is possible to compare and evaluate different treatments and interventions. In my view, therefore, it will be helpful to begin with a glance at the theoretical background, and to postpone my commentary on the papers themselves until the end of the book.

In my conclusion I shall attempt to draw out some of the lessons to be learnt from this collection of articles, and to highlight some of the current questions and issues which are of importance to psychiatrists, psychologists, social workers and others who are struggling to provide more effective treatment approaches in their work with troubled young people. I shall commence, however, with a short discussion of three theoretical viewpoints, all of which have directly affected the development of the helping process.

THEORETICAL APPROACHES

(a) Psychoanalysis

Of all the theories of adolescence it is probably true to say that the psychoanalytic approach has had the greatest impact upon treatment, but I would argue that the sociological viewpoint, as well as – more recently – behavioural and cognitive advances are important in helping us to think about the nature of intervention. The psychoanalytic view takes as its starting point the upsurge of instincts which is said to occur at puberty. This increase in instinctual life, it is suggested, upsets the psychic balance which has been achieved by the end of childhood, causing internal emotional upheaval and leading to a greatly increased vulnerability of the personality (Freud 1937). This state of affairs is associated with two further factors. In the first place, the individual's awakening sexuality leads him or her to look outside the family setting for appropriate "love objects", thus severing the emotional ties with the parents which have existed since infancy. Secondly, the vulnerability of the personality results in the employment of psychological defences to cope with the instincts and anxiety which are, to a greater or lesser extent, maladaptive.

Blos (1962, 1967), a prominent psychoanalytic writer, has described adolescence as a "second individuation process", the first having been completed towards the end of the third year of life. In his view (for summary see Muuss 1980), both periods have certain things in common: an urgent need for psychological change which helps the individual adapt to maturation; an increased vulnerability of personality; and finally, both periods are followed by specific psychopathology should the individual run into difficulties. Furthermore, an analogy can be drawn between the transformation in early childhood from a dependent infant to a self-reliant toddler, and the adolescent transition to adult independence. In both there is a process of disengagement involving a loosening of emotional ties and a move towards a new stage of autonomy. Other features of adolescent development which are of significance to the psychoanalytic viewpoint include regression – a manifestation of behaviour more appropriate to earlier stages of development – and ambivalence.

According to the psychoanalysts ambivalence accounts for many of the phenomena often considered incomprehensible in adolescent behaviour. For example the emotional instability of relationships, the contradictions in thought and feeling, and the apparently illogical shift from one reaction to another reflect the fluctuations between loving and hating, acceptance and rejection, involvement and non-involvement which underlie relationships in the early years, and which are reactivated once more in adolescence. Such fluctuations in mood and behaviour are indicative also of the young person's attitudes to growing up. Thus, while freedom may appear the most exciting of goals, there are also moments when, in the harsh light of reality, independence and the necessity to fight one's own battles becomes a daunting prospect. At these times childlike dependence exercises a powerful attraction and is manifested in periods of uncertainty and self-doubt, and in behaviour which is more likely to bring to mind a wilful child than a young adult.

A consideration of ambivalence leads us on to the more general theme of non-conformity and rebellion, believed by psychoanalysts to be an almost universal feature of adolescence. Behaviour of this sort has many causes. Some of it is a direct result of ambivalent modes of relating. In other circumstances, however, it may be interpreted as an aid to the disengagement process. In this context, if the parents can be construed as old-fashioned and irrelevant then the task of breaking the emotional ties becomes easier. If everything that originates from home can safely be rejected then there is nothing to be lost by giving it all up. Non-conformity thus facilitates the process of disengagement, although as many writers point out, there are a number of intermediate stages along the way.

To summarize, three particular ideas characterize the psychoanalytic position. First, adolescence is seen as a period of marked vulnerability of personality, resulting primarily from the upsurge of instincts at puberty. Secondly, an emphasis is laid on the likelihood of maladaptive behaviour, stemming from the inadequacy of the psychological defences to cope with inner conflicts and tensions. Examples of such behaviour include extreme fluctuations of mood, inconsistency in relationships, depression and non-conformity. Thirdly, the process of disengagement is given special prominence, for this is perceived as a necessity if mature emotional and sexual relationships are to be established outside the home.

This survey of the psychoanalytic approach to adolescence would not be complete without some mention of identity and identity-crisis, and of the work of Erik Erikson in particular. In many respects Erikson towers above all other writers in this area. Although a psychoanalyst, he is able to take account of social and cultural circumstances, and his writings constitute a great deal more than standard textbooks. *Childhood and Society* (1963) and *Identity: Youth and Crisis* (1968) are viewed as works of literary merit as well as classics in psychology. Perhaps most important, Erikson has, in some subtle way, come to be seen as one of the great commentators on youth. The phrase "identity crisis" has passed into our everyday vocabulary, and he himself points out (1968) that it can now be used in journalism, for example, "African state faces identity crisis after independence", or among students, in an announcement he noticed at Harvard: "Identity Crisis. 6.00 p.m. Friday. Room B128. All welcome." Erikson's contribution is thus far more than that simply of a psychoanalytic theorist, a fact which causes some headaches for anyone attempting to summarize his views (see Chapter 11 for additional comments).

Let us start by noting that Erikson sees life as a series of stages, each associated with a particular developmental task of a psychosocial nature. In infancy, for example, the task is to establish a sense of *basic trust*, and to combat *mistrust*. The maternal relationship is considered here to be crucial in creating a foundation upon which the infant may build later, trusting relationships. For adolescents the task involves the establishment of a *coherent identity*, and the defeat a sense of *identity diffusion*. Erikson believes that the search for identity becomes especially acute at this stage. He lays some stress on the phenomenon of rapid biological and social change during adolescence, and points especially to the importance for the individual of having to take major decisions at this time in almost all areas of life. In many of his writings Erikson either states or implies that some form of crisis is necessary for the young person to resolve the identity issue and to defeat identity diffusion which, according to Erikson, has four major components. In the first place, there is the problem of *intimacy*. Here the individual may fear commitment or involvement in close interpersonal relationships because of the possible loss of his or her own identity. This fear can lead to stereotyped, formalized relationships, to isolation, or the young person may, as Erikson puts it "in repeated hectic attempts and dismal failures, seek intimacy with the most improbable partners" (1968, p. 167). Secondly, there is the possibility of a *diffusion of time perspective*. Here the adolescent finds it impossible to plan for the future, or to retain any sense of time. This problem is thought to be associated with anxieties about change and becoming adult, and often: "consists of a decided disbelief in the possibility that time may bring change and yet also of a violent fear that it might" (1968, p. 169).

Next there is a *diffusion of industry*, in which the young person finds it difficult to harness his or her resources in a realistic way in work or study. Both of these activities represent commitment and as a defence against this the individual may either find it impossible to concentrate, or may frenetically engage in one single activity to the exclusion of all others. Finally, Erikson discusses the choice of a *negative identity*. By this is meant the young person's selection of an identity exactly the opposite to that preferred by parents or other important adults. "The loss of a sense of identity is often expressed in a scornful and snobbish hostility towards the role offered as proper and desirable in one's family or immediate community. Any aspect of the required role or all of it – be it masculinity or femininity, nationality or class membership – can become the main focus of the young person's acid disdain" (1968, p. 173).

These four elements, therefore, constitute the main features of identity diffusion, although clearly not all will be present in any one individual who experiences an identity crisis. In addition to such concepts, one other notion needs to be mentioned as an integral feature of Erikson's theory, that of *psychosocial moratorium*. This means a period during which decisions are left in abeyance. It is argued that society allows, even encourages, a time of life when the young person may delay major identity choices and experiment with roles in order to discover the sort of person he or she wishes to be; while such a stage may lead to disorientation or disturbance it has, according to Erikson, a healthy function. As he says: "Much of this apparent confusion thus must be considered social play – the true genetic successor to childhood play" (1968, p. 164).

(b) Sociology

Erikson's mention of "social play" reflects his special position within psycho-analysis, for he is a writer who encourages one to consider not only the internal psychological world of the young person but to recognize social factors and take account of these in making sense of identity development. Nonetheless, in general, the sociological view of adolescence has a very different perspective from that of psychoanalytic theory. While there is no disagreement between the two approaches concerning the importance of the transitional process from childhood to maturity, the two viewpoints diverge on the causes of this process. While one concentrates on internal factors, the other looks to society and to events outside the individual for a satisfactory explanation. For the sociologist and social psychologist "socialization" and "role" are two key concepts. Socialization means the process whereby individuals in a society absorb its current values, standards and beliefs. Everyone in society learns through the agents of socialization, such as school, home, the mass media etc., the expecta-tions associated with various roles, although, as one might imagine, expecta-tions are not necessarily clear cut. Furthermore, socialization may be more or less effective, depending on the nature of the agents to which the individual is exposed, the amount of conflict between the different agents and so on. During childhood the individual, by and large, has his or her roles ascribed by others, but as he or she matures through adolescence greater opportunities are avail-able, not only for a choice of roles, but also for a choice of how those roles should be interpreted. As will become apparent, it is implicit in the social-psychological view that both socialization and role assumption are more problematic during adolescence than at any other time.

Why should this be so? In attempting to answer this question one can first of all consider roles and role assumptions. It is the belief of most sociologists that a large proportion of an individual's life is characterized by engagement in a series of roles – the sum total of which is known as the role repertoire. The years between childhood and adulthood, as a period of emerging identity, are seen as particularly relevant to the construction of this role repertoire, for the following reasons. First, features of adolescence such as growing independence from authority figures, involvement with peer groups, and unusual sensitivity to the evaluations of others, all provoke role transitions. Secondly, any inner change or uncertainty has the effect of increasing the individual's dependence on others, and this applies particularly to the need for reassurance and support for the self-concept. Thirdly, the effects of major environmental changes are also relevant in this context; different schools, the move from school to university or college, leaving home, taking a job, all demand involvement in a new set of relationships, which in turn lead to different and often greater expectations, a substantial reassessment of the self, and an acceleration of the process of social-ization. Role change, it will be apparent, is thus seen as an integral feature of adolescent development.

While role change may be one source of difficulty for the adolescent, it is certainly not the only one. Inherent in role behaviour generally are a number of potential stresses; some of which appear to be particularly relevant to young people. Role conflict is one example, where the individual occupies two roles. The expectations associated with both roles are incompatible; the individual may be caught between two people or two sets of people who expect different forms of behaviour. Another example is role discontinuity. Here there is a lack of order in the transition from one role to another. One only has to think of the inexperience among school leavers of the work situation, or the grossly inadequate preparation for parenthood in our society to appreciate the point. Thirdly, we may note role incongruence, when the individual is placed in a position for which he or she is unsuited; in other words, the role ascribed by others is not the one the individual would have chosen. Good illustrations of this in the adolescent context would be parents who hold unrealistically high expectations of their teenage children, or who, alternatively, fight to maintain their adolescent sons and daughters in childlike roles.

Implicit in these theoretical notions is the view that the individual's movement through adolescence will be very much affected by the consistent or inconsistent, adaptive or maladaptive expectations held by significant people in his or her immediate environment. Up to this point our discussion has concentrated on the features of role behaviour which lead sociologists and social-psychologists to view adolescence not only as a transitional period, but as one that contains many potentially stressful characteristics. However, the process of socialization is also seen by many as being fraught with conflict at this stage. Socialization processes inevitably interact with social change, and one can note two particular changes which have occurred in the last decade or so; the prolonged dependence of young people as a result of both increased opportunities for secondary and higher education, as well as growing youth unemployment, and the decline in the role of the family. Sociologists believe that these phenomena have had a number of consequences. In the first place, industrialized societies have witnessed increasing age segregation, with a decline in the time adults and teenagers spend together. Secondly, the peer group has assumed an ever more important role, precisely as a result of the abdication of responsibility by parents in the upbringing of their teenage children. Finally, the adolescent is exposed to a large variety of socialization agencies including secondary school, the peer group, adult-directed youth organizations, the mass media, political organizations and so on, and is thus presented with a wide range of potential conflicts in values and ideals.

To summarize, the sociological or social-psychological approach to adolescence is marked by concern with roles and role change, and with the process of socialization. There can be little doubt that adolescence, from this point of view, is seen as being dominated by stress and tension, not so much because of inner emotional instability, as with the psychoanalysts, but as a result of conflicting pressures from outside.

(c) Cognitive and behavioural approaches

Such views contrast strongly with cognitive and behavioural approaches, neither of which encompass expectations of disturbance or stress. Behaviourism has little to say about particular developmental stages, but its concern with more general issues of psychological functioning, such as learning, makes it relevant to the adolescent context. A good review may be found in Conger and Petersen (1984), who outline the principles of learning theory and draw attention to the different types of learning occurring in young people (see also Chapter 10).

Of particular importance here is the distinction between classical and operant conditioning. In the former a reflexive response becomes associated with a previously neutral stimulus. In one of the most famous psychological experiments Pavlov, the Russian physiologist, showed how a dog could be taught the response of salivation to the sound of a buzzer by presenting the buzzer at the same time as presenting some mouth-watering food. In operant conditioning the response to be learnt is not automatically elicited by a known stimulus but must be gradually and painstakingly developed. The individual's own response is instrumental in producing the reward. In other words it operates to bring about the reward, hence the term operant conditioning. In some learning situations, particularly those in which the desired response is a fairly simple one, the experimenter or teacher may simply wait for the response to occur by chance. For example, in another classic experiment B.F. Skinner showed how a pigeon could be taught to turn its head to the right continually by rewarding it with a food pellet every time the behaviour was manifested. In more complex situations, however, the experimenter may not wait for the desired behaviour to occur by chance, but may take steps to increase the likelihood of the response occurring. For example, in training an autistic child to speak the teacher or psychologist may spend a lot of time actually demonstrating the desired behaviour before the child first imitates what is required and so can be rewarded.

These descriptions of classical and operant conditioning may seem a long way from working with troubled adolescents, but it is the understanding of these fundamental processes, and of the nature and importance of reward or reinforcement, that have led to the development of treatment approaches such as behaviour therapy, biofeedback and the token economy model for use in group settings. All these hinge upon the concept of reinforcement, the idea that events which follow a response are likely to have a direct effect on whether that response will occur again. Early work by psychologists interested in this field focused on issues such as the nature of reinforcers, the importance of the time interval between the target behaviour and the appearance of the reinforcer, and what has become known as the schedule of reinforcement (i.e. whether behaviour needed to be reinforced every time it occurred or only at intervals, as exemplified in the situation which exists in gambling). More recently there have been disputes in the literature as to whether reinforcement is always necessary for learning, and attention has been drawn to the existence of social learning, or learning by imitation. Furthermore, learning theorists have become more interested in the characteristics of the environment in which learning takes place, as well as in the links between learning and cognition, exemplified in the expanding field of cognitive behaviour therapy (see Chapter 9). This bridge between the two fields – learning and cognition – is a significant one, bringing together workers from different backgrounds, and is, one hopes, a reflection of increasing co-operation between experimental, educational and clinical psychologists.

It is evident that an understanding of cognition in adolescence has also played a significant part in the introduction of new concepts of treatment. The work of Jean Piaget, the Swiss psychologist, is the most obvious starting place for a consideration of cognitive development during the teenage years. It was he who first pointed out that a qualitative change in the nature of mental ability, rather than any simple increase in cognitive skill, is to be expected at or around puberty, and he has argued that it is at this point in development that formal operational thought finally becomes possible (Inhelder and Piaget, 1958). A full description of Piaget's stages of cognitive growth is not possible here. Most readers will be familiar with his assertion that in early adolescence the individual moves from a stage of concrete operations to one of formal operational thought. With the appearance of this stage a number of capabilities become available to the young person. Perhaps the most significant of these is the ability to construct ''contrary to fact'' propositions. This change has been described as the shift of emphasis in adolescent thought from the ''real'' to the ''possible'', and it facilitates hypothetico-deductive logic. It also enables the individual to think about mental constructs as objects that can be manipulated, and to come to terms with notions of probability and belief.

Studies show that intelligence is likely to play a role in the development of formal operational thinking. Yet this variable is not sufficient to explain why formal operations appear in one child at 12, and in another at 16. Inhelder and Piaget (1958) paid remarkably little attention to this problem, contenting themselves simply with some speculation about the relation between intellectual and social development.

They appear to suggest that as social pressures operate on the individual, encouraging him or her towards maturity and independence, so intellectual skills develop, enabling the young person to cope with the new demands of a more adult life. This is hardly a very satisfactory explanation, although it may indeed turn out that social and intellectual maturation are correlated. Surprisingly there is little in the literature which sheds much light on such an important topic, as Neimark (1975) indicates. We may ask what other factors might be involved. Intelligence only contributes a small proportion of the total variance. Perhaps attention should be paid to the type of school and the attitudes of teachers. Studies have indicated that self-image might be important, but what about achievement motivation, or position in the peer group? Also the impact of parental attitudes and the home environment should undoubtedly be examined. At this point, it must be accepted that there are no definite answers to the question of what determines the appearance of formal operational thinking.

To study adolescent reasoning is obviously another way of looking at cognitive development. David Elkind (1967) represents a good example of someone seeking to extend Piaget's original notions in this way. He argues that while the attainment of formal operational thinking frees the individual in many respects from childhood egocentrism, paradoxically at the same time it entangles him or her in a new version of the same thing. This is because the achievement of formal operational thought allows the adolescent to think about not only his own thought, but also about the thoughts of other people. It is this capacity to take account of other people's thinking, argues Elkind, which is paradoxically the basis of adolescent egocentrism.

Essentially the individual finds it extremely difficult to differentiate between what others are thinking about and his own pre-occupations. He assumes that if he is obsessed by a thought or a problem then other people must also be obsessed by the same thing. One example given by Elkind is that of the adolescent's appearance. To a large extent teenagers are preoccupied with the way they look to others, and they make the assumption that others must be as involved as they are with the same subject. Elkind ties this type of egocentrism in with the concept of what he calls "the imaginary audience". Because of this egocentrism the adolescent is, either in actual or fantasized social situations, anticipating the reactions of others. However, these reactions are based on a premise that others are as admiring or critical of him as he is of himself. Thus he is continually constructing and reacting to his "imaginary audience", a fact which, according to Elkind, explains a lot of adolescent behaviour – the self-consciousness, the wish for privacy, and the long hours spent in front of the mirror. Recent work (reviewed in Conger and Petersen, 1984) has provided strong corroboration for Elkind's views (see also Chapter 9).

These views have been extended by both Kohlberg (1969) and – more recently – by Selman (1980). In what has become known as the cognitive-developmental approach the young person is seen as progressing through a series of stages which are linked to cognitive development but which have direct relevance to social maturation. While Kohlberg has been concerned with moral development, Selman's focus has been on social perspective-taking, and it is this latter approach that has had a particular impact on intervention strategies.

Before describing the way this has happened it may be worth briefly recapitulating Selman's stages. He sees four major stages of social cognition:

Stage 1: the differential or subjective perspective-taking stage (ages 5–9)
Here children are beginning to realize that other people can have a social perspective which is different from their own.

Stage 2: self-reflective thinking, or reciprocal perspective-taking (ages 7–12)
At this stage the child realizes not only that other people have their own perspective, but that they may actually be giving thought to the child's own perspective. Thus the crucial cognitive advance here is the ability to take into account the perspective of another individual.

Stage 3: third person, or mutual perspective-taking (ages 10–15)
The perspective-taking skills of early adolescence lead to the capacity for a more complex type of social cognition. The young person moves beyond simply taking the other person's perspective (in a back and forth manner) and is able to see all parties from a more generalized third-person perspective.

Stage 4: in-depth societal perspective-taking (age 15 +)
During this stage the individual may move to a still higher and more abstract level of interpersonal perspective-taking which involves co-ordinating the perspectives of society with those of the individual and the group.

The delineation of such a process carries the work of Piaget, Kohlberg and Elkind one step further, introducing new concepts, and indeed a new perspective into work with troubled young people. As Buss and Enright point out in Chapter 11, we have needed more than the straightforward outline of formal operational thought to explain fully the development of identity and to provide a theoretical framework for such things as social skills training. The notion of formal operations, and the theory relating to it, does of course cover a range of cognitive abilities. What it lacks is an acknowledgement of the social input, and perhaps more important, a framework which draws attention to the interplay between different aspects of cognition. After all, where therapeutic work with young people is concerned, their level of social perspective-taking is of far greater importance than their ability to construct contrary-to-fact hypotheses in science subjects.

There is no doubt that Selman's approach to the social development of the individual has very considerable implications, not least because such a view must help us to understand better those who function poorly in social situations and those who, for whatever reason, are disadvantaged in their relationships with both adults and peers. The combined views of the cognitive-developmental theorists have opened up a new way of looking at the disadvantaged or immature adolescent, the implications of which have still not been fully assimilated. Readers will appreciate, in many of the contributions to this Handbook, how valuable professional workers are finding the cognitive-developmental approach, and will perceive that a wealth of opportunities for the development of new treatment strategies are available as a result of the work of these theorists.

THE ROLE OF THEORY

Writers differ considerably in the degree of vulnerability they see as integral to the process of adolescent development. While some view this stage in the life cycle as being more problematic than almost all other stages, carrying with it a high risk of stress or disorder, other theorists pay little attention to the question of vulnerability, preferring to consider broad principles of maturation or psychological function.

Such a debate has been considered in great detail elsewhere (e.g. Rutter, 1979; Coleman, 1980; Conger and Petersen, 1984) and will not be recapitulated here. What should be noted, however, is that reviews of research evidence indicate clearly that the great majority of adolescents pass through this stage of development with relatively little trauma. The concept of adolescence as a period of "storm and stress" for all is not borne out by the facts. Nonetheless there is, as with any other stage in the life cycle, a minority who run into difficulties and we are concerned here with this group. We have considered a range of theories and we must now turn to the question: What do these theories have to offer those working with troubled young people?

It is obvious that theories offer a framework within which to conceptualize treatment, and furthermore any one theory provides an impetus towards a particular approach to treatment. Thus, for example, learning theory encourages the therapist to take note of behavioural contingencies, the nature of the rewards available, and the general context in which behaviour is occurring. Sociology emphasizes the importance of roles, group processes and the conflicts between different norms and expectations. The cognitive-developmental approach focuses on the interaction between cognition and social maturation, providing a framework within which to consider social skills, the development of the self-concept, peer relationships and so on. Each theory, therefore, highlights different aspects of the individual's personality and functioning.

Theoretical perspectives help us in two other ways. First, they indicate particular areas of vulnerability. For example, Erikson's work has alerted us to the critical importance of identity development, the likelihood that many will feel raw and uncertain in this area, and what might go wrong in the course of achieving a stable identity. Psychoanalysts have also emphasized the probability of regression, and therefore of childish or even infantile behaviour in adolescence. They have drawn attention to the disengagement process, and the likely consequences of this, such as a sense of loss and depression, mourning or even bereavement. They have noted the need for strong and sometimes inappropriate psychological defences, and have underlined the role of ambivalence. All this of course provides a key to a greater understanding of the particular areas of vulnerability most common among troubled young people.

A second fundamental contribution of theory generally is to alert practitioners to the features of adolescence which make work with this group especially difficult. One such example would be "family enmeshment". Some knowledge of disengagement, and of the paradoxes and ambiguous feelings experienced in such a process, helps us to cope with the problems inherent in trying to work with teenagers who are both separate from and at the same time completely entangled with their families (see Chapters 2, 3, and 4). Questions such as: To what extent is the young person to be seen as a fully responsible individual? To what extent can the young person take decisions on his or her own behalf? How far must parents be involved, or at least informed, of what is going on in treatment? Can taking sides be avoided where there is conflict between parent and teenager? are all an inevitable part of working with young people, and theories should help prepare us for the difficulties that therapists will experience in their work with adolescents.

Family enmeshment is obviously not the only feature of the adolescent world that makes intervention problematic. We have already referred to ambivalence, and it should come as no surprise to any of us to find that the ambivalence young people feel towards their parents is expressed just as strongly in relationships they have with adults, especially in those relationships where dependence is expected or indeed required if any help is to be effective. A number of other features of adolescence may also be mentioned as factors to be taken into account in the treatment situation.

The role of the peer group, for example, should never be ignored. As a result of the process of disengagement from parents and family, peers play an especially important part for the teenager as both support and reference group. Peers can be powerful aids to treatment (see Chapter 8), but they can also render completely ineffective any therapeutic initiative if involvement in that initiative is perceived by the young person as running counter to what is acceptable within the peer group. Issues of authority and leadership are another minefield where work with young people is concerned. Chapter 5 reflects on the qualities of leadership necessary for intervention with groups of young people, and some awareness of the problems adolescents are likely to have with authority will help immeasurably in planning and preparing adults for this role.

Lastly, the topic of cognitive development should be mentioned. A number of chapters draw attention to the problems of working with the younger adolescent, and there is no doubt that, in thinking about appropriate intervention, some acknowledgement of the cognitive maturity of the young person in question is essential. This may be because he or she has poorly developed social skills or perspective-taking ability, in which case some remedial programme can be incorporated as part of the treatment. Alternatively it may be that the adolescent's present level of cognitive maturity will rule out one type of intervention and favour another. In any event there seems little doubt now that one contribution of theory has been to make all of us aware of the importance of cognitive ability for the success of treatment and this is apparent in many of the chapters which follow.

Considerations such as these will, I hope, provide a perspective on the articles in this book. Contributions vary in the degree to which they draw upon a particular theory. Almost all, however, approach adolescence with theoretical concepts in mind, and an awareness of these will undoubtedly help the reader make the best use of the material.

REFERENCES

Blos, P. (1962). *On Adolescence*. London: Collier-Macmillan.

Blos, P. (1967). The second individuation process of adolescence. *Psychoanalytic Study of the Child*, **22**, 162–186.

Coleman, J.C. (1980). *The Nature of Adolescence*. London: Methuen.

Conger, J. and Petersen, A. (1984). *Adolescence and Youth* (3rd Ed). New York: Harper and Row.

Elkind, D. (1967). Egocentrism in adolescence. *Child Development* **38**, 1025–1034.

Erikson, E. (1963). *Childhood and Society*. Harmondsworth: Penguin.

Erikson, E. (1968). *Identity: Youth and Crisis*. London: Faber.

Evans, J. (1982). *Adolescent and Pre-adolescent Psychiatry*. London: Academic Press.

Freud, A. (1937). *The Ego and the Mechanisms of Defence*. London: Hogarth Press.

Inhelder, B. and Piaget, J. (1958). *The Growth of Logical Thinking*. London: Routledge and Kegan Paul.

Kohlberg, L. (1969). *Stages in the Development of Moral Thought and Action*. New York: Holt, Rinehart and Winston.

Muuss, R. (1980). *Theories of Adolescence* (4th Edn). New York: Random House.

Neimark E.D. (1975). Intellectual development during adolescence. In *Review of Child Development Research*, Vol. 4, Horowitz, F.D. (Ed). Chicago: University of Chicago Press.

Rutter, M. (1979). *Changing Youth in a Changing Society*. London: The Nuffield Provincial Hospitals Trust.

Selman, R. (1980). *The Growth of Interpersonal Understanding*. New York: Academic Press.

Steinberg, D. (1983). *The Clinical Psychiatry of Adolescence*. London: John Wiley & Sons.

REFERENCES

2. Adolescent individuation and family therapy

DAVID A. BERKOWITZ

INTRODUCTION

Despite the separateness of ego boundaries and the relatively advanced degree of self-object differentiation apparent at the time of normal adolescence, it is useful for purposes of understanding and treatment to think in terms of an adolescent-family system or unit. Unlike the earliest mother-infant unit as described by Sander (1962) and Winnicott (1960), by adolescence some autonomy of the self has been differentiated out of this system. However, similar to the earliest mother-infant unit, the adolescent-family unit's unique set of developmental tasks or issues are being negotiated in the interaction between family and adolescent. Furthermore, as in earlier phases of development, the parental response to the adolescent's strivings plays a crucial role in determining the outcome of this developmental phase.

My intent in this chapter is to describe the main developmental issue confronting the adolescent-family system, some of the major problems of the disturbed adolescent, the central difficulties of treatment, and the related role of the family. The predominant focus will be on external factors arising from the family as these influence the internal intrapsychic issues of the adolescent. Family resistances to the developmental task and to the adolescent's treatment will be illustrated. Finally, some therapeutic implications of these observations will be discussed.

Working with troubled adolescents
ISBN 0-12-179720-1

Because he or she is part of a system, the adolescent's delicately balanced internal forces are in constant interaction with external forces of the family. My thesis is that the extrapsychic counterpart to the adolescent's regressive dependent strivings is the family's prohibition, however unconscious and covertly conveyed, against separation-individuation. Parentally induced guilt reinforces and is the external complement to the intrapsychic or internal guilt and "projected" dependency of the adolescent. Precisely because we are dealing with a system, the family's prohibition against separation contributes significantly to the failure of individuation and to the related special difficulties of adolescent treatment. I will therefore suggest that treatment of the family, concurrent with individual therapy for the adolescent, can be an important adjunct to address the special difficulties of forging an alliance in adolescent treatment.

TASKS OF ADOLESCENCE: THE ADOLESCENT

The developmental task from the side of the adolescent has been amply elaborated by A. Freud (1958), Blos (1967) and others (Erikson, 1956; Jacobson, 1964; Shapiro, 1963) and it will only briefly be summarized here. Blos (1967) has referred to adolescence as the "second individuation" phase, noting that adolescent individuation reflects those structural changes that accompany the emotional disengagement from internalized objects. He states that what is in infancy, in Mahler's (1963) phrase, a "hatching from the symbiotic membrance to become an individuated toddler", becomes in adolescence the shedding of family dependencies and the loosening of infantile object ties in order to become a member of the adult world. The disengagement from internalized objects opens the way in adolescence to the seeking of external and extrafamilial objects. For the adolescent who is severely disturbed or "borderline", the developmental task of individuation is made even more problematic by intense issues of aloneness and abandonment anxiety as well as heightened impulsivity and lack of control, lower level defences, low frustration tolerance, and deep distrust (Adler and Buie, 1979; Gunderson and Singer, 1975; Kernberg, 1975; and E. Shapiro, 1978).

The major task confronting the adolescent-family unit is thus that of individuation through the adolescent's gradually attenuating dependency on the family in order that he or she may begin to prepare and be prepared for a life outside of the family.

The consequent difficulties in the successful negotiation of this developmental task are widely appreciated. "It is by now axiomatic," writes Blos, "that without a successful disengagement from infantile internalized objects, the finding of new, namely extrafamilial, love objects in the outside world either is precluded, hindered, or remains restricted to simple replication and substitution'' (Blos, 1967, p. 164). ''Ego disturbances, apparent in acting out, in learning disorders, in lack of purpose, in procrastination, in moodiness and negativism, are frequently the symptomatic signs of a failure in the disengagement from infantile objects, and, consequently, they represent a failure of individuation itself'' (Blos, 1967, p. 166).

Success or failure of individuation – and we must think of these as relative terms – depends on a variety of both internal and external factors which can influence the individuation process and the difficulties the adolescent has in being in treatment.

Anna Freud (1958) has documented the internal difficulties inherent in the adolescent task and the concomitant interferences to treatment. Many of the latter arise from the adolescent's desperate attempts to defend himself against the regressive dependent strivings with which he is struggling. The adolescent needs to defend against the instinctual upsurge and against the infantile object ties, defence against the latter sometimes resulting in flight. Treatment problems result from the unavailability of libido for investment in the past or in the therapist because it is tied up both in mourning old objects and in seeking new ones. Anna Freud invokes this economic viewpoint to explain such common problems as the adolescents' reluctance to co-operate, their lack of involvement in the therapy or in the relationship with the therapist, their battles for the reduction of weekly sessions, their lack of punctuality, their missing of treatment sessions for the sake of outside activities, and their propensity to suddenly break off treatment altogether.

TASKS OF ADOLESCENCE: THE FAMILY

The major external resistances arise from the family, and before we focus on them, let us briefly review the developmental task from the side of the parents. For the adolescent's development to be successful, the family must promote the individuation process during this period. In order to do this, the family must provide a facilitating or ''holding environment'' (Winnicott, 1955, 1960, 1969) during the child's adolescence. In Winnicott's original description of the ''holding environment,'' the mother ''survives'' her child's instinctual assaults without retaliation or withdrawal, thus demonstrating to the infant her own autonomy and independent existence. We have elsewhere (Shapiro, Zinner, Shapiro and Berkowitz, 1975; Berkowitz, Shapiro, Zinner and Shapiro, 1974a) described the requisite holding environment during adolescence as one that provides a consistent context within which the child can develop an integrated self-concept and an integrated conception of others in his development of what Erikson (1956) has termed an ''ego identity''.

In writing about schizophrenic families, in a similar vein, Brodey (1965) ascribed to the parent the task of relating to the child with an awareness of his "objective existence", allowing the child separateness while remaining within "responsive communicative distance". The family, then, must provide an empathic setting in which the child is aided gradually to separate and differentiate himself from it without being devalued or threatened by a withdrawal of support.

The task of this phase is a developmental one for the parents, as well, and offers them an opportunity to arrive at what Benedek (1959) has called a "new level of integration". While this stage in the life of the parents holds the potential for further growth, or "generativity" in Erikson's (1956) term, it is inevitably stressful and too often one of despair. Let us briefly contrast two mothers of hospitalized adolescents, the first untreated and the second after treatment, to illustrate this aspect of the task.

The first mother referred to her hospitalized daughter as "the problem" and proclaimed that she wanted to see her married, settled and especially "happy". She stated that she was closer to her daughter because "girls need more protection and are more helpless". In an initial interview she was able to acknowledge tearfully that she was herself filled with despair now that the "nest is empty". She has always felt abandoned by her husband, a scientist who works every evening. Therefore, the mother took up residence for a good part of the year in the city where the daughter was living, leaving her husband to his computers. She has no friends and is terribly lonely.

The second mother demonstrated the ability to resolve a similar difficulty through family treatment. At the beginning she constantly tried to raise her own self-esteem through the accomplishments of her husband and children. She continually berated her hospitalized adolescent daughter for poor grades in school and felt that all the problems resided with the daughter. However, through family treatment the mother came to realize that she was herself feeling impoverished. Once acknowledging this, she was able to discover within herself dormant interests and talents. She struggled to overcome her anxiety in entering a complicated and creative profession, which provided her much satisfaction in the long run. Gradually, she was able to support her self-esteem from within, mitigating to an extent the previous reliance on her husband and daughter.

RESISTANCES OF THE FAMILY

For many adolescents, difficulties both in attending to the developmental task and in becoming engaged in and remaining in treatment are inextricably connected to external factors as well. These external factors or interferences to development also function as external resistances to the treatment (R. Shapiro,

1978) and interact with the internal resistances of the adolescent. Let us now address deviations and resistances to the family's facilitation of adolescent development.

Elsewhere (Berkowitz, 1981) I have described the families of the severely disturbed adolescents. In these borderline cases, the adolescent offspring is either neglected (Gunderson, Kerr and Englund, 1980), "bound" (Stierlin, 1977), or, as is more commonly described, rewarded for regressive behaviour such as clinging dependency, and threatened with emotional abandonment for attempts to separate and become autonomous (Masterson, 1972; Masterson and Rinsley, 1975; Shapiro, *et al.*, 1975; Zinner and Shapiro, 1975).

In contrast to providing a facilitating environment, and despite heartfelt avowals to the contrary, many of these families often resort to a variety of counter-separation attitudes and behaviours under the impact of the adolescent period. To varying degrees, these parents attempt to hold their borderline adolescent close, to possess their child, and to prevent individuation. Strictness regarding the adolescent often is rationalized by the parents as based on the existence of dangers outside the home – rapists, murderers, sex, drugs, etc.,* – and real events are cited as justification for a paranoid and phobic view of the world. Inevitably, these parents find fault with their children's object choices outside the family. Occasionally in therapy they may admit their wish to have been able to stop the passage of time when the children were small. Under tactful questioning, such families reveal that no one has much of a life outside the family. These parents have few friends, and the children often feel responsible for their parents' well-being.

In one case, a 21-year-old borderline adolescent became depressed and suicidal on repeated attempts to leave home. The mother brought to the therapist a list which carefully chronicled her daughter's injuries and accidents since she was a toddler. She broke her arm while ice skating many years ago, and now she is forbidden to skate because they feel that it could very well happen again. The mother states that she would like to keep her adolescent daughter "chained up" so that they could know where she is at all times. The father tacitly agrees to keeping the daughter bound to the home.

One form that object possession takes is the attempt to channel the adolescent to live out parental aspirations (Berkowitz *et al.*, 1974a, b). To be sure, the process of "programming" begins early and these youngsters can describe having always felt like their parents' "puppets" and robots. It is not until they reach the stage of adolescence proper, however, with its inherent drive towards, and implicit demand for, individuation that their compromised autonomy becomes conflictual. And then what may appear to the clinician as guilt because

---

*Clinically speaking, expressions of concern by the parents about these specific items often reflect a reaction to the underlying issue of separation.

of oedipal success almost invariably proves to be guilt over becoming one's own person. Such separation guilt has been described by Modell (1965). Often just to be in treatment may create a loyalty conflict for the adolescent (Boszormenyi-Nagy, 1972).

For an illustration of this type of interference with autonomy, a medical student entered psychotherapy on the verge of dropping out of school. He described how his physician-father had subtly devalued any and all other interests he had dared to express while growing up. The father would always attempt to dissuade him by saying, "Well, that's interesting, but . . ." followed by several reasons why that field would make a poor choice of career. The father's hope was that his son would not only become a physician, but would ultimately join him in a partnership in his own subspeciality. At times the father confided in the son the wish that he had owned a family business to pass on to him and his siblings so that they could all be together. When the son, in the latter stages of his training, expressed interest in any other subspecialities, the father again made derogatory comments, attempting to undermine any field of medicine other than his own.

The son's response included failing and temporarily dropping out of school, an angry defiant attitude toward his instructors and a guilty depression with suicidal ideation. Following an argument with his father, he had a fantasy of slashing his wrists in front of him. Earlier attempts at autonomy in his life were replete with self-defeating overtones, and feeble acts of defiance were always coupled with injuries to the self. Later, after returning to medical school, he felt acutely that the choice was not his own but represented submission to the father. He toyed with the idea of choosing a subspeciality that the father opposed in order to spite him and thought of dropping out of medicine altogether. With delight, he recounted an anecdote of a medical student who, on receiving his diploma, handed it to his parents and went off to become an artist.*

Motivation for self-defeat with such patients is not primarily based on a conflict concerning oedipal success, since what appears to the outside observer to represent forward movement by the patient in his career unconsciously represents to him further submission to the omnipotent control of the parent. The self-defeating efforts at individuation of this patient and others like him (e.g. his dropping out of school) represent his conflictual attempts at taking an autonomous stance while simultaneously appeasing his guilt about separation – i.e his guilt about choosing a path different from that prescribed by his father.

In their desperate attempts to fend off perceived separation and loss, families may resort to increasingly regressive behaviours, including angry repudiation of the separating member whose move toward autonomy has become person-

---

*Of interest is that one of the patient's favourite pastimes and talents was constructing intricate puppets on a string, reflecting his own feelings of being controlled.

alized as a rejection (Zinner and Shapiro, 1975; Shapiro *et al.*, 1975), or such counter-separation manoeuvres as bribes, threats of abandonment through illness and death, flaring of real physical illness, suicide or incest.

A severely diabetic mother would position herself in the kitchen eating ice cream and cake when her adolescent daughter arrived home from an evening out. When the daughter expressed her alarm, the mother's reply was, "Oh, what do you care anyway?" Here the clear intent was to keep the daughter bound to the home by inducing guilt.

Another case illustrates graphically some of the issues of separation and loss and an extreme family attempt to cope with that. A father of several adolescent children lost his wife to cancer. As she was slowly dying, he began to have incestuous relations with each of his adolescent sons. He disregarded his daughters, saying, "Forget about them; girls only grow up to marry and leave you, and you can't count on them." The sexual relations with the sons continued for several years, until one of them announced his intention to marry. A violent argument over these plans ensued, culminating in the father's suicide.

It is often in the service of keeping the departing adolescent at home that the parents collusively provide incestuous relations, covertly agreeing that violating such a taboo is better than losing their offspring. Gutheil and Avery (1977) have described frank incest between a father and his adolescent daughters as an attempt to forestall the loss through separation of the daughters by providing all stimulation and excitement within the family bounds. In their case, overtly sexual behaviour was used in the service of preventing an abject dread of loss rooted in the preoedipal development of each of the parents. The mother's covert complicity not only allowed her to escape the gratification of an internally prohibited sexual relationship with her husband, but (similar to the previous case) also unconsciously attempted to ensure the intactness of the family beyond the phase-appropriate period. This finding is consonant with Framo's (1970) suggestion that, by offering themselves, the parents can inculcate a life-long, built-in persuader against the offspring's ever finding a life outside the family.

Thus, although the basic issue is similar in a variety of cases, manifestations of a counter-separation stance by the family vary on a continuum from subtle attempts to coerce the adolescent to more blatant attempts to control and compel him.

MOTIVATION FOR FAMILY RESISTANCES

For parents to function successfully as facilitators of the adolescent individuation process, they must have had relatively good developmental experiences in their own families of origin. They need to have emerged from their own struggles over individuation with psychological integrity, relative maturity, and sufficiently adequate capacity for regulating narcissistic equilibrium to enable them to survive the "assault" by the adolescent in his necessarily stormy attempt to disengage himself.

In phase-appropriate development in accord with the new maturation both in the ego and in the drives, the adolescent begins to define himself as separate and to think independently. In the cases we are considering, rather than greeting this stage of their offspring's development with pleasure and pride, incipient adolescent individuation is met with anxiety and prohibition. In these cases, a regression in family functioning is set into motion by the phase of adolescence with its threat to the parents of separation and abandonment, resulting in the counter-separation behaviours described.

In this regression, the parents fail to relate to the child as a separate object and as an independent centre of his own initiative. Rather, they relate to him as an extension of themselves. Where it occurs, this empathic failure can often be understood on the basis of vulnerable parental narcissism. Due to the parents' own underlying early narcissistic fixations, the child or adolescent is perceived as a "selfobject", in Kohut's (1971) words, i.e. an object which is psychologically "experienced as part of the self" rather than being perceived as separate and independent. Since the "other" is vitally needed to function as part of the self, either used to complete the self through merger or to provide it with stability, cohesiveness, and a sense of worth through mirroring, the "other" cannot be perceived as separate and independent (Ornstein, 1977).

The tendency to misinterpret adolescent separation as a narcissistic injury is illustrated by a father who was prone to outbursts of rage regarding the autonomous behaviors of his adolescent children, which he experienced as beyond the realm of his control. In speaking to his daughter about his rageful outbursts in response to the childrens' attempts to seek objects outside of the family during adolescence, he said:

> I get just as involved with Hal's life as I get in Susan's . . . Okay, if I was out with you or if I was watching you, for instance, out on a date, I would be as uncomfortable as hell too, because it would for some reason, I would hate to see you, what I would think of as making love to a guy. Somehow this would, uh, this would I think, I think I would get angry because I would feel frozen out of it . . . I do get caught up in, I would get just as caught up in seeing Hal in a clinch with a girl as I would seeing you in a clinch with a guy, you know.

Vulnerable parental narcissism, with its possessiveness and its claims for absolute and omnipotent control, is often rooted in the parents' unresolved grief over past losses, be those acute and discrete, or (more often) chronic and cumulative, resulting from frustrating and depriving relationships in which the parents felt emotionally abandoned in their families of origin. Separation of the offspring in such families then raises the spectre of loneliness, abandonment, rage and emptiness which relates to the original traumatic losses or cumulative sense of loss. If they can prevent separation of the offspring, it is as if they can mitigate the old hurts and deprivations or recapture and replace or restore aspects of the old objects.

SOME THERAPEUTIC IMPLICATIONS

The family's response to the experience of separation and loss related to the adolescent individuation process and the necessity for the therapist to be ready and willing to meet this response in a flexible manner are illustrated by two adolescent cases.

The first case exemplifies failure of treatment when the adolescent was away from home. The parents opposed the treatment because they found it threatening in the same manner that they found her emerging autonomy threatening. Hence there was no alliance with the family, which might possibly have contained the patient had it existed.

An intelligent young college student entered psychotherapy because she had unsatisfactory relationships with men and performed poorly in one field of study after another. She changed fields several times, each time feeling terribly inadequate and intellectually inferior. Her immigrant father, a domineering and wealthy business man, had never allowed her to associate with young men of a different religion and could not understand why she was "wasting" her life in college anyway. Her mother, who essentially shared the father's view, called the patient to say that she was hurting her father who feels that his children just take his money but do not really love him, and that if she loved her father she would come home. The father was very involved in a family business which had been built up from nothing by the grandfather, The patient's younger brother had rebelled completely and broken all ties with the family. Now nearing retirement, the young woman's father had designated the patient as his successor in the family business. In light of his own great need, he could not understand her needs and independent career aspirations which seemed "frivolous" to him, and he devalued each of her fields of study as potentially leading to a financially destitute state.

This young woman's failure in her studies can be understood as an expression of guilt over separation, fuelled by the family, reflecting her conflict over betraying family loyalties, and as an attempt to thwart her own moves towards autonomy and ensure her safe return to the fold. It is as if she were saying unconsciously, "If I am not cut out for any of these fields of endeavour and do not have what it takes, then I really belong back in the family business. My father is right, and in his way, I will circumvent my own ambivalence about ever separating from the family."

Her father constantly urged her to stop therapy, suggesting that she was "wasting" money on "outside" help when she should be "confiding" in him. After about five months of therapy, following the daughter's visit home, the father began to telephone her daily, saying that he was dreaming about her and missed her. At the same time, he began to pressure her about money and asked her whether she really "needed" therapy.

In a telephone call, he told the therapist that an "estrangement" took place on his daughter's part when she went away to college, as she had wanted to become more independent. He then launched into a tirade against some neighbors who advised the children to leave home, particularly one who "meddled and analyzed". This was followed by a question about the therapist's religious values and practices and a question about how long the daughter's treatment would take. Shortly after that, she terminated therapy.

In the second case, a college student entered psychotherapy because of depression over separation from home where he had been both loved and needed, owing to the parent's previous losses. When the therapist was willing to meet with the family as requested, they seemed to be relieved that the therapist was not advocating a dramatic separation of their adolescent from them. Often when parents are reassured implicitly that the goal of therapy is not a radical separation, they are able to actively support the adolescent's treatment.

CONCLUSION

The critical adolescent developmental task of separation-individuation is negotiated in the interaction between family and adolescent. Successful maturation requires the helpful participation of the parents in providing a facilitating environment, a setting in which the adolescent is emotionally supported in his attempts to develop an integrated identity as a psychologically differentiated person. Where the parents themselves suffer unresolved narcissistic fixations rooted in frustrating relationships in their own early development, there is a regression under the threat of their adolescent offspring's separation. In this regression, the parents are less able to relate to the adolescent as a separate and independent center of his own initiative, but tend to relate to him as an extension of themselves, a selfobject whom they feel they have the unquestionable right to possess and control. The resulting counter-separation attitudes and behaviours of the parents present a profound interference to the adolescent developmental task.

In his classic paper on "Indications and contraindications for exploratory family therapy", Wynne (1963) suggested that family therapy was useful for the clarification and resolution of any patterned intrafamilial "relationship difficulty", i.e. problems in reciprocal interaction to which each person is contributing, collusively or openly; relationship problems in which all of the participant family members have a vital and continuing stake, on either a conscious or an unconscious level. In other words, we are interested here in the interplay between the individual and the family and in the extent that external interferences or "external resistances" (R. Shapiro, 1978), reinforce, fuel and perpetuate the difficulties of and the internal resistances to treatment of the individual identified patient.

I am suggesting that work with the family, as an adjunct to individual therapy for the adolescent, is useful for addressing certain external interferences to the adolescent's treatment. While family involvement is of less importance with a more neurotic adolescent and may require only a diagnostic assessment interview or none at all, it becomes of increasing importance with the more severely disturbed adolescent patient where problems of individuation are paramount. In these latter cases, concurrent family treatment may not only be indicated, but may prove absolutely necessary, if progress is to be made. Especially in these latter cases, it is essential to have a working alliance with the family (Shapiro, et al., 1977). Such an alliance is built upon attempts to understand empathically all the family members, with sensitivity to their life stresses, unresolved griefs and emotional abandonments. In the context of such an alliance, projections may be taken back, denied affects may be reclaimed (Berkowitz, 1977) and intrapsychic conflicts which have been managed by externalizing them into the interpersonal family setting may be reinternalized.

In this more favourable setting, the adolescent's tendency to defy treatment gives way to a more manageable therapeutic situation as the family's prohibition against the individuation of their adolescent offspring is addressed. The result can be the resumption of the developmental task of progressive individuation for the adolescent-family unit.

REFERENCES

Adler, G. and Buie, D. (1979). Aloneness and borderline psychopathology: the possible relevance of child development issues. *International Journal of Psycho-Analysis* **60**, 83–96.

Benedek, T. (1959). Parenthood as a developmental phase. *Journal of the American Psycho-analytical Association* **7**, 389–417.

Berkowitz, D. (1977). On the reclaiming of denied affects in family therapy. *Family Process* **16**, 495–501.

Berkowitz, D. (1981). The borderline adolescent and the family. In *Major Psychopathology and Family Therapy*, Lansky, M. (Ed.). New York: Grune and Stratton.

Berkowitz, D., Shapiro, R., Zinner, J. and Shapiro, E. (1974a). Family contributions to narcissistic disturbances in adolescents. *International Review of Psychoanalysis* **I**, 353–362.

Berkowitz, D., Shapiro, R., Zinner, J. and Shapiro, E. (1974b). Concurrent family treatment of narcissistic disorders in adolescents. *International Journal of Psychoanalytic Psychotherapy* **3**, 379–396.

Blos, P. (1967). The second individuation process of adolescence. *The Psychoanalytic Study of the Child* 22, 162–186. New York: International Universities Press.

Boszormenyi-Nagy, I. (1972). Loyalty implications of the transference model in psychotherapy, *Archives of General Psychiatry* 27, 374–380.

Brodey, W. (1965). On the dynamics of narcissism: I. externalization and early ego development. *The Psychoanalytic Study of the Child* 20, 165–193. New York: International Universities Press.

Erikson, E. (1956). The problem of ego identity. *Journal of the American Psychoanalytic Association* 4, 56–121.

Framo, J. (1970). Symptoms from a family transactional viewpoint. In *Family Therapy in Transition*, Ackerman, N. (Ed.). *International Psychiatry Clinics* 7, 125–171.

Freud, A. (1958). Adolescence. *The Psychoanalytic Study of the Child* 13, 255–278. New York: International Universities Press.

Gunderson J. and Singer, M. (1975). Defining borderline patients. *American Journal of Psychiatry* 132, 1–10

Gunderson, J., Kerr, J., and Englund, D. (1980). The families of borderlines. *Archives of General Psychiatry* 37, 27–33.

Gutheil, T. and Avery, N. (1977). Multiple overt incest as family defense against loss. *Family Process* 16, 105–116.

Jacobson, E. (1964). *The Self and the Object World*. New York: International Universities Press.

Kernberg, O. (1975). *Borderline Conditions and Pathological Narcissism*. New York: Jason Aronson.

Kohut, H. (1971). *The Analysis of the Self*. New York: International Universities Press.

Mahler, M. (1963). Thoughts about development and individuation. *The Psychoanalytic Study of the Child* 18, 307–324. New York: International Universities Press.

Masterson, J. (1972). *Treatment of the Borderline Adolescent: A Developmental Approach*. New York: John Wiley & Sons.

Masterson J. and Rinsley, D. (1975). The borderline syndrome: the role of the mother in the genesis and psychic structure of the borderline personality. *International Journal of Psycho-Analysis,* 56, 163–177.

Modell, A. (1965). On having the right to a life: an aspect of the superego's development. *International Journal of Psycho-Analysis* 46, 323–331.

Ornstein, A. (1977). Childhood disorders and the psychopathology of the self. Presented at Tufts Symposium, Boston, October, 1977.

Sander, L.W. (1962). Issues in early mother-child interaction. *Journal of the American Academy of Child Psychiatry* I, 141–166.

Shapiro, E. (1978). The psychodynamics and developmental pathology of the borderline patient: a review of the literature. *American Journal of Psychiatry* 135, 1305–1315.

Shapiro, R. (1963). Adolescence and the psychology of the ego. *Psychiatry* 26, 77–87.

Shapiro, R. (1978). The adolescent, the therapist, and the family: the management of external resistances to psychoanalytic therapy of adolescents. *Journal of Adolescence* I, 3–10.

Shapiro, E., Zinner, J., Shapiro, R. and Berkowitz, D. (1975). The influences of family experience on borderline personality development. *International Review of Psycho-Analysis* 2, 399–411.

Shapiro, E., Shapiro, R., Zinner, J. and Berkowitz, D. (1977). The borderline ego and the working alliance: indications for family and individual treatment in adolescence. *International Journal of Psycho-Analysis* 58, 77–88.

Stierlin, H. (1977). *Psychoanalysis and Family Therapy*. New York: Jason Aronson.

Winnicott, D.W. (1955). The depressive position in normal emotional development. In *Collected Papers, Through Pediatrics to Psychoanalysis*. New York: Basic Books.

Winnicott, D.W. (1960). The theory of the parent-infant relationship. *International Journal of Psycho-Analysis* **41**, 585–594.

Winnicott, D.W. (1969). The use of an object. *International Journal of Psycho-Analysis* **50**, 711–716.

Wynne, L. (1963). Indications and contraindications for exploratory family therapy. In *Intensive Family Therapy, Theoretical and Practical Aspects*, Boszormenyi-Nagy, I. and Framo, J. (Eds.). New York: Hoeber.

Zinner, J. and Shapiro, E. (1975). Splitting in families of borderline adolescents. In *Borderline States in Psychiatry*, Mack, J. (Ed.). *Seminars in Psychiatry*. New York: Grune and Stratton.

3. Treating the male college student from a family systems perspective

RICHARD FULMER AND JO ANNE MEDALIE

INTRODUCTION

Leaving home is an important event in the individual life cycle of each college student. Typically, counsellors of college-age youth have viewed the late adolescent developmental transition primarily from an intrapsychic perspective with its focus on identity formation and the development of the self (Erikson, 1968). We have attended to such inevitable intrapsychic struggles as the conflict between dependence and autonomy, gender identity, intimacy with peers, and the formation of an effective style of work. We have viewed the student as if he were emerging from a static family context whose impact was felt largely through internalization of past events. The process of sorting out these archaic influences required revising ego-ideals and super-ego demands by modifying internalized prohibitions and requirements.

This ego psychological approach did not explicitly take into account, however, the fact that the student is not an isolated person behaving solely in response to inner impulses. He is actually a member of an ongoing family system which continues to exert both overt and covert influences and which he, in turn, influences. This appreciation for the current impact of family members on each other has, of course, always been a major aspect of family therapy. Some family therapists have attempted to integrate family and individual

Working with troubled adolescents
ISBN 0-12-179720-1

approaches (Pinsof, 1983; Feldman, 1985). In addition, some psychoanalytic thinkers have also begun to consider the role of current family dynamics (Levenson, 1972, pp. 167-174; Calogeras and Alston, 1985; Brandt and Silverman, 1985).

When the son leaves home for college, he is not the only family member passing through a developmental stage requiring a change of behaviour and a new inner and contextual definition of self. Recent work on adult development, particularly the mid-life crisis or transition (Williams, 1977; Gould, 1978; Levinson, Darrow, Klein, Levinson and McKee, 1978; Sales, 1978), highlights our awareness of the concurrent developmental tasks of the parental generation which interact powerfully with the late adolescent's life.

This chapter is based on a longer article (Fulmer, Medalie and Lord, 1982) detailing our experience as counsellors during a period when the college at which we worked admitted only male students. We thus focus on the problems of college men and their families. The issues confronting women making the transition to college are both similar and different, and we will not attempt here to apply our viewpoint to their situation.

Our clients may present with such symptoms of psychological distress as depression, procrastination, difficulties in concentration, academic failure, difficulties in social relationships with peers of either sex, problems of identity formation or overt conflicts with parents. Our thesis is that when a student develops such problems, they are often related to some current aspect of his role in the family system.

A developmental view of family systems (Carter and McGoldrick, 1987) has provided us with a powerful tool for understanding the structure and dynamics of predictable issues and conflicts during periods of change in the individual life cycle. In addition, the perspective of adult development has heightened our awareness of the normative developmental issues of the student's "significant others". When these viewpoints are combined, we have found ourselves increasingly able to help our clients to focus more precisely on seemingly inexplicable pressures in their current lives.

THE FAMILY AS A SYSTEM

Recent theory and practice in family therapy view the symptoms of any one family member as the product of the whole family acting as a system. Thus the individual with the most obvious psychological distress (the "Identified Patient") is displaying such symptoms in response to the explicit and implicit emotional communications made by other members of his family to him and to each other. Relationships are considered as three-person events. For example, an over-close relationship between a son and his mother may be seen as a function of a too-distant relationship between that mother and the father and a conflicted relationship between the father and the son. As the family develops, the proximity between different members must be allowed to vary to fit each person's changing needs.

The family life cycle

While each family member is developing through the stages of his or her individual life cycle, the families of the patients we see are all going through a specific family life cycle stage with its own particular tasks. The son *appears* to be the one undergoing the most change and stress. He is leaving a familiar environment of family and school in which his status has been rising and is entering an unfamiliar and challenging environment in which his status might be relatively low. This stage is characterized (Carter and McGoldrick, 1987) by the following changes in family roles and relationships.

The relationship between the son and his parents becomes more distant and less intense, especially if the son leaves home to live at the college. His parents may miss him and he may yearn for his old position in the family, but the task appropriate for this stage is his *separation* from his family. With the adolescent physically absent, fewer demands are made on the role of the *parent*, and the roles of *husband* and *wife* are intensified in a way that is reminiscent of the early years of the courtship and marriage. They have the opportunity to communicate directly with each other without their child to act as a buffer, go-between, distraction or support for either parent.

These changes may be quite positive, but they almost always carry anxiety with them. The couple may have some chronic problems in their marital relationship that have been submerged or ignored by their attention to their children. When the opportunity (and, perhaps, the necessity) of negotiating these issues arises, the parents may understandably be very reluctant to confront them.

The decrease in child care responsibility also allows parents to develop in the areas of work and recreation. Mothers who have delayed pursuing education or a career may now be free to give it full time. Fathers may intensify their current work involvement or feel free to use their new time for more recreation with peers.

Another major task for the parents' generation at this stage is to become reinvolved with their own aging parents. As the grandparents' generation enters old age, they may need and welcome more attention and care from their children. Of course, to intensify these relationships carries risk and anxiety and a necessary readjustment to changed roles.

Other siblings in the family may be affected in diverse ways according to their gender, birth order and role in the family system. The first or last child to leave the home may have especially poignant meanings for the parents. Younger siblings may wish to emulate or be very different from older ones. In virtually all cases the family at home will be shrinking. This change will cause many complicated losses (of a big brother or confidant) and gains (of getting one's own room or own "day in the sun") for the remaining siblings.

This family life cycle stage is a growth phase in which everyone can gain, but like any growth, it involves loss. Because the losses inherent in this stage are not usually recognized in our culture, families often do not realize that there are reasons for mourning even at this time of growth and accomplishment. Paul (1967) has written extensively about the negative effects of insufficient mourning in families, but usually in relation to family events that are readily identified as occasions for grief, such as deaths. It is our thesis that even positive events inevitably carry certain losses. If these are not mourned, the grief may emerge in some disguised form, such as depression or vengefulness (Searles, 1965). We contend that it is *the family's resistance to the task of separation* that is the basis of many of the psychological problems seen in the college-age son (or other family members) at this time.

How family and son interact to resist separation

These are some of the indirect ways in which a family's interaction pattern may interfere with an orderly separation:

1. The son may develop such academic, emotional or behavioural problems that his parents feel it necessary to become reinvolved with him.

2. One of the parents (usually the one thought of by other family members as the most "emotional") may become depressed. The other parent may also be covertly depressed, and, in order to protect himself emotionally, may withdraw from his mate. The son may then be drawn back into the family to help the overtly depressed parent and to allow the covertly depressed parent to continue to mask his own feelings.

3. The parents may become involved in protracted conflict and the son may reinvolve himself in what might have been an old role as mediator.

4. Another sibling may develop emotional or behavioural problems which family members might use to distract themselves from their own sad feelings or from a problematic relationship between the parents.

5. The son may become severely depressed over the loss of a girlfriend from "home". The attachment to such a girlfriend has helped ease the transition from family to college by permitting the boy to separate from his parents and at the same time remain in close touch with them on his frequent weekend visits home. These romantic relationships, gratifying as they were when both participants were in high school, usually become conflicted and devitalized during the student's freshman year, and begin to break up when the girlfriend herself is preparing for college. The student's apparently

incommensurate and often disabling grief can be explained if the girlfriend is seen as a "transitional object" (Winnicott, 1971). Such an object has an exclusive, irreplaceable quality to its owner. While the girlfriend may be replaceable, what she stands for is not – the student's family. Thus the student's loss takes on an extraordinary intensity because he is losing both the girl herself, and his heretofore hidden and almost surely conflicted relationship with his family. He is also forced to face the fact that his protracted involvement with her has impaired his social development in his new environment, his college.

6. Some students resist the challenge of becoming more differentiated as persons by remaining inappropriately dependent upon their parents for direction and guidance. They may select a career goal suggested by parents without considering its "fit" with their actual interests and abilities. An overtly dependent son may also seek advice about which academic courses to follow, despite the fact that most parents are unqualified or have too little information to help in such a decision.

7. Another "arrest" in the separation process can be seen in the student who consciously and explicitly denies his attachment to his mother. On the surface, he appears to have separated himself without feeling a sense of loss. His complaint is that he has been unable to find a girlfriend, ostensibly because of his shyness and fear of rejection. He expresses positive feelings about leaving home where he feels controlled and in conflict with one or both parents. In such cases there is usually evidence of a highly ambivalent mother-son relationship in which the mother has over-compensated for her suppressed resentment at thwarted ambitions by overcontrolling her son during his adolescence. Such a relationship is usually complemented by a distant, dominating husband/father. In unconscious reaction to mother's lack of empathy, the son has defensively cut himself off from her. This detachment, however, becomes a characteristic of the son, rendering him unable to invest in appropriate extrafamilial love relationships.

THE ADULT DEVELOPMENT PERSPECTIVE

In addition to the individual psychodynamic and family systems perspectives, we use an adult development framework in viewing the transition to college. The current developmental stages of both parents and students contribute significantly to both their relationships with each other and to the dynamics of the family system. The student is in the "early adult transition" (Levinson, 1978) in which the broad developmental tasks include identity formation and intimacy (Erikson, 1968). His parents are facing "the mid-life transition" in which the developmental issue is characterized by "generativity versus stagnation'' (Erikson, 1968). Their parents' relationship with one another and with their college-age child will be influenced by how well or how poorly they are meeting or have resolved their respective developmental tasks.

Psychosocial tasks of the mother in middle adulthood

The socio-cultural circumstance of the modern American middle-class woman has shaped the central developmental task of mid-life. Smaller families, longer lives and separation of extended families prompt even the most traditionally-orientated contemporary middle-class woman to seek alternatives to the family as her exclusive source of interest and competence, especially by the time children are preparing to go off to college. A mother faces not only a "role loss" (Bart, 1971) that is inevitable with children's changing needs and status, but also an actual or threatened loss of her children's emotional attachment to her. In the process of developing herself further as a person, the woman may be confronted with doubts about her adequacy to learn, achieve or compete "out in the world". She must resist the temptation to leave it to her son to achieve vicariously for her. We contend that her son's successful separation will be directly related to her ability to solve her own life stage problems.

Though diminished in functions and probably in emotional intensity, the mother's role *vis-à-vis* her son is by no means over. Her task now is to redefine her relationship to an emerging young adult. She must deal with the expectation that the son will take on the tasks of feeding and clothing himself and monitoring his own physical and emotional health. To the extent that she gradually renounces these roles, the son is induced to accept them. In establishing new generational boundaries with her son, the mother has to decide how much she should expect to know about what is going on in her son's life at this point. He might be expected to share less of his personal life with his mother as sexual matters play an increasing role in his life. He is also expected to become more self-sufficient in caring for his physical needs. At the same time, a new sharing might occur as a mother appropriately now turns to her nearly adult son to ask advice about her problems with a younger sibling. She must also come to terms with occasional demands for regression to the old mother-child role relationship as when the son returns from college with his dirty laundry or sees fit to spontaneously return for a home-cooked meal when she has made other social plans.

A mother's ambivalent feelings about giving up her mothering role are captured in the following story of a mother whose son had just graduated from college.

The mother told us how she had conscientiously encouraged independence in her son as he was growing up and especially when he left home, only to succeed too well. As her son successfully made the transition to college, she suddenly had to negotiate dinner engagements with him. The final "insult" was that when he did

come to dinner, he now brought her flowers as a house gift! With a mixture of
pride and sadness, she observed, "I lost a child and gained a relative".

Concomitant with the changing mother-son relationship is the task of
revitalizing the couple relationship. In some marriages, this relationship yields
less satisfaction during peak child-rearing years (Williams, 1977), perhaps
because neither partner has time to give it the necessary attention. When that
time becomes available, each mate may have to stretch to become more accom-
modating and empathic to the needs of the other.

The interests of the newly differentiated wife-mother may not be synchro-
nous with her husband's current needs which stem from age and developmental
differences. For husbands who are well into their fifties, there is a lessening of
involvement in careers and an increased interest in sharing more leisure activities with a wife who, for her part, may be at her peak involvement in a relatively
new occupation or interest. She may therefore be unable to take time off from
her job for an extended vacation desired by her spouse. If her husband's need
for support and companionship is thwarted by her ambitions, he may
experience envy or resentment of his wife's new interests. Resentment about
having long-deferred nurturant needs left unsatisfied may cause tensions in the
couple's sexual relationship when the wife becomes more active. Thus, in addition to separation and detachment from her son, the mother may experience
conflict in establishing a new level and quality of attachment and separateness
with her husband.

Psychosocial tasks of the father in middle adulthood
A father in his early forties is likely to be going through the "mid-life transition"
(Levinson, 1978). He now realizes he has limited time to accomplish his life
goals and begins to evaluate his past life and achievements in these years. His
task with respect to achievement is to realistically accept his limits or, if possible,
to develop in new occupational directions.

Men who have failed to work on this mid-life task may attempt to resolve their
frustrations vicariously. They may pressure their sons to realize their own
unfulfilled dreams, most frequently in high status professions such as law or
medicine. A better resolution is for a father to revise his present aspirations or
turn to some fulfilling interest that was set aside in his youth in favour of his
present occupation.

The father's major task in relation to his son during the college years is to let
go of the reins of authority and acknowledge his limited power to control his
son's life. As his son moves away from his control, the father has also to face his
declining "instrumental" functions as interpreter of reality, mentor, role
model and material provider. Thus, although not as intimately involved in child
care as mother, a father may experience an unexpectedly acute "role loss" and
decrease in self-esteem when his authority over and contact with his son

diminish. He may experience envy and resentment as his son turns to new mentors he meets at college. This is especially the case with a man who has not been able to satisfy needs for leadership outside of the family setting.

Psychosocial tasks of the son

During the period when his parents may be in the process of a mid-life re-evaluation of their work and interpersonal commitments, the college student is beginning the process of commitment to adult roles. His psychosocial task is to begin to renounce his emotional and physical dependency on his mother, differentiate his interests from his father's, develop some realistic achievement strivings and evolve an autonomous personal identity that will link him to society.

To become more autonomous the son must accept the responsibility of working for himself, finally becoming his own authority. He must discipline himself and measure himself by his own standards of success, "dethroning" his father from the seat of authority over him. The counsellor sees many students who have passively resisted this task. For example, a young man who does well in humanities but not in mathematics or science chooses engineering because his father believes this is a practical and "manly" occupation. In evaluating his dogged commitment to a field in which he performs poorly, it is apparent that the son has been unable to differentiate his own values and goals from his father's. While the student's archaic dependency wishes may require a rigid adherence to paternal expectations, the problem may also be associated with the current father-son relationship. In the latter case, the student dares not question his goals or acknowledge his deficiencies because he fears that his father cannot tolerate his withdrawal or challenge to his authority.

Work inhibitions are often indicative of an inability of the student to develop an unconflicted, autonomous relationship with his father. A typical example is of a student who begins to manifest a "success phobia" early in his college career. He first demonstrates that he can master his academic work in the first term or year of college, only to slide into an academic decline following his success. Frequently, the father of such a student is a disappointed blue-collar worker who had to abandon more ambitious plans in his youth because of economic hardships. He shows his ambivalence towards his son's achievement by making snide remarks about the "smart-assed" college boys who work as his supervisors while giving indirect evidence of being inwardly proud of his son. At the same time, the mother, not fully aware of her husband's unarticulated ambivalence, vocally supports the son, thereby seeming to undermine her husband. The conflicting messages communicated to the student imply that his success will please his mother but diminish his father, resulting in a work inhibition. In such cases, the middle-aged father's failure to "make peace" with himself about his failed ambition keeps him from giving wholehearted support to his son. While ambivalence and guilt about surpassing the father may represent the residues of earlier oedipal rivalries, its current edition in the ongoing family system has a new life all its own.

Another kind of work inhibition is seen in the sons of confident, highly successful fathers. In these cases it is not a "success phobia", but rather a fear of failure that inhibits the son's achievement. The father may prod his son to follow in his footsteps without a sense of his son's unique potentialities and needs. These men seem unable to be proper mentors to their sons, regarding them instead as narcissistic extensions with no separate identity of their own. Such fathers remain absorbed in their own competitive achievement goals well into middle adulthood. They fail to come to terms with the tasks of generativity and are therefore regarded by their sons as unreachable, idealized competitors rather than as supports. For instance, it is not unusual for college counsellors to find sons of prominent physicians among students who are having difficulty passing organic chemistry or other premedical screening courses. This failure threatens the son's conscious dream of becoming a doctor like his idealized father. His fear that he cannot equal his father's achievement, however, inhibits him from even attempting to achieve in this field. He and his father implicitly expect him to always remain in second place. Such a father has been unavailable to help his son differentiate a distinctive career direction that would not be in direct competition with himself. The mother in such cases is often a well-educated woman who has put aside her own interests to serve her dominating, self-absorbed husband. She ofters no alternative model for achievement in interests other than those of the father.

Interaction between the student leaving home and parents' decision to divorce
In addition to having an impact on his parents' individual developmental tasks, the student's move from home to college may affect the marriage itself. It has become increasingly common that parents separate or divorce when either the student or a sibling leaves home. The change in the structure of the family system itself frequently leaves the student vulnerable to the needs of the weaker of the two parents, sometimes with disabling, suppressed anger at the parent who takes the initiative in the separation.

> A freshman experiencing intense bouts of depression which interfered with his work reported that the extremely hostile, conflicted marriage of his parents broke up only months before he came to college. Denial prevented his making any connection between his current depression and the impending divorce. Although his parents had fought for years, it was not until the day that the son received his acceptance to college that his father announced his decision to leave. The father departed under the pretext that it would make his son eligible for financial aid. The son felt alienated from his father and burdened by his mother's anxiety over the loss of her marriage. For the father, the son's acceptance to a good college signalled a successful conclusion to his parental responsibility and so to the

marriage itself. For the son, the father's decision to leave at that point only served to reinforce his anger at having been a pivot in the conflict between his parents. For the mother, the dissolution of the marriage upon her son's departure made it difficult for her to let go of him. The son's anger toward his father and guilt about his mother resulted in a disabling depression which undermined his attempt to become independent.

IMPLICATIONS FOR TREATMENT

We see our patients in weekly psychodynamically oriented psychotherapy. Treatment extends from brief consultations (two or three sessions) to weekly sessions throughout the academic year. This short-term treatment precludes the use of classical techniques such as free association and the resolution of a regressive transference neurosis. We do, however, draw meaning from our client's associative responses. We also regularly interpret negative transference reactions when they interfere with the therapy or can be shown to be *in vivo* cases of a maladaptive pattern of feeling and behaviour. Even if it were possible, however, we do not consider classic psychoanalysis appropriate for the majority of our patients. Their characters are not sufficiently formed to sustain extended treatment. We focus on those aspects of our patients' problems which are the result of conflict in resolving current developmental tasks, rather than enduring personality characteristics. Thus we attempt only to clear away barriers to development in brief, focused treatment with the expectation that the burgeoning energies of this developmental phase will then find gratifying solutions to the phase-specific tasks. Our effort to combine the psychodynamic, developmental and family systems points of view has influenced our work at each stage of the therapy in the following ways.

Inquiry

We focus the therapy on the maladaptive behavior the student presents. We therefore actively inquire for concrete examples, attempting to place the symptoms in a context of time, place and interpersonal milieu as well as in relation to the patient's inner life. In addition to a thorough psychodynamic/developmental history, we broaden the inquiry to include what each of the student's parents know about his symptoms, how they found out (or did not find out), how each parent has reacted (or would react), and what interactions the student has had with each parent concerning his problems. We also ask for information about the parents' respective work situations as well as the student's view of their ongoing relationship with each other. We especially focus on recent or anticipated changes in any of these areas. We keep in mind the respective ages of the student's parents, both presently and at crucial points in the past, as possible guides to developmental issues in the parents' lives that may have impinged on the student's current conflicts.

We also attempt to discover something about the current life situations of the student's siblings. Are they successful or problematic? At what life cycle stages are they? Sometimes when a student's sibling is preparing to leave home, the student may *then* receive some unusual pressure from his family and develop symptoms for the first time.

In addition to the standard (and necessary) questions about the student's separate dyadic relationships with each parent, we also inquire about the relationships of his family members with each other. We try to discover (if possible from his report) the sequences or patterns in which these relationships occur. For instance, it may not be sufficient to know that a student has an "intrusive" mother. It is also useful to know how he reacted to her various intrusive behaviours, and what behaviour from himself and other family members (particularly his father) elicited or allowed that intrusiveness.

We inquire about the student's various roles in the family system as they developed through his life. What complementary roles did other family members play that allowed him to play his? What is his current role in the system? We consider certain themes especially salient for this developmental period. We focus our questions on the patient's understanding of his family's attitudes toward work, success, ambition, family loyalty, competition, and separation-individuation. Such questions might include: "Who was considered successful in your father's family? Your mother's? Who was the black sheep? Whom did you (and each sibling) take after? How did your father leave his home? Your mother? Have you heard any family stories about that?"

We also ask questions in a style that helps the student make discriminations between his parents and allows us to discover relational patterns and habitual sequences of interaction. For example, "Who would be most upset if you . . . (failed this course, killed yourself, got a girlfriend, changed your major?) What does (the other parent) do when that one is upset? Then what do you do?" (Penn, 1982).

Establishing a focus

A contextual formulation of the symptom

In a recent article on remedying a "bogged down treatment" Cooper and Witenberg (1985) recommend developing a "coherent overview" of the patient. Their standard for such an overview is that the therapist should be able to "tell a story in which the patient is the main character whose life has psychological themes extending from childhood to adulthood" (p. 41). The story we attempt to formulate and share with the student connects the student's symptoms to his family life, past and present (Held and Bellows, 1983).

We also explicitly reframe maladaptive behaviour in terms of the student's delay in completing a developmental task of the adolescent era. This often supplies a motivation for dealing with the symptom. For instance, the student may see his failure to attend class as an appropriate rebellion against the perceived incompetence or arbitrariness of his teacher, ignoring the self-defeating nature of his protest. To show how this behaviour fails to move him ahead in development may help to make the symptom ego-dystonic.

Setting a goal

One of our greatest contributions to our clients is to help them define a problem that can be worked on in short-term psychotherapy. We encourage the student to set a concrete developmental goal related to the "coherent overview", e.g. attending classes regularly, studying persistently, choosing a field of study, becoming assertive in a relationship with roommate or girlfriend, or deciding whether to drop out of school. The therapy then is focused on the vicissitudes of behaviour, thought and feeling relevant to this goal and the "story" it exemplifies.

Interpretation of resistance

The student's resistance to achieving this goal is interpreted in terms of the classic psychoanalytic triad – unacceptable impulse, anxiety and defense. These are analysed as they appear in his report of his behaviours outside the hour. When a parallel process occurs in the negative transference we do interpret it. The structure we supply in our active inquiry, focusing and goal-setting does not, however, encourage the development of a regressive transference. We therefore concentrate on the student's resistance to problem-solving in the world outside of the therapy.

It is in the student's struggles to achieve the agreed-upon goal of the therapy that the central conflict is revealed, especially in relation to his family, past and present. In our interpretations, we try to cast his struggle in those terms, viewing the symptomatic behaviour as an example of the family drama. This elicits and identifies the student's primitive feelings in relation to his archaic images of his family members. Once he realizes these feelings are understood and accepted by the therapist, he often gains some distance from them.

Whatever the student's view of his parents' relationship and how that affects him, we generally focus on both how it has contributed to his current character and the developmental task of renouncing his responsibility for it. Our interventions are aimed at clarifying the ways in which symptoms are a function of overreaction to family pressures, encouraging the renunciation of these pressures, and establishing a differentiated (but non-rejecting) relationship to each parent. The student's responsibility for *his* side of the relationship is stressed and, where applicable, his inappropriate feelings of responsibility for his parents' relationship with each other is analysed. This process of first eliciting infantile feelings about pathological patterns of family interaction and then viewing his parents' motives for these patterns from a greater emotional distance has several therapeutic advantages. It makes the symptom explicable and, therefore, more susceptible to mastery. By explaining parents' past behaviour, it puts responsibility on the student for solving his school-related difficulty. Most of all, it encourages an emotional detachment from his parents in the therapy that is analogous to his age-appropriate need to detach from them.

Working through

The refining and retelling of the student's story through this middle phase of treatment is analogous (but not equivalent) to the "working through" of classical analysis. As treatment progresses we may also encourage (especially in cases of depression) mourning for lost opportunities, loss of childhood status or of the student's old role in his family. For students with adequate ego strength, we may support concrete actions that foster the separation process. This may include encouraging them to open their own bank accounts or to move out of their parents' home. For students living at school who are not addressing the task of effective detachment from parents, we may challenge excessively frequent visits home that prevent the development of campus social life. Further examples of such active interventions may be found in Carter and Orfanidis's article on "Family Therapy with One Person . . ." (1976) and Wachtel and Wachtel's book, *Family Dynamics in Individual Psychotherapy* (1986).

It is possible to utilize school holidays, especially at Christmas or intersession, as opportunities to advance the separation process. Counselling can help the student to anticipate problematic family situations and develop new methods for dealing with them. For instance, students may wish to anticipate and plan for a non-defensive confrontation with an intrusive parent or develop a non-attacking approach to a distant one. Following up these plans in sessions after the holiday can discover important changes in the emotional distance between the student and his family.

Systems thinking has another application in working with individuals (Martin, 1977). By considering the family context that "requires" the student's symptom, the therapist can anticipate how the family will homeostatically resist if his troublesome behaviour is indeed removed. He can even help the student plan for his family's reaction to the changes that individual therapy may be effecting in his behaviour. Such anticipation may then increase the student's confidence in his new direction.

Termination

Our treatment year corresponds to the academic year, so our therapy has a built-in time-limited quality. This both requires and aids us in the process described above of focusing on symptoms, setting goals and interpreting resistance in relation to those goals. These time limits, made clear early in the therapy, regulate the depth of transference and set a problem-solving atmosphere. We do probe for negative transference feelings around the termination and attempt to at least acknowledge if not resolve them. In cases where the student is either especially fragile or, on the other hand, mature enough to support an extended therapy, we may also make a private referral.

Referral

For individual therapy

Referral to outside treatment resources is an important function of the college psychological counsellor. Assessing presenting problems in terms of whether they represent transient developmental conflicts amenable to short-term, focused psychotherapy is the first task. Problems stemming from long-term character pathology, serious developmental arrests, and borderline or psychotic states are, beyond support during crises, generally best dealt with in more extensive treatment than most college counselling services can offer. The judgement of *who* and *when* to refer is frequently facilitated by an awareness of family system constraints.

Since college psychological services usually do not charge a fee and are confidential, students can seek counselling there without parental involvement. When an outside referral is suggested, however, the *status quo* between son and his parents is apt to become unsettled. Parents become involved when their son must leave college or requires financial support for treatment. Idealizations about the son's developmental progress must then be confronted. A recommendation for treatment outside of college may ring alarm bells about unacknowledged conflicts among family members.

We have found that referral of college students to psychotherapy should be viewed as a process rather than as a cut and dried procedure. The process itself may develop into a useful therapeutic intervention often requiring a series of consultations. Some students are reluctant to enlist their parents' financial support for treatment on the grounds of increasing their dependency. It is useful to challenge this rationalization, pointing out how therapy poses a threat to the existing family system. The consultation may expose the student's resistance. He may learn about transference phenomena, seeing similarities in the way he deals with the counsellor and with his parents. This insight may enable him to face his anxiety about the loss of his primary objects.

Enmeshment between children and parents may only become visible after a treatment recommendation is made. We help the student to anticipate each parent's likely response to the treatment recommendation. Parents who are especially threatened by the prospect of their child's further development may resist the referral. We may even offer to speak with parents about the recommendation in cases where the student is particularly immature and his parents unusually controlling or intrusive. The referral may be facilitated by emphasizing the seriousness of the son's problems but minimizing the parents' feelings of failure and blame. The consultant's direct contact with the parent may also provide insight into the workings of the family which the son was unable to articulate during the evaluation. Feedback to the student may enable him to see how his family dynamics had prevented him from facing his conflicts sooner or forced him to escalate his cry for help. This observation may de-idealize parents enough for the son to commit himself to treatment.

If a therapy referral is to "take" it must not be vulnerable to resistance based upon financial considerations. Anticipating and working out details of how therapy is to be financed is essential. Negotiation between student and parents about their mutual responsibilities for financing therapy may offer an opportunity for boundary setting. Such boundaries are a necessary first step in resolving the intrapsychic conflicts toward which individual therapy is aimed.

For family therapy

For severe cases of separation conflict, it may be appropriate to refer appropriate students for family therapy. Because the task of this life cycle stage is separation, some individually-oriented therapists may hesitate to make such a referral. They might think that family therapy (by attempting to "improve communication" in the family) would increase rather than decrease the student's connection with his parents. A sophisticated family therapist will not have this goal, however, and will work to increase differentiation and separation between student and family without an angry "cut-off" (Bowen, 1978). The present authors have also found it useful in some cases to see the student individually and refer the rest of his family for therapy as a group to help them adjust to his distancing himself from them. Often a short-term of family therapy can resolve some of the more severe and blatant symptoms. It can then be followed by a more extended individual therapy for the student and (sometimes) couples therapy for the parents.

Suggesting family therapy to parents can also be a delicate task because it may imply to already defensive parents that they are responsible for their son's problems. We have found it most useful to not mention possible parental or marital conflicts as a source of difficulty or potential focus of the therapy. We cast the referral as an opportunity for parents to help the family therapist help their son (Anderson and Stewart, 1983), thereby enlisting co-operation without unnecessarily arousing their resistance.

REFERENCES

Anderson, C. and Stewart, S. (1983). *Mastering Resistance: A Practical Guide to Family Therapy*. New York: Guilford Press.

Bart, P. (1971). Depression in Middle-Aged Women. In *Woman in Sexist Society*, Gornick, V. and Moran, B. (Eds). New York: Basic Books.

Bowen, M. (1978). *Family Therapy in Clinical Practice*. New York: Jason Aronson, Inc.

Brandt, D. and Silverman, H. (1985). The impact of maternal personality on individuation during adolescence. *Psychoanalytic Psychology* **2:3**, 267–273.

Calogeras, R.C. and Alston, T.M. (1985). Family pathology and the infantile neurosis. *International Journal of Psychoanalysis* **66:3**, 359–373.

Carter, E. and McGoldrick, M. (1987). The Changing Family Life Cycle and Family Therapy: An Overview. In *The Changing Family Life Cycle: A Framework for Family Therapy*. (2nd Edn), Carter, E. and McGoldrick, M. (Eds). New York: Gardner Press.

Carter, E. and Orfanidis, M.M. (1976). Family Therapy with One Person and the Family Therapist's Own Family. In *Family Therapy: Theory and Practice*, Guerin, P.J., Jr. (Ed.). New York: Gardner Press.

Cooper, A. and Witenberg, E. (1985). The "bogged down" treatment: A remedy. *Contemporary Psychoanalysis* **21:1**, 27–41.

Erikson, E. (1968). *Indentity: Youth and Crisis*. New York: W.W. Norton.

Feldman, L.B. (1985). Integrative multi-level therapy: A comprehensive interpersonal and intrapsychic approach. *Journal of Marital and Family Therapy* **11:4**, 357–372.

Fulmer, R.H., Medalie, J., Lord, D.A. (1982). Life cycles in transition: A family systems perspective on counselling the college student. *Journal of Adolescence* **5**, 195–217.

Gould, R.L. (1978). *Transformations: Growth and Change in Adult Life*. New York: Simon and Schuster.

Held, B.S. and Bellows, D.C. (1983). A family systems approach to crisis reactions in college students. *Journal of Marital and Family Therapy* **9:4**, 365–373.

Levenson, E.A. (1972). *The Fallacy of Understanding*. New York: Basic Books.

Levinson, D., Darrow, C., Klein, E., Levinson, M. and McKee, D. (1978). *The Seasons of a Man's Life*. New York: Alfred A. Knopf.

Martin, F.E. (1977). Some implications from the theory and practice of family therapy for individual therapy (and vice versa). *British Journal of Medical Psychology* **50**, 53–64.

Paul, N. (1967). The Role of Mourning and Empathy in Conjoint Marital Therapy. In *Family Therapy and Disturbed Families*, Zuk, G. and Boszormenyi-Nagy, I. (Eds). Palo Alto: Science and Behavior Books.

Penn, Peggy (1982). Circular questioning. *Family Process* **21:3**, 267–280.

Pinsof, W.M. (1983). Integrative problem-centered therapy: Toward the synthesis of family and individual psychotherapies. *Journal of Marital and Family Therapy* **9:1**, 19–36.

Sales, E. (1978). Women's Adult Development. In *Women and Sex Roles: A Social Psychological Perspective*, Frieze, I., Parsons, J., Johnson, P., Ruble, D. and Zellman, G. (Eds). New York: W.W. Norton.

Searles, H.F. (1965). The Psychodynamics of Vengefulness. In *Collected Papers on Schizophrenia and Related Subjects*. New York: International Universities Press.

Wachtel, E. and Wachtel, P. (1986). *Family Dynamics in Individual Psychotherapy*. New York: Guilford Press.

Williams, J. (1977). *Psychology of Women: Behavior in a Biosocial Context*. New York: W.W. Norton.

Winnicott, D.W. (1971). *Playing and Reality*. New York: Basic Books.

4. Some techniques for working with resistant families of adolescents

DAVID WILL

INTRODUCTION

This paper provides an overview of different types of resistance that can occur in the course of conjoint therapy with the families of adolescents, and then describes some techniques that I have found useful in working with such families in an outpatient psychiatric clinic. Its emphasis is practical and based on a number of different theoretical models which reflect the eclectic nature of my clinical work. I believe that many of the insights afforded by different schools of family therapy are complementary rather than antagonistic, and that no single therapeutic school provides a panacea for all the ills of all families (Lishman and Will, 1979).

This paper's aim is to provide some general principles that may prove helpful in working with resistant families. It cannot hope to encompass the detail and sophistication of the technical writings that have emanated from particular schools of therapy (e.g. Haley, 1971, 1976; Watzlawick, Weakland and Fisch, 1974; Palazolli, Cecchin, Prata and Boscolo, 1978; Box, Copley, Magnagna and Moustaki, 1981; Minuchin and Fishman, 1981). What it may achieve, however, is a *broadly based* approach to the common clinical problem of the resistant family. In this respect is is similar to the important contributions made by Treacher and Carpenter, 1982; Carpenter, Treacher, Jenkins and O'Reilly, 1983; and Kingston, 1984.

Working with troubled adolescents
ISBN 0-12-179720-1

I will start by describing some of the types of resistance that occur in family therapy and will then look in turn at three main types of technique designed to tackle resistance: directive techniques designed to lower the family's anxiety, directive techniques designed to increase anxiety and strategic techniques designed to exploit resistance.

THE PHENOMENON OF RESISTANCE IN FAMILY THERAPY

Most symptoms can be seen as serving a function for the family system arising when a family's coping mechanisms have been unable to deal with a particular problem in a functional way. Any attempt to challenge the dysfunctional solution which the family has developed will lead to the possibility that the original problem will re-emerge. Consequently, *all families will be resistant to therapy but some are more resistant than others.* The response of the highly resistant family is based on defiance rather than compliance (Fisher, Anderson and Jones, 1981). Here is a vignette which illustrates high resistance.

The K family was referred to the psychiatric clinic with a history of severe anorexia nervosa in their 14-year-old son, Derek, the youngest child. Two older siblings had recently left home after considerable strife between themselves and the middle-aged parents. The family had a history of looking after invalids and the onset of Derek's symptoms coincided with the death, two years previously, of the last of these invalids, maternal grandmother. The parents made it clear that they were not happy being seen conjointly at the first assessment interview, during which Derek was virtually mute, father obstreperously defensive and mother passively so. Both parents wanted an individual medical approach to be taken to Derek and expressed considerable surprise at being involved themselves. "Derek's the problem, not us," said father. For the next few interviews one or other of the parents failed to attend. Father phoned between appointments to say that his wife was not strong enough to stand these senseless sessions. Each interview with the family or parts of the family became monotonously similar. Derek's hostile silence became more and more entrenched and the parents' demands for medical solutions and their complaints about the uselessness of the sessions became more and more strident. Derek's weight continued to fall and the therapists' anxiety increased. The therapists came to dread appointments with the family.

In essence then, a highly resistant family shows defiance towards the therapists, who may be repeatedly attacked as the existence of family problem is repeatedly denied by family members. Interviews can become monotonously repetitive and the therapist(s) often become more anxious than the family members. Why do some families show such a degree of resistance?

For family therapy to proceed relatively smoothly the family must have some motivation. This motivation is usually *anxiety*. When a family accepts the need for therapy it is usually because the anxiety generated by symptomatic behaviour or by its consequences becomes greater than the anxiety the symptomatic behaviour serves to avoid. Thus for the K family to accept therapy it would be necessary that the anxiety about having a family member starving to death became harder to bear than the anxiety that the family would collapse if it did not contain an invalid. For therapy to proceed without excessive resistance there has to be *an optimal level of anxiety* within the family; anxiety should be neither too high, lest therapy is too threatening, nor should it be too low, lest there is no motivation for therapy.

Resistance occurs when the family's anxiety is too high or too low. Techniques for working with resistant families may be designed *directly* to lower or raise anxiety, or may be designed *strategically* to exploit resistance to a therapeutic end. I shall now describe some common examples of both types of resistance.

Families whose anxiety level is too high

These families may resist treatment because they are terrified of the imagined consequences of change, of the revelation of secrets or of the imagined power of the therapist. These anxieties may be conscious or unconscious and their elucidation may be straightforward or complex (see Box, 1979). In all such families, however, resistance is accompanied by manifest anxiety rather than by denial. The therapist is made to feel as if she/he is walking on egg shells or as if she/he is being excessively intrusive or clumsy should she/he begin to explore sensitive issues.

One very common *imagined consequence of change* in families of adolescents is to fear that maturation and separation of a child from the family will result in disastrous consequences. On the other hand such a fear may be relatively realistic when an emotionally barren marital couple are aware of how bleak marital life would be were their "problem" teenager to proceed with separation and individuation.

The Q family presented as an elderly couple whose 17-year-old daughter, Mandy, had a four-year history of severe bulaemia nervosa. Mandy was in fact the illegitimate product of an affair the father had with another woman, who had died soon after Mandy was born. Both parents lived vicariously through their daughter. Mother lavished much time and money on her "little doll", choosing all Mandy's clothes. Father had encouraged his daughter to take up skating and spent hours coaching her. The parents did nothing together and, without Mandy as a focus, knew that their marriage would be dead. All three dreaded the prospect of Mandy's separation and bitterly resisted therapy.

Fears about imagined consequences of adolescent maturation can be quite unrealistic but sustained by *Family Myths* (Byng-Hall, 1973). For example, in the K family there was a family myth that mother was weak and fragile. Hence, adolescent strivings for autonomy which involved disagreements with mother were seen as dangerous and potentially destructive towards her. Derek's anorexia was motivated in part by a desire to avoid maturation and the concomitant disagreements with mother that it would entail.

The revelation of family secrets is often feared as catastrophic and, as with myths, such secrets may be real or imagined (see Pincus and Dare, 1978). Sometimes a real and imaginary secret may co-exist. This was the case in the N family in which the main secret was to do with adoption. The family presented as two rather elderly parents with a phobic 16-year-old son, Robert, and a normal 17-year-old daughter, Sarah, whom the parents saw as abnormally rebellious. At the first interview both parents became anxious and defensive when questions were asked about the children's early development.

At the end of the interview the parents asked to be seen separately from the children and revealed the "real" secret, namely that Sarah was adopted, a fact which she knew but which was kept hidden (or so they thought) from Robert. The reason for this real secret being kept revealed the imaginary secret. Mother said they had kept the fact of Sarah's adoption secret from Robert, since, if he found out, Robert would undoubtedly turn on Sarah and want her out of the family. This is fact was a projection of the parents' imaginary secret onto their son. Both parents shared a secret bad-blood fantasy in terms of which their adoptive daughter's normal steps towards adolescent maturation were seen as evidence of a disastrous moral weakness in her genetic make up.

Fantasies about the *imagined power of the therapist* can be a prime source of high levels of familial anxiety, and can be relatively realistic or of a transference-type. Relatively "realistic" fantasies can be evoked by the professional identity of the therapist. For example, as a psychiatrist, I am often asked to see delinquents to provide psychiatric reports for a Children's Hearing. Almost invariably the parents and/or the youngster have some apprehension that the youngster will be found to be mad and "put away", for otherwise why should they have to see a psychiatrist? Similarly, social workers may find themselves confronted by families who implicitly assume that they are being seen with a view to a social worker's removing their children into care.

In addition to such fantasies about the therapist, many families will show transference-like responses to the therapist. However, it is the family therapy group in the Adolescent Department of the Tavistock Clinic who have made the most sophisticated study of family group transference as tellingly described by Box (1981) and Copley (1981).

Families whose anxiety level is too low

The second group of highly resistant families comprises those families whose anxiety level is too low. Such families deal with anxiety by denial, projection and projective identification. When confronted with this sort of family the paradigmatic experience of the therapist is that of a sense of increasing personal anxiety in the face of a family group which denies anxiety. Various levels of *denial* are possible and I will use the family in which anorexia nervosa has occurred to illustrate these various levels.

Level 1. Parents and/or other family members acknowledge that the anorexia nervosa is an expression of psychological problems in the anorexic patient and in the family. Only the patient denies this.

Level 2. Parents and/or other family members acknowledge that the anorexia nervosa is a problem with some psychological antecedents in the anorexic patient but none in the family.

Level 3. Parents and/or other family members acknowledge that the anorexia nervosa is a problem of *a purely physical kind* and are only interested in obtaining physical treatment for the patient.

Level 4. The whole family joins with the anorexic in denying there is a problem, e.g. the parents of a skeletal 15-year-old who had been starving herself for two years, and who both maintained that their daughter's self-starvation was a minor consequence of the menarche which was bound to settle in time.

Level 5. The whole family *and* associated caring professionals deny that there is a problem, e.g. the GP who refused to refer a very severe anorexic, detected by an educational psychologist, for psychiatric treatment on the grounds that the parents saw no problem and he felt their views should be respected.

Denial reduces the family's anxiety to inappropriately low levels and the therapist may find him/herself desperately trying to convince the family that they have problems! The family usually parries such attempts with ease: they are quite normal, there are thousands of families like themselves, the therapist must have an over-fertile imagination. Denial is often accompanied by *projection*, e.g. any problems that emerge in sessions are produced by the therapist as in "We had no problems until we started to come here". Families of anorexics can create intricate and sticky webs of projection in which the unwary therapist gets trapped: the anorexia is due to hormones, drugs, too much or too little sunlight, anything that is, but stresses in the family.

Projective identification (see Zinner and Shapiro, 1972; Box, 1978) is an almost invariable accompaniment of denial. The family can deposit its anxiety into the therapist. Hence the not uncommon process whereby the therapist becomes progressively more anxious lest an anorexic patient starves to death while the patient and her family remain blandly unconcerned. Projective identification can also lead to a kind of mirroring in which intrafamilial conflicts become enacted by various members of the same treatment team or by different professionals involved with the family.

For example, a 15-year-old anorexic came very close to starving in an adolescent psychiatric unit because the staff were enacting an intrafamilial conflict. The girl's parents had been split, mother wanting to take a firm line over her daughter's diet, father wanting to be indulgent. The staff in the unit mirrored this split, half of them wishing to institute a regime of supervised feeding for the girl, the other half seeing this as "collusion with the symptom" and vigorously opposing supervised feeding. While the staff enacted the parental conflict, the anorexic continued to starve herself and her parents were able to unite in an attack on the unit where treatment was obviously getting nowhere.

SOME TECHNIQUES FOR DEALING WITH RESISTANT FAMILIES

Directive techniques designed to decrease inappropriately high levels of anxiety
As we have seen, inappropriately high levels of anxiety may be produced by fears about the imagined consequences of change, about the revelation of secrets, and about the imagined power of the therapist. In essence such fears can be tackled using the same basic techniques that obtain in individual dynamic psychotherapy. First, the therapist must be aware of such fears as possible sources of anxiety and resistance. Secondly, through the elucidation and interpretation of such fears, their power can first be clarified and then diminished (see, for example, Byng-Hall, 1973; Pincus and Dare, 1978; Box 1978, 1981).

There are, however, a few very simple techniques that can obviate or at any rate reduce resistance due to high levels of anxiety. For example, it is preferable to avoid the revelation of a secret without first engaging and preparing a family. Common situations that can generate secrets are adoptions and illegitimacy. It is vital to establish whether or not information about these areas is openly available to all family members. Having provoked one or two families' fury, anxiety and resistance by inadvertently revealing secrets such as these, I find it prudent to assume that such information is secret until I find it to be otherwise.

Another very simple technique that can avoid the development of excessively high levels of anxiety is *obtaining a therapeutic mandate*. By the simple expedient of asking "can we talk about this?" it is possible to avoid the premature exposure of potentially anxiety-provoking material. I like to obtain such a mandate in family sessions before explaining, for example, the reasons parents had for adopting children or the history of previous marriage(s) of parents in reconstituted families. A therapeutic mandate may not be obtained initially but the refusal to discuss a particular area can provide useful clues about the nature of family myths or secrets. More importantly, by respecting a family's anxieties it is possible to avoid raising them to anti-therapeutic levels.

Related to the therapeutic mandate is the technique of using a *tactical individual session* with highly anxious families. Thus, if it becomes clear, for example, that there is a severe marital problem whose immediate exposure will be too anxiety-provoking, I may set up an individual session with the identified adolescent patient *for purely tactical reasons*. Often parents will perceive this as an acknowledgement that there is some validity in their concerns about their youngster and this can be sufficiently reassuring to allow them to face their own marital problems. Obviously a potential hazard of this technique is apparent collusion with a family's scapegoating mechanisms. However, if this hazard is borne in mind, the judicious use of the tactical individual session with the identified patient can significantly reduce excessive levels of parental anxiety.

Sometimes high levels of anxiety can be *exploited* in order to reduce resistance to therapy. The commonest situation in which this technique can be helpful is that in which there are intense anxieties about separation. A family that is initially resistant to conjoint therapy may change its tune if offered an alternative that is even more anxiety-provoking. For example, the members of the T family, father, mother and 14-year-old anorexic Jenny, were initially violently opposed to attending for conjoint family therapy. This was a highly enmeshed family in which the prospect of the girl's separating from her parents provoked great anxiety. The therapist told the family that long-term inpatient treatment for Jenny was indicated. The family were made so anxious by this suggestion and the separation it would entail, that they readily agreed to conjoint family therapy on an outpatient basis.

Directive techniques designed to increase inappropriately low levels of anxiety
As we have seen, inappropriately low levels of anxiety which lead to resistance to therapy may be produced by denial, projection and projective identification. These can be confronted in a number of ways and the family helped to reintroject its own anxieties.

Denial can be confronted head on by *authoritarian techniques* designed to increase anxiety by exploiting the expert status of the therapist. This entails a frontal assault on the family's view of the problem. For example, the D family were referred because the 10-year-old son was showing a marked deterioration in his school performance. The other family members were mother, a 13-year-old daughter and a 12-year-old son. It transpired that the father had been imprisoned some 18 months before referral for incestuous activity with the two oldest children. In the initial family interview mother declared that she was not prepared to discuss the incest, since that would lead to the opening of old wounds and was a subject that had been exhaustively discussed in the past. However, therapists were struck by much unfinished business. There was intense rivalry between mother and daughter for the parental role in the family and a marked split in the siblings with a victim subsystem and an isolated 10-year-old. The therapists concluded that the presenting problem and other current stresses in the family were residues of the trauma of the incest. Accordingly, they confronted mother's denial head on, e.g. "As experts we can tell you that we must talk about the incest and its consequences if we are to help your family function more happily." This was accepted by the mother.

Such an authoritarian use of the expert can be *amplified* in a number of ways. For example, a co-therapist may be introduced to provide strength in numbers. The use of a one-off consultation with an individual "expert" or with a consultation team behind a screen may be helpful. Papp (1980) has discussed how such a team can function as a "Greek Chorus" and underline and emphasize the authority of the therapist.

A second type of frontal assault on denial is effected by *precipitating a crisis* which can increase the level of anxiety within the family. For example, the P family comprised mother, father, two younger children and the identified patient, James, aged 15, who had a two-year history of intermittent but severe solvent abuse. James had been referred to the clinic on two previous occasions but with little success. The parents had ceased to live as man and wife, but continued to live under the same roof. Each would taunt the other with accounts of their sexual exploits with others. It seemed to the therapist that James' solvent abuse was a frantic attempt on his part to bring his parents together by providing them with a common problem to deal with (see Framrose, 1982). The parents, however, refused to be involved together in treatment. James then started to truant, which enabled the therapist to precipitate a crisis by referring James to a Children's Hearing. This involvement of the legal system provided the parents with a healthy confrontation with reality as a result of which they ceased denying their part in the problem and agreed to attend conjoint interviews together.

Some defensive *projections* can be dealt with by the use of a consultation with an "expert". This technique can, for example, be useful in *demedicalizing* anorexia nervosa and in *depsychiatrizing* school phobia. In both these instances referral to a specialist is used paradoxically to "de-specialize" a problem.

For example, the M family, father, mother and the 16-year-old anorexic daughter Susan, only wished to see Susan's anorexia as a medical problem. They refused to acknowledge that family stress and psychological factors were important and instead projected all responsibility for the anorexia onto mysterious physical factors. The therapist was able to use a consultant physician as an expert who could demedicalize the problem. The family were told by the therapist that he might be wrong in his assessment of Susan's anorexia and so he had requested a second opinion from an expert in the physical aspects of anorexia nervosa. The family went to see the consultant physician who, after conducting a meticulous examination, was pleased to be able to tell the family that there was no physical cause for their daughter's anorexia. It is possible to amplify this technique by getting the physician to put the referring psychiatrist in a one-down position, e.g. "Dr Will was rather silly to refer your daughter to me since it is so obvious to an expert like myself that her problems are not caused by physical factors''.

In a similar sort of way the easiest means of depsychiatrizing school phobia is often referral to a psychiatrist. Families of severe school phobics often deny the relevance of family factors in the condition, instead projecting their responsibility by attributing the phobia to internal factors in the child such as ''nerves'' or ''extreme sensitivity''. Such families can sometimes convince themselves and GPs, schoolteachers or educational psychologists that their child is so vulnerable to anxiety that she/he is clearly a ''psychiatric case'', and that no pressure be put upon the child to attend school. A psychiatric consultation can be useful in order to depsychiatrize the problem and help family members withdraw their projections. Only a psychiatrist is seen as having the power to pronounce the child sane or psychiatrically normal.

Projective identifications can often be undermined by adequately addressing interprofessional systems issues. As we have seen, some resistant families are able to project intrafamilial conflicts and anxieties into the treatment team (see also Britton, 1981). I always expect that, unless active steps are taken to prevent it, a resistant family will attempt to exacerbate all possible sources of conflict between myself and other involved professionals. Thus, for example, when I have seen a resistant anorexic family for the first time, I assume that the family will disagree with my assessment and will try to get the referring agent (usually the GP) to side with their view of the matter against mine. Consequently, I will usually telephone the GP soon after my first meeting with such a family to warn him that the family may attempt such a manoeuvre. This may or may not be sufficient to contain the situation.

For example, the L family presented with a 15-year-old anorexic daughter and from the beginning of the first interview the parents showed great resistance to talking about anything other than drugs, hormones and diets, while their passive daughter sat mute. At the end of the first session a contract was made for the second session, offering a tactical individual interview for the girl with one therapist and a conjoint interview for the parents with myself. I was sufficiently uneasy about the family's motivation to telephone the referring GP to forewarn him of the possibility of the family's returning to see him to complain about our assessment and to attempt to play the GP off against us. The GP was very sympathetic and co-operative and 'phoned a couple of days later to say that the family had indeed tried to do this but that he had told them that we were the experts and knew best. The family, however, failed to keep their next appointment. On telephoning them I discovered that they had gone privately to another GP who had done what they wanted, which was to refer their daughter to an organically orientated psychiatrist. Their daughter was now an inpatient in an adult psychiatric unit and was receiving the drugs that the parents had demanded of us to prescribe.

Clearly, as this example shows, some resistant families are so expert at playing professionals off against one another that they remain in control of therapy.
However, good intercommunication between the different professional systems
involved is an absolutely essential prerequisite when working with resistant
families, as, for example, when working with resistant families of school
phobics. Here I often adopt a very firm approach, directing the immediate
return of the youngster to school. However, I always assume that, unless there is
adequate interprofessional liaison, the family will succeed in convincing
another involved professional – be it the school doctor, the GP, the head-
master, the guidance teacher, the educational psychologist or the local authority
social worker – that no pressure should be put on the child. For a directive treatment approach to have any hope of success in the situation, every single professional involved with the child and family must be consulted and a jointly agreed
plan developed. Some basic principles of the kind of tensions that can arise
between professionals and some guidelines for their management can be found
in Evans (1970).

Strategic interventions

The essence of strategic interventions is the redirection of conscious and unconscious resistance to a therapeutic end. The mutative mechanisms of such interventions have been conceptualized in different ways: as the production of a
therapeutic double-bind that places the family in a no-win situation
(Watzlawick et al., 1974); as a sort of cognitive bombshell whose explosion leads
to cognitive and hence behavioural change (Palazolli et al., 1978); or as an intervention that exploits the hate in the family's transference to the therapist (when
the hated therapist tells the family members to do one thing, their hostility will
lead them to do the opposite). I cannot hope to attempt a review of the literature
on strategic interventions in a paper of this length. (Some useful reviews and
bibliographies include Raskin and Klein, 1976; Weeks and L'Abate, 1978;
Dell, 1981.) Instead, I wish to indicate in general terms some of the uses that can
be made of such interventions in work with resistant families.

There is a still-burgeoning enthusiasm for strategic interventions because
they comprise a relatively new and exciting technique and there are those who
feel that strategic work represents a new therapeutic paradigm that can and
should be applied to all problems in all families (K. Tomm, personal communication). I do not share this view, but instead use strategic interventions selec-
tively. A review by Fisher et al (1981) provides a useful classification of such
interventions and some guidelines for their use. Their review deals with paradoxical interventions but the classification put forward can be generalized to
strategic interventions as a whole. Three main types of intervention are
described: Reframing, Escalation and Redirection.

Reframing involves the reinterpretation of the meaning a family places on symptomatic behaviour. Given its cognitive nature, it is a technique best suited to families who possess some capacity for insight. For example, in the treatment of the K family, a one-off consultation provided a reframing of the meaning of Derek's anorexia. The family were told by the therapists that an appointment had been made for a second opinion on their problems to be obtained from "an expert on anorexia nervosa" (myself). They were given an appointment for a month hence, being told that the expert's time was precious and his appointments booked far in advance. I carried out a Milan Group-type interview (see Palazolli, Boscolo, Cecchin and Prata, 1980), with the two original therapists observing behind a screen, and a reframing intervention was arrived at. I told the family that Derek's anorexia had been doing the family a great service since it was Derek's way of not growing up. Derek knew that neither of his parents could cope with the stresses of another adolescent growing up and leaving the family and was protecting them from such stresses by starving himself so as not to grow up. Although the family initially responded to this intervention as if it were crazy, they attended conjoint family sessions regularly thereafter.

Escalation involves the prescription of symptomatic behaviour more extreme than the presenting symptoms. For example, the Z family presented with a 15-year-old daughter, Jane, who had a three-year history of school phobia that had proved resistant to the attempts of several agencies to modify it. In addition mother had been agoraphobic for some 10 years and unable to venture outside of the house unaccompanied. Jane's school phobia was clearly meeting mother's needs for support and company. The therapists therefore prescribed a routine that escalated the symptomatic behaviour. Amongst other things, Jane was told to spend all her time in the same room as her mother and to sleep in the same bed as her. The effect of this prescription was dramatic; not only did Jane return quickly to school but, within a week, mother had take her first unaccompanied bus trip in 10 years.

Redirection attempts to bring symptomatic behaviour under voluntary control by prescribing the circumstances during which it is to occur. An example of the use of this technique was the treatment of the Y family, comprising mother and three sons aged 17, 15 and 13. Ronnie, the middle son, was referred for stealing. It gradually became clear that his stealing served a homeostatic function for the family, being designed to ensure that family life did not become too good. Things had been good in the past only to be shattered when the father left the family for another woman. The family appeared to be functioning in terms of a myth, that if things became too good again, the same sort of catastrophe would ensue. Accordingly mother and the three boys were seen separately and mother was told to leave her purse with £2 in it, unattended on the kitchen table every Friday night. The boys were told that they should decide amongst themselves every Friday who should steal the money. Mother and the boys were instructed not to reveal these instructions to each other. Following this intervention Ronnie's stealing ceased to be a problem.

When and how should strategic interventions of this sort be used? I feel that it is important to stress that their use should not be taken lightly and, above all, require previous experience of family therapy. Clinical examples such as the three given above can seem glib and straightforward in print and yet all three followed lengthy deliberation and discussion. The greatest danger of the indiscriminate use of strategic interventions lies in their possible use as a means of acting out a negative counter-transference. If a therapist is feeling furious and frustrated with a family, glib recourse to a strategic intervention can merely represent an act of hostility on the therapist's part. Although the inexperienced therapist may be most prone to this sort of behaviour, experienced therapists are not immune from this temptation. I think this is one reason why many experienced strategic therapists rely heavily on consultation with colleagues (e.g. Palazolli *et al.*, 1978, 1980; Papp, 1980).

Fisher *et al.* (1981) have provided some sensible guidelines for the indications and contra-indications for strategic interventions. They stress that disorganized and chaotic families are *not* suited to strategic approaches. This makes *a priori* sense since all strategic interventions require a degree of family homeostasis which can be challenged and changed. Fisher and his colleagues also suggest that strategic interventions should not be used in families who are compliant and who will respond to conventional directive or interpretative interventions. I share this wish to *reserve* strategic interventions for families who will not respond to conventional therapy, but I realize that many would disagree, feeling that strategic interventions can be so efficient and effective that they should be used whenever possible.

In my own practice I only use strategic interventions *from the outset* with families who have a history of failure to respond to more directive or interpretative approaches. Such families represent a minority of referrals, and this means that I will often start off therapy by using a directive or interpretative approach and will then change to a strategic approach. Such a changing of therapeutic horses in midstream may be seen by some as irresponsibly eclectic, but I can see no way of avoiding it unless one chooses to use strategic interventions from the outset with every family or eschews their use altogether. Besides, therapeutic use can be made of the changeover from one style to the other.

At the very least, the changeover can be used as an opportunity to put oneself in a one-down position, e.g. "I've been discussing my attempts to help you with my colleagues who have pointed out that I have been quite incorrect in my approach up till now." Further therapeutic *amplification* of the change can be obtained by using a screened consultation as the changeover point. It can sometimes be useful to use an "outside" expert actually to interview the family and announce the change of tack (as in the K family). At times it can be expedient to accompany the change of tack by a change in therapist, e.g. "Your problems are too much for a therapist of my limited experience to deal with so I am referring you to a much more experienced person."

I offer these suggestions as tentative guidelines only. Strategic techniques are new enough to be exciting and new enough for their full potential not to be recognized. They are also fashionable and consequently run the risk of being overused. Time and clinical experience will doubtless help to refine our views on the indications and contra-indications for their use.

I should like to acknowledge the collaboration of my colleagues, David Baird, Frank Baird and Chris Lewis in much of the clinical work described in this paper.

REFERENCES

Box, S.J. (1978). An analytic approach to work with families. *Journal of Adolescence* **1**, 119–133.

Box, S.J. (1979). The elucidation of a Family Myth. *Journal of Family Therapy* **1**, 75–86.

Box, S.J. (1981). Working with the dynamics of the session. In *Psychotherapy With Families*, Box, S.J., Copley, B., Magnagna, J. and Moustaki, E. (Eds), pp. 69–74. London: Routledge and Kegan Paul Limited.

Box, S.J., Copley, B., Magnagna, J. and Moustaki, E. (Eds) (1981). *Psychotherapy With Families*. London: Routledge and Kegan Paul Limited.

Britton, R. (1981). Re-enactment as an unwilling professional response to family dynamics. In *Psychotherapy With Families*, Box, S.J. *et al.* (Eds), pp. 48–58. London: Routledge and Kegan Paul Limited.

Byng-Hall, J. (1973). Family myths used as a defence in conjoint family therapy. *British Journal of Medical Psychology* **46**, 239–250.

Carpenter, J., Treacher, A., Jenkins, H. and O'Reilly, P. (1983). 'Oh No! Not the Smith's again!' An exploration of how to identify and overcome 'stuckness' in family therapy. Part II: Stuckness in the therapeutic and supervisory systems. *Journal of Family Therapy* **5**, 81–96.

Copley, B. (1981). Introducing Families to Family Work. In *Psychotherapy With Families*, Box, S.J. *et al.* (Eds), pp. 35–47. London: Routledge and Kegan Paul Limited.

Dell, P.F. (1981). Some irreverent thoughts on paradox. *Family Process* **20**, 37–51.

Evans, J. (1970). Conflicts, crises and tensions in a residential unit. *Proceedings of the Fifth A.P.S.A. Conference* 61–71.

Fisher, L., Anderson, A. and Jones, J.E. (1981). Types of paradoxical intervention and indications/contraindications for use in clinical practice. *Family Process* **20**, 25–35.

Framrose, R. (1982). From structure to strategy with the families of solvent abusers. *Journal of Family Therapy* **4**, 43–59.

Freud, S. (1910). *"Wild" Psychoanalysis* (Standard Edition XI), pp. 221–227.

Haley, J. (1971). *Changing Families*. New York: Grune and Stratton Inc.

Haley, J. (1976). *Problem-solving Therapy*. San Francisco: Jossey-Bass Inc.

Kingston, P. (1984). 'But they aren't motivated . . .' issues concerned with encouraging motivation for change in families. *Journal of Family Therapy* **6**, 381–403.

Lishman, J. and Will, D. (1979). Family Therapy. A choice of frameworks. *Journal of Family Therapy* **1**, 383–395.

Minuchin, S. and Fishman, M.C. (1981). *Family Therapy Techniques*. Cambridge, Mass: Harvard University Press.

Palazolli, M.S., Cecchin, G., Prata, G. and Boscolo, L. (1978). *Paradox and Counterparadox*. New York: Aronson.

Palazolli, M.S., Boscolo, L., Cecchin, G. and Prata, G. (1980). Hypothesizing-circularity – neutrality: three guidelines for the conductor of the session. *Family Process* **19**, 3–12.

Papp, P. (1980). The Greek chorus and other techniques of paradoxical therapy. *Family Process* **19**, 45–57.

Pincus, L. and Dare, C. (1978). *Secrets in the Family*. London: Faber.

Raskin, D.E. and Klein, Z.E. (1976). Losing a symptom through keeping it. *Archives of General Psychiatry* **33**, 548–555.

Richter, H.E. (1974). *The Family as Patient*. London: Souvenir Press.

Treacher, A. and Carpenter, J. (1982). 'Oh No! Not the Smiths again!' An exploration of how to identify and overcome 'stuckness' in family therapy. Part I: Stuckness involving the conceptual and technical aspects of therapy. *Journal of Family Therapy* **4**, 285–305.

Watzlawick, P., Weakland, J. and Fisch, R. (1974). *Change*. New York: Norton.

Weeks, G. and L'Abate, L. (1978). A bibliography of paradoxical methods in psychotherapy of family systems. *Family Process* **17**, 95–98.

Zinner, J. and Shapiro, R. (1972). Projection identification as a mode of perception in families of adolescents. *International Journal of Psychoanalysis* **53**, 523–530.

5. Social work skills in group work with adolescents

ANDREW KERSLAKE

THE HISTORICAL BACKGROUND

Low intensity groups led by field social workers have been an important part of social work with adolescents in Britain for about the last 15 years. A characterization of such groups would be: two leaders, the group meeting once a week, normally after school, and the programme lasting for around 10 weeks. Initially the impetus for the development of this style of work came from a variety of sources. Legislative changes in the late 1960s, under the title of Intermediate Treatment, encouraged new approaches to work with adolescents. Social work training began to place an increasing emphasis on the importance of the peer group as an influence on adolescent behaviour, together with the theory that groups were capable of producing significant behavioural change. A move to working in groups was also seen as time saving. Finally, if for no other reason, many social workers felt frustrated with traditional one-to-one interventions.

All seasoned social workers have at some point in their career had the painful experience of sitting across from a youngster who has chosen to be verbally non-communicative. The worker's statements and questions are responded to in the same manner – either silence or monosyllables. After ten minutes of the monologue the worker feels angry and after another ten minutes he begins to feel inadequate. If by some unfortunate coincidence he should run into the same kind of response on the same day with another youngster, the professional may begin to

Working with troubled adolescents
ISBN 0 – 12 – 179720 – 1

question whether or not he is cut out to work with anyone under 21. (Reid, 1980 p. 211.)

The creation of large, unified social services departments, staffed by many newly qualified workers, proved an acceptable breeding ground for adopting a different approach to working with adolescents. However, this change in working methods also posed problems and difficulties.

Like many approaches that grow rapidly, expectations often become generalized and overstated. By the late 1970s a considerable confusion had arisen concerning what form social work with adolescents should actually take and whether it was or was not intermediate treatment (Jones and Kerslake, 1979). This confusion was not only terminological, it also extended into practice. Should this work be a specialist or a generic social work activity? Who should it be for? Those involved in groupwork programmes often ranged from adolescents simply known to social work agencies, to those on court orders, to young people in residential care. This breadth of clientele was reflected in the aims for the groups, which as Bottoms (1983) states were "staggeringly vague and wide". In his research review he does however go on to outline three strategies that groups often held in common: delinquency prevention, prevention of custody or residential care, and an improvement in personal functioning (Bottoms, 1983).

Achieving these aims was clearly well beyond the capabilities of what so far had been fairly low intensity interventions. The groups were unlikely to avoid delinquency as their programmes were neither constructed around its causation nor tackled reasons for offending. They were unlikely to avoid care or custody as they were simply not matched in intensity to the level of problems creating the demand for an institutionalized response. Finally, their ability to demonstrate an improvement in personal functioning was limited by the lack of clear goals and tasks in the group programmes. Rather than furthering the original aim of Intermediate Treatment, i.e. intervention intermediate in intensity between supervision and residential care, the groups had tended to replace the lower intensity statutory functions of supervision, i.e. "to advise assist and befriend". The content of the group programmes also tended to reflect this by consisting of games or activities, designed to improve or create relationships between supervisor and supervisee.

As a consequence of these problems, in the 1980s attention and practice began to shift from field social worker-based interventions. Recent policy, particularly in the field of delinquency, has moved in two separate and contradictory directions. On the one hand, under financial pressure to provide alternatives to care and custody, agencies have gradually created a series of specialist projects staffed by specialist workers. Yet on the other hand, following a mixture of diversion, decarceration and non-intervention policies (Miller, 1978; Schur, 1973), there has been an increased emphasis on pre-court forms of action. Despite this, and perhaps recognizing that many of social workers' adolescent clients are non-delinquent, a considerable number of low intensity groups remain. However, this shift in emphasis is not without significance. It represents part of a wider reaction to social work intervention as vague, unmeasurable and potentially damaging. If this form of work with adolescents in groups is to survive and develop, social workers need to respond by being both precise and non-labelling in the construction and implementation of groupwork programmes. This means being clear about how such groups are planned, what skills are demanded, and how those skills should be evaluated. The remainder of this chapter concentrates on these issues.

LEADERSHIP PREPARATION

Four particular areas of preparation confront the social worker(s) prior to the first meeting of a group: establishing appropriate aims and objectives, gaining the support and validation of the parent agency, preparing the programmes and emotional preparation.

Aims and objectives

A variety of checklists are now available (Hodge, 1977; Jones and Kerslake, 1979; Scottish I.T. Resource Centre, 1981) which outline in a comprehensive and practical form the tasks a social worker needs to cover before the commencement of a groupwork programme. The central theme to these approaches is that of starting from a clear goal or purpose based on evidence of need. Upon this many other decisions depend, such as the programme content, the number of group members, how frequently it should meet, etc. However, this needs-based approach is not always followed. As Hodge argues:

> Motives for starting a group should be related to a perceived need in the agency's clients and not primarily to the social groupworkers own need for self-development, self-expression or curiosity. (Hodge, 1977, p. 8.)

Personal interest, however, is not the only distraction. There is always the danger of starting from something other than need when, as economists would put it, "items are fixed in supply". These pre-conditions are not always clearly stated, but are often disguised by agencies when there is an insistence that either certain workers are involved, or certain group members attend or particular premises are used.

In all of these examples someone is saying, "Whatever you are planning, you have to do it within this framework or take into account these constraints." Whilst constraints are realistic and are always going to exist, if planning *starts* from limitations, then the possibility of the group meeting needs other than those of the adolescents becomes greater. These problems can be illustrated from the historical background. Here the need to limit delinquent behaviour and avoid residential care or custody was apparent from workers' caseloads. The "item fixed in supply" was that social workers could only allow time for one group session a week. An approach based on need should have dictated either arguing for more time or workers for the agency or offering lower priority but achieveable aims for the group. There is good research evidence to argue for aims that are limited but precise (Rutter and Giller, 1983; Goldberg and Connelly, 1981). Projects that have a single, identifiable and achieveable goal tend to be not only more successful but are also better able to describe and account for their success. The alternative – groups which allow a dangerous mis-match between achieveable and fantasy aims – can lead to difficulties. For example:

1. One or two adolescents possessing problems demanding far more time and/or control than other group members.

2. A disparity between one worker and another, or between workers and members, over the purpose of meeting and therefore over programme content.

3. An inability to tackle serious problems, yet claiming that the group has this as an aim.

If in the adolescent these problems are linked to delinquency, then the appearance of the group "failing" may actually promote the adolescent into care or custody, rather than divert him or her from that outcome. This process, known as "net widening", has been one of the main criticisms levelled at low intensity groupwork with adolescent offenders (see Thorpe, et al., 1980; Rutherford, 1986).

The model for planning aims and objectives is therefore a sequential one. The first step calls for a review of how adolescent needs are currently being met, their effectiveness, and the potential for alternatives within the workers' agency. If a low intensity, social worker-led group is then felt to be appropriate, it is still important to reflect on which needs and/or problems the approach is not going to tackle. In reviewing the efficacy of this type of intervention previous research evaluation can be helpful. Rutter and Giller (1983) discuss, in reviewing the effectiveness of Intermediate Treatment groups, the need for contact and work with families. Jones (1979) looks at the issues of sustaining the effects of the programme beyond the duration of the group.

Next, the more practical questions concerning the group's resources and boundaries should be answered. Resolution of these questions can also be aided by using research. For example (see Hare, 1962), in determining how many members should be invited, the smaller the group:

1. The easier it becomes to work with.

2. The pace of group development gets faster and cohesion is achieved sooner.

3. More complex tasks can be tackled and greater individual contact within the group becomes possible.

However, "small is not always best":

1. The marginal resource costs are greater per member.

2. It might limit the use of some techniques, such as role play.

3. The greater the possibility that the group might avoid rather than confront reality (see Grunsell, 1978).

Finally, there is a need to discuss the aims and boundaries of the group with the potential group members, by face to face contact with those running the group.

Agency preparation

Agency preparation means making sure that the groupwork programme is congruent with the agency. Simply put: that the work happens because of, rather than despite, the parent agency. The social worker's task is to get the agency to recognize the groupwork programme as a legitimate part of that worker's tasks and duties. The consequences of not doing so only increase pressure on the individual worker and potentially denigrate any successful outcomes. The goals are therefore both political and strategic, the aim being to obtain recognition and support. If the group is effective and successful, and similar needs are still evident amongst other adolescents, then it should become an established part of that agency's responses. For that to occur the agency needs to recognize the group's existence. Support can vary from colleagues asking how the group is progressing through to covering the groupworker's other tasks. Failure to gain agency acceptance can mean any of the following difficulties:

1. Pursuing the work in your own time.

2. Failure to gain support, supervision or consultancy for what you are doing.

3. An inconsistent approach being offered to agency clients, leading to confusion over who gets what kind of service and why.

4. Groupwork with adolescents being viewed as your own idiosyncratic idea; best left for you alone to practise.

Programme preparation

One of the contributory factors leading to a decrease in the importance of low intensity groups for adolescents was the gap between leadership ability and expectations. To a casual observer it would often have been hard to determine the goals of the groups from an examination of their content. As Jones, in his research, revealed:

> It is also debateable whether the programmes of these groups can really be described as groupwork, where there is a conscious and planned attempt to work with processes within the group, as compared to arranging and supervising an activity programme for a group of young people. The groups varied in the extent to which they used the processes and dynamics of the group to influence the adolescents, but with limited experience and expertise in groupwork, some of the social workers were dissatisfied with their performance. (Jones, 1979, p. 41.)

The irony is that a considerable wealth of material is now available from which social workers can design a groupwork programme (see Priestley, McGuire, Flegg, Hemsley and Welham, 1978; Armstrong, 1979; Dearling, 1979; Lennox, 1982; Ball and Sowa, 1985). Many of these approaches use structured interventions in the form of either role plays, games or exercises. Whilst such material provides a basis for programming it also offers the temptation to select a ready-made package, and apply it to a group.

Designing a successful programme means knowing in advance what you are going to do and why you are going to do it; being able to explain how you hope it can aid achievement of the aims for the group; and rehearsing the programme, yet being able to abandon any particular individual exercise if it does not feel right at the moment of implementation. Learning skills in designing and implementing a group programme is similar to learning skills in any other area. You begin with basic rules, e.g. the selection of an appropriate series of exercises or activities. At first they feel unnatural, they are part of another person's abilities rather than your own. The tendency is to hide this apprehension by saying, "I could not do that", or "they would laugh at this"; in effect presenting anxiety as inability. Gradually, through rehearsal and practice, the skills become part of your style of work. In groups this means maintaining a balance between objectivity and flexibility, to know when to go on to the next task, when to extend an exercise to a greater depth of discussion, and when to make things light or become serious. Achieving this balance means that the programme for each session forms the framework for working, rather than the goal. Provided that group aims take priority over the programme, the dangers of overusing exercises and structured experiences should be limited (see Anderson, 1980).

In low intensity groups, which meet only once or twice a week for a limited time span, there is a need to be conscious of the limitations this places upon programming. At the end of any one session the group participants have to return to their home, neighbourhood, school or community – locations which are likely to re-stimulate problems. Unlike day or residential care, "loose ends" left from a group session are less likely to be picked up by another caring individual. Awareness of this vulnerability should encourage workers to structure each session, to complete work within given time spans and to have clear objectives.

Emotional preparation

In establishing the aims and objectives, preparing the programme and gaining agency acceptance, it is easy for workers to avoid their own emotional preparation. Add to that pressure a dash of defensiveness and an assumption that qualified social workers should automatically have a stock of skills, and a recipe for poor work is constructed.

Part of the social worker's task is to get in touch with adolescence and to have a model of "normality" to work with (Laufer, 1980). There are various ways of achieving this. It is useful to review your own adolescence, your relationship with your parents, your siblings and your peers. How did your public, visible image differ from your private feelings? How does this view of your adolescence compare to that of others? It can be helpful to use not only the social work literature, but also works of fiction, e.g. Bleasdale (1976), as a route to gaining understanding. If you have had little contact with adolescents in the past, spending some time in youth clubs is a good way of gaining "first-hand" experience. Considering how you communicate is also important. Talk to the adolescent as a child and you patronize, even if the behaviour was childish or, more likely, regressive. Talk as an adult, or make assumptions concerning knowledge, and you run the danger of being misinterpreted or not understood.

Constructing a model of "normality" is particularly important where social workers hold legal powers, if "normal", but testing behaviour, is not to be interpreted as "difficult" or problematic. Without such a perspective it is easy to see how a worker's personal difficulties in encountering adolescence can be translated as the adolescent's individual problem rather than that of the worker.

Further preparation needs to take into account the "group" context of meeting. First, even groups which only meet once a week still have an intensity that is not possessed by individual social worker/adolescent contact. Secondly, power automatically shifts from the worker to being shared (sometimes not always comfortably) with the group. Thirdly, the worker needs to be sensitive to the unique position that he or she holds. It calls for the effective use of a variety of roles; from authority figure to counsellor to friend; from leader to facilitator to participant. The aim (as discussed in worker evaluation below) is not only to understand and practise these different roles, but also to be able to move cleanly and in a way that is understood by the adolescent, from one role to another.

Finally, work in groups frequently entails working with a co-leader. Because workers share a common knowledge base, or an office, or an interest in adolescence, the assumption should not be made that they also share the ability to work together. Before a group programme begins, the values and beliefs that each worker holds and their attitudes to each other need to be rigorously tested. Ball and Sowa (1985) suggest ways of clarifying common values and there is also a computer programme which enables workers to plan, test and evaluate their leadership together (Kerslake and Charlton, 1985).

How social workers prepare will vary according to knowledge and experience, yet their interventions should have common foundations. There is the need to be "present" – to be relaxed and sensitive to what is going on, not with your mind on other work outside the group. There is a need to have a model of "normality" (probably combined with a sense of humour), and to enter the group *with* a flexible but well-prepared programme and a clear idea of your ultimate objective, but *without* anything of yourself that you need to prove or protect. Finally, there is a need to remain honest, not only because adolescents, lacking adult pretention, have a unique ability to uncover lies, but also because many of social work's adolescent clients will have been frequent recipients of deceit. As Reid (1980) states, by the time an adolescent enters a group, he or she will probably have been lied to by parents, relatives and possibly teachers, the police, and other social workers. Having learnt to adapt to an adult world which seems filled with phoniness and manipulation, the social worker who simply asks for trust, without demonstrating their own trust and commitment, is going to fail.

It may be felt that preparation has been discussed at length and at the expense of work within the group. However, as Douglas argues:

> There is mounting evidence that the single factor which is responsible for the breakdown of more groups than any other is lack of adequate preparation. Obviously preparation cannot take into consideration all the possible changes that may occur, but it must provide a secure basis from which to start. (Douglas, 1976, p. 56.)

LEADERSHIP STYLES IN THE GROUP

So far the term "leadership" has been used to describe a social worker's role in working with a group that he or she has formed. It is not an ideal term. We all have different ideas of what being a leader means, yet the word acts as a reminder of the responsibility social workers need to accept when they form groups. Many of the leadership models available are rather static and reflect ideal types rather than practical approaches (Lippit and White, 1962; Fielder, 1965). The use of the word "style" also has significance. It is intended to imply not only different styles of work between workers, but also that an individual worker's style needs to change during the life span of a group. This idea of a changing leadership style, which reflects the development of the group, has already been explored in terms of group models by Whittaker (1970). Table 1 suggests an alternative model of leadership development for social workers working with adolescent groups.

Initially the worker's role reinforces the preparatory work. This includes repeating the ideas that have previously been discussed individually, about the

Table 1 *Theoretical models of leadership style*

Leadership style	Task	Stage of development	Example
Originator	Responsible for: bringing the group members together; honestly outlining the goals and potential content of the group; establishing that the goals are congruent with the needs of the members; marshalling personal resources.	Pre-affiliation (Garland *et al.*, 1965) Forming (Tuckman, 1965)	"It is clear that during the early stages of group development the central issue for the group worker is the establishment of a sense of direction and purpose and to bring this about he must be prepared to use his authority whilst being sensitive to suggestions, feelings and initiatives which come from group members." (Waterhouse, 1978, p. 132.)
Enlightened autocrat	Establishes: (a) by personal example, a consistent pattern to the group, e.g. times of starting and ending. (b) a basis for democratic decision-making and "lends a model" of how this might be achieved. (c) a programme which offers safety by its structure, but increasingly allows greater choice to group members. Is clear in enforcing parameters of acceptable behaviour. Works to control deviant power of any one member over another.	Power and control (Garland *et al.*, 1965) Storming (Tuckman, 1965)	"You need to decide what your boundaries are in your relationships with the group and individual group members. What is the role that you are going to adopt within the group? Workers are naturally keen for group members to like them, but this can lead to difficulties if this can not be balanced with the responsibilities workers carry for keeping the group within agreed boundaries." (Ball and Sowa, 1985, p. 4.)

Table 1 *Cont'd*

Leadership style	Task	Stage of development	Example
Boundary maintainer and facilitator	Continually encourages members to help each other. Patrols the boundaries of the group and enforces them by reminders rather than overt control. Acts as a social worker by creating environments in which adolescents can safely bring problems forward for discussion at their own pace. Programme less structured and democratically planned. Is aware of and looks towards positive completion of group programme.	Maturation phase (Sarri and Galinsky, 1967) Performing (Tuckman, 1965)	"A lot of time is spent emphasizing the good qualities of individuals, often qualities they are trying to fight against because they are seen as weak or 'soft'. Self-image is essential to the establishment of the ability in an individual to cope with these pressures of normal life. Unless he believes that he has the qualities to cope with those pressures in a different, more constructive and less self-damaging way, then the whole effort is wasted." (Wealdon Centre, 1977, p. 265.)

purposes of the group, and how they might be achieved. In any group, before trust and confidence can be established, members need to know exactly what they are committing themselves to, and what is expected of them. In part this can be covered by explanation, but workers also need to provide examples which can be readily understood. This can mean starting on work that is central to the purpose of the group rather than tangential; making sure that everyone makes a contribution when people may be shy or embarrassed; being prepared to lead; and placing an emphasis on successful achievement of tasks. Obviously, many of these features of leadership continue throughout the life of the group, but they are particularly crucial at the beginning. If the confidence of group members is lost then it is often hard to regain. The central theme is that if you are responsible for bringing individuals together, you are also responsible for making sure that the group works.

The next task acts as a bridge between the first and second stages of leadership style. There is a need to begin to establish the boundaries, rules and structure of the group, i.e. a controlled framework within which tasks can be completed and objectives achieved.

> It is important and only fair to adolescents in group work that limits of acceptable behaviour, expectations, goals and sanctions should be clearly and unequivocally stated. . . . Not only will the worker's own organization and the public at large expect a degree of control, but the worker too will be aware that if she does not maintain the group structure and allows subcultural influences to develop and subvert the process, work will not be done. (Derricourt and Penrose, 1984, p. 31.)

This second leadership stage is described as "enlightened autocrat". It should not be confused with dictator or megalomaniac. The aim is not to collect arbitrary power, but to provide a framework which is constructive and to the members' benefit. Any boundary, rule or structure that the worker cannot explain or argue for, to the group, is probably best discarded. However, each part of the framework is slightly different. Defining boundaries entails outlining limits, such as acceptable and unacceptable behaviour, or describing issues such as confidentiality. Rules are the means by which those boundaries are then maintained. Structure represents the vehicle by which the group's objectives are achieved. As in constructing the group programme, no pre-determined format is offered, although suggestions for good practice can be made. In rule-making some of these are:

1. As few rules as necessary to maintain the boundaries of the group.
2. All rules should be based on common sense and be enforceable.
3. Rules should be formulated by co-operation, neither any member or leader having an automatic veto.
4. The consequences of rule-breaking should be described and understood.
5. Workers must agree about how rules should be applied.

6. Rules must apply equally to workers and members, e.g. attendance and punctuality.

In terms of boundaries and structure, a common fault of social workers in groups is to try and achieve a democratic style of work too soon.

> Our dilemma with the groups of youngsters is that on the grounds of knowledge or information (the first precondition of wise choice) we cannot expect them to have enough of either commodity necessary to make properly informed decisions. Yet if we veto a democratic process on that basis, we would never reach the situation where the practice of choosing (the second precondition) was ever fulfilled. Our answer is to approach self-government gently and developmentally from the premise that to be free is to know how to use self-government and democracy. (White and Brockington, 1978, p. 91.)

In the initial stages of a group, easy acquiescence often hides a false consensus, as group members find their feet and compare this group to others such as school, or friendship groups. After an identity is established, leadership can become much more of a struggle. Attempts to generate discussion or confront problems may be met, at worst, by refusal to attend, or at best, diffidence, silence or non-co-operation. Survive this and the next test becomes managing choice. If you fail to give sufficient information you end up with weak or unimplementable decisions; offer information and you are accused of dominating the discussion. Even securing participation in the things the group members want can be both tiring and frustrating. Many workers will have experienced times when the simplest of tasks promotes disagreements, tears, fights, rage, storming out of the room, etc. The pressure on the worker is to give in, or complete the task themselves. The alternative, as Grunsell puts it, is to command overtly:

> A whirlwind drive through the centre to cajole, bully and carry all the kids out on a trip. "You'll never know whether you like it till you try. I don't give a damn what you think. Stop yapping! Just *move*". That's what the kids wanted and it was awful. (Grunsell, 1978, p. 41.)

Most of the group development theories anticipate difficulties and testing behaviour fairly early in a group's life. In adolescent groups this is no different, only perhaps more visible. As discussed earlier, given the failure of many adults towards adolescents in trouble, it is of little surprise that when a caring, sharing social worker arrives, rather than being given an open-armed welcome, young people are rightly suspicious. The worker needs to both earn and demonstrate trust. Achieve that goal and the third stage, when the group really begins to work towards its objectives, becomes a possibility.

The third style, of boundary maintainer and facilitator, is rather akin to that of a plate juggler. You rush from one pole to another keeping everything spinning, yet the act is supposed to look effortless. Movement into this stage can sometimes go almost unnoticed. Suddenly, something that used to be a struggle seems a lot easier. By this time workers should be looking to members to play a bigger part in decision-making and there should be a lessening of structure. A mark of progress is often being able to surrender the props that seemed so important in the early stages. As White comments, it might be group members who are reluctant to give this structure up:

> Yet surprisingly, they accepted a degree of structure, and all of them responded to english and maths and commented on its usefulness. In truth, of course, such slots presented a framework of security. . . . From their comments it is clear that we could have introduced even more structure than we did. To be given choice and apparent freedom to select can be very threatening for young people. (White, 1980, pp. 166–167.)

LEADERSHIP EVALUATION

Monitoring progress and outcome is vital if both social workers and agency are to demonstrate that the group's objectives have been achieved. Evaluating leadership is not only an important part of that process, but also necessary for the worker's own personal development. Rutter and Giller, in looking at the outcome of residential care, identify the importance of individual characteristics over regime.

> But the features found to characterize "successful" institutions have not been those which differentiate so-called therapeutic and corrective regimes. Rather, the relevant features seem to involve a combination of firmness, warmth, harmony, high expectations, good discipline, and a practical approach to training (Rutter and Giller, 1983, p. 318.)

Just as emotional preparation can be overlooked amongst the plethora of other tasks before a group begins, so examining worker style can be lost in evaluating the group's outcome. At best we tend to rely on impressions rather than a structured approach to analysis. Dearling (1979) suggests a simple six-point staff development exercise, for use by workers in Intermediate Treatment centres. This can be easily adapted to field social workers' leading groups and used in consultancy/supervision.

1. Re-state what you think the objectives of the group programme are.
2. Give two reasons why you think the group is successful/unsuccessful.
3. In which parts of the work are you: a) most interested. Why? b) least interested. Why?
4. What sort of work are you particularly good at, i.e. discussions, structured exercises, activities, counselling, residential trips?
5. List any weaknesses in your work with the group, which you are aware of, or have been pointed out to you.

6. Co-led groups: Do you think that the staff work together as a team? What do you consider your individual contribution to be? List reasons for your answer.

This type of analysis is a useful starting point for an examination of group leadership issues. Heron (1975 and 1977) suggests a more detailed approach to examining the characteristics of social worker interventions. Although his model stretches across a range of professional roles, it has a particular applicability to work with groups. The detail of his description is helpful, in that he describes positive and negative interventions (those where the outward appearance is therapeutic, but the outcome is not). He terms the latter degenerative interventions. Heron's original model was based on six categories or types of intervention: prescriptive, informative, confronting, cathartic, catalytic and supportive. Using the model as a basis, it is possible to simplify the titles and provide a description of the meaning of each.

Directive interventions. These attempt to lead, influence and/or direct the adolescent towards particular forms of behaviour. This can occur in two areas:

> future behaviour, where the worker may give advice, suggest, command, request, or demonstrate/role play behaviour before the adolescent attempts the same;
> current behaviour, where the worker may verbally direct/monitor/correct or evaluate performance, or non-verbally do the same by eye contact, touch or gesture.

Informative interventions. These seek to give knowledge relevant to the adolescent's needs and interests. This can be done by:

> giving general knowledge;
> giving knowledge that is specific to a particular task, need or interest;
> giving knowledge that is about the adolescent or a particular situation, in which he/she is closely involved.

Informative interventions should enhance, not suppress, the adolescent's need to participate actively in the learning process.

Confronting interventions. These directly challenge the attitude, behaviour or belief of the adolescent. We are often bad at confrontation because, perhaps perversely, we do not use it often enough. The consequences of this are either confrontations that become wrapped in rationalities and only confuse the recipient, or confrontations that emerge in anger or authoritarian control because we have bottled up our feeling for too long. When confrontations are punitive and attacking, they generally fail because the adolescent backs off, hardens his/her defences and counter-attacks in some way. Successful confrontations are those which are clear in their intentions but supportive in their implementation. The adolescents essentially need to feel you are on their side.

Tension-relieving interventions. These are interventions which allow the adolescent to bring to the surface painful emotions. Care should be taken that:

we don't miss emotional cues, when the adolescent is ready and willing to discuss a subject of importance;
that having exposed emotion we don't back off/and close those feelings down, because of our own hesitancy;
that emotional issues are tackled in a conducive environment, where you are free of disruption or disturbance.

Self-discovery interventions. These are interventions which although emanating from the worker allow the adolescents to pursue their own path, by their own route. However, it does not imply abandonment. The worker still needs to use other intervention styles in being both supportive and encouraging. Some of the assumptions behind such an approach are that:

adolescents are experts about themselves;
individuals often need help to utilize fully their own resources;
the effects of learning can be more lasting when we discover things for ourselves.

Supportive interventions. Being supportive means more than the rather lazy ''grunts of agreement'' we often offer others. It is all too easy for these to confirm people's problems rather than help resolve them. At one level, support means a range of verbal and non-verbal actions. At another, it is a powerful statement about your attitude towards the recipient. You cannot genuinely be supportive without at the same time affirming the worth and value of the adolescent and doing so in an unqualified manner.

In addition to the six categories, there is also a need for a seventh which acknowledges the impact that power differentials can have on social worker/ adolescent relationships.

Interventions which lessen status differences. It is easy for adolescents to feel powerless when in individual contact with social workers. These can centre on adult/ adolescent differences, worker/client conflict and whose territory you meet on. Social workers who are unsure of their own authority when experiencing leadership problems within the group are always vulnerable to using status as a means to regain control.

Taking the seven categories as a basis for evaluation, social workers can develop their own analytical tools. Ranking the categories, from those they feel most to least competent in using, is a starting point. Taking each category in turn and looking at how they occurred in the group programme could prove valuable. Find examples from your own practice of how you use the categories both negatively and positively, e.g.

Degenerative supportive interventions:

mis-using your own experience, such as "when I was your age", or "when you are older you will . . .";

appearing to support negative behaviour, such as bullying, by not intervening;

avoiding giving genuine praise by adding "but if only you had . . ." after your encouragement, or patronizing an adolescent on an achievement which you might not see as significant.

Positive supportive interventions:

being able to offer physical contact from touch to full embrace as a means of showing support;

being prepared to join in and reveal your weaknesses as a way of encouraging others;

an ability to show feelings of liking, affection and fondness.

Most social workers with adolescents, apart from trainee saints, will have both positive and negative interventions as part of their practice. The negative ones most often occur when we feel tired or vulnerable. Recognizing them as warnings is a strength rather than a weakness. By identifying positives as well, they can help to constitute a route to improved practice.

CONCLUSION

Social work with adolescents in the kind of groups described in this chapter is not an easy task. It commands fewer resources than residential or day care, yet exposes workers to many of the problems of demanding relationships encountered in those settings. It calls for the worker to assess realistically the needs of adolescents supervised by the agency, to define achievable goals for the limited life of the group and to accomplish a host of practical tasks in preparing and following a groupwork programme. In addition, in establishing trusting relationships with the group members, it is likely to challenge both the worker's personal values and emotional strengths. If successful, few outside the group will understand the effort involved to achieve that outcome. If it fails, the worker's error will probably be seen in trying at all, rather than in needing help to get it right next time.

Low intensity groups are not likely to bring about major personal change. More intensive interventions, whether at a personal, family, community or political level, find that hard enough to achieve. However, neither should such groups trivialize by offering limited programmes or objectives which substitute physical activity for problem-solving. Well-led and well-designed groups can offer their participants a sense of belonging, the achievement of a particular task or skill, feelings of self-worth, and some personal insight into behaviour with ideas of how to avoid damaging outcomes – valuable benefits to those who have rarely achieved such feelings before.

REFERENCES

Anderson, J. (1980). Structured Experiences In Growth Groups in Social Work. *Social Casework*, 277–287.

Armstrong, H. (1979). *The Youth Games Handbook*. Scottish I.T. Resource Centre.

Ball, L. and Sowa, T. (1985). *Groupwork and I.T. – A Practical Handbook*. The Junction Project.

Bleasdale, A. (1976). *Scully*. London: Hutchinson.

Bottoms, A. (1980). *Feasibility Report for Research into Intermediate Treatment*. National Youth Bureau.

Dearling, A. (1979). *The Use of Recording in I.T.* I.T. Mailing, No. 4, National Youth Bureau.

Derricourt, N. and Penrose, J. (1984). Group Work with Young Offenders. *Social Work Education*, Vol. 4, No. 1, 29–33.

Douglas, T. (1976). *Groupwork Practice*. London: Tavistock.

Fielder, F. (1965). The Contingency Model. In *A Theory of Leadership Effectiveness in Basic Studies in Social Psychology*, Proshansky, H. and Seidenberg, B. (Eds). New York: Rinehart & Winston.

Garland, J., Jones, H. and Kolodny, R. (1965). A model for stages of development in social work groups. In *Explorations in Groupwork*, Bernstein, S. (Ed). Boston: University of Boston Press.

Goldberg, M. and Connelly, N. (1981). *Evaluative Research in Social Care*. Heinemann.

Grunsell, R. (1978). *Born to be Invisible*. London: Macmillan.

Hare, P. (1962). *A Handbook of Small Group Research*. New York: The Free Press of Glencoe.

Heron, J. (1975). *Six Category Intervention Analysis*. University of Surrey.

Heron, J. (1977). *Dimensions of Facilitator Style*. London: British Postgraduette Medical Foundation.

Hodge, J. (1977). Social Groupwork-Rules for Establishing the Group. *Social Work Today* **8**, 8–11.

Jones, R. (1979). *Fun and Therapy: Consumer and Social Worker Perceptions of Intermediate Treatment*. National Youth Bureau.

Jones, R. and Kerslake, A. (1979). *Intermediate Treatment and Social Work*. London: Heinemann.

Kerslake, A. and Charlton, D. (1985). *Developing Adolescent Projects: A Computer Assisted Training and Consultancy Package for Social Workers*. University of Bath.

Laufer, M. (1980). Which adolescents must be helped and by whom? *Journal of Adolescence* **3**, 265–273.

Lennox, D. (1982). *Residential Group Therapy for Children*. London: Tavistock.

Lippitt, R. and White, R. (1962). Leader Behaviour and Member Reaction in Three "Social Climates". In *Group Dynamics: Research and Theory*, Cartwright, D. and Zander, A. (Eds). New York: Columbia University Press.

Miller, J. (1978). *Systems of Control and the Serious Juvenile Offender*. Washington: Washington, D.C. Department of Justice.

Priestley, P., McGuire, J., Flegg, D., Hemsley, V. and Welham, D. (1978). *Social Skills and Personal Problem Solving*. London: Tavistock.

Reid, K. (1980). Some Common Problems in Working with Adolescents. In *Social Work with Adolescents*, Jones, R. and Pritchard, C. (Eds). London: Routledge and Kegan Paul.

Rutherford. A. (1986). *Growing out of Crime*. Penguin.

Rutter, M. and Giller, H. (1983). *Juvenile Delinquency: Trends and Perspectives*. London: Penguin.

Sarri, R. and Galinsky, M. (1967). A conceptual framework for group developments. In *Readings in Group Work Practice*. Vintner, R. (Ed). Michigan: Campus Publishers.

Schur, E. (1973). *Radical Non-Intervention*. Englewood Cliffs, NJ: Prentice Hall.

Scottish I.T. Resource Centre (1981). *The I.T. Resource Manual*. I.T. Resource Centre and Lothian Regional Council.

Tuckman, B. (1965). Some Stages of Development in Groups. *Psychological Bulletin* **63**, 384–399.

Thorpe, D., Smith, D., Green, C. and Paley, J. (1980). *Out of Care: The Community Support of Juvenile Offenders*. London: George Allen and Unwin.

Waterhouse, J. (1978). Group Work in Intermediate Treatment. *British Journal of Social Work* **8**, 127–144,

Wealdon Centre. (1977). The Wealdon Centre in *Intermediate Treatment: 28 Choices*. D.H.S.S. Development Group, 262–267.

Whittaker, K. (1970). Models of Group Development: Implications for Social Group Work Practice. *Social Service Review* Sept 1970, 308–22.

White, R. (1980). *Absent with Cause*. London: Routledge and Kegan Paul.

White, R. and Brockington, D. (1978). *In and Out of School*. London: Routledge and Kegan Paul.

6. Innovation in an adolescent unit: the introduction of small group work

DEREK STEINBERG

An organization that deals with difficult problems for which there is no predictable, straightforward blueprint for success has to meet two major challenges: to maintain a reasonable sense of stability and security for its staff and clientele, but at the same time try new approaches. Stability has its "dark side" – institutionalization. But so has experimentation and innovation, because they entail risks. In the stress-prone environment of psychiatric units there is always the endemic problem that staff will be tempted to stick with what they know, with what seems to work more or less well, and use such energy and initiative as they have left over for reacting to emergencies. Even psychiatric hospitals, units and teams which regard themselves as progressive are as vulnerable to being unnecessarily conservative as the more easily maligned old-fashioned institutions. Innovation is an issue for all services.

This chapter is about the introduction of small group work to a stable, well-established adolescent unit which was already doing a satisfactory job. There is a little about small group therapy with adolescents, but it is mostly about another group of people: ourselves, the staff.

THE UNIT AT BETHLEM

Recent developments at the Adolescent Unit at the joint Bethlem Royal and Maudsley Hospital have been fairly fully described in a recent book (Steinberg,

Working with troubled adolescents
ISBN 0 – 12 – 179720 – 1

1986). The unit was one of the first in the United Kingdom and among the first in the world to specialize in work with adolescents. It opened in 1949, one year after the unit at St Ebba's in Epsom, now at Long Grove (Sands, 1953; Warren, 1952). I worked as a psychiatric trainee at the Bethlem unit in 1971, returning as consultant psychiatrist "in overall charge" in 1975.

I found a most experienced group of staff, with the emphasis of management on individual work with the adolescent and separate work with parents. A lot of work was done with the young people together, particularly in the school and in games and outings, and the unit had a strong corporate identity. However, while the staff were well attuned to the currents of feelings and behaviour throughout the unit, these were not particularly a focus for exploration or work by patients, their families or the staff themselves. An important characteristic of the unit was its division into two wards: one, upstairs, for boys, with Philip Connell as consultant, and, downstairs, Wilfrid Warren's girls' ward. Joining, with a little trepidation, such a distinguished organization, I felt I had two general obligations: to keep it as good as it was, and to help it change.

Before describing the groups, which were both an instrument of change within the unit and evidence of its development, two things should be said about a policy which the senior staff increasingly shared and which has stood the test of time. We did not see the unit as developing into a therapeutic community, still less being primarily a psychotherapeutic resource. It was felt that the primary purpose of a hospital-based adolescent unit was to provide a general psychiatric service for boys and girls who needed the basic skills of psychiatrists and psychiatric nurses. These skills certainly included the ability to use socio-therapeutic and psychotherapeutic methods, but not as an alternative to using behaviour therapy programmes, medication and investigating and managing physical aspects of disorder. A psychiatric hospital unit justified its expense and complexity by being generally-orientated and eclectic, and by taking as wide a range of patients for as wide a range of psychiatric reasons as possible (Steinberg, 1981, 1982, 1983). Meanwhile the increasing number of people skilled in family work, and indeed the achievements of family approaches (e.g. Dare, 1985 and 1986), led to many hard-to-handle adolescents being "held" successfully in their homes, as outpatients; while similar methods, integrated with consultative work (Caplan, 1970; Steinberg and Yule, 1985), meant that many disturbed youngsters could be managed in children's homes which would otherwise have wanted them transferred.

The result of trying to keep adolescents from hospital admission, and focusing the inpatient work on general psychiatric tasks, was that our inpatients began to include an increasing number of boys and girls with psychoses and with physical and intellectual problems.

GROUP WORK WITH ADOLESCENTS

We believed that definite limits were necessary to help the boys develop an awareness of their own behaviour and to modify it . . . they could "do tricks" on the
pipes on the ceiling, but they were not allowed to play on the fire escape.
(Stranahan, Schwartzmann and Atkin, 1957.)

These are not ordinarily part of the preoccupations of group psychotherapists;
people working with adolescents, however, know that these are exactly the sort
of matters to allow for, to have rules about, if work is to remain viable.

Why do group work at all? We could find no convincing evidence that group
work with adolescents achieved any particular goals; nonetheless the field has
quite an extensive literature (e.g. Evans, 1965; Kraft, 1968; MacLennan and
Felsenfeld, 1968; Frank and Zilbach, 1968; Berkowitz, 1972; Meeks, 1974;
Abramowitz, 1976; Acton, 1970; Bruce, 1975, 1978; O'Brian, Bruggen and
Dunne, 1985). Yet there is much convincing evidence to support the everyday
impression that informal group activity with peers is powerfully influential for
good or ill during adolescence (e.g. see Coleman, 1980; Brittain, 1968; and
review in Wolkind and Rutter, 1985). It seemed to us that however else we
worked with adolescents, e.g. individually or in families, we could all learn
something if organized, supervised work in groups became part of the unit's
programme.

In any case, much of the life of the unit already operated on a group or small
group basis. Much of the teaching in the school, our occupational therapist's
work, and creative and recreational activities such as painting, pottery, music,
drama, cooking, camping, outings and games (quite apart from informal
gatherings in the ward) took place naturally on a small group basis. Understanding of what went on in such groups, however, was unevenly spread; some
staff used theoretical positions they were familiar with, some used their intuition, and some were not particularly conscious of group processes operating at
all. We were using various group activities as key therapeutic and educational
tools, and indeed as a major part of our rationale for providing residential treatment, without giving group work as such the critical attention it deserved.

Systematic group work, then, would help affirm an important part of the
unit's milieu, develop its effectiveness, and provide a focus for learning, teaching and research about groups in general.

Some theoretical principles for small group work

The strongest principle we used was pragmatic rather than theoretical or ideological: small group activities were already an influential part of the unit's social
environment. Therefore we would organize ways of seeing what went on in
them and examining what we found.

Secondly, as many clinicians have found, a large proportion of adolescents feel less vulnerable in groups, less uncomfortably isolated with the therapist, and less exposed to overwhelming and mixed feelings about the adult concerned (e.g. Evans, 1965). These are feelings which professional workers would sometimes reciprocate too, especially since hopeless and despairing adolescents tend to project such feelings onto the therapist in the guise of attributed qualities.

For many staff and adolescent patients, the key psychodynamic and psychotherapeutic principle of transference (see Brown and Pedder (1979) for a good, brief account) is more accessible and usable in group work than it is in individual work. Among staff whose work is not usually perceived as operating at levels where transference and countertransference occur – such as many teachers and nurses – it is relatively unusual for supervision time to be set aside to look specifically at such feelings. The small groups and their supervision were set up as, among other things, a bridge between expert ''psychotherapy'' and the important, demanding but less intensively supervised day-to-day transference of feelings between staff and patients.

Acton (1970), while pointing out that the literature on group work with adolescents is frustrating and disappointing, stresses four important principles, which we adopted in our own work. The group therapists should be active, not passive; firm limits should be set on behaviour in the groups; the impression that adolescents are prepared to learn more from peers than from adults needs recognition; and the feelings generated in the therapist should be regarded as significant.

Bruce (1975 and 1978), following Winnicott (1971), emphasized the importance of demonstrating staff survival. The principle here is that the adolescent push towards independence, with its implicit or explicit challenge to adults, is accompanied by an unconscious fantasy of destroying and replacing them. To adapt an aspect of attachment theory (e.g. Bowlby, 1979), the adolescent needs a safe base in terms of his or her relationships in order to conduct social and personal experiments, which at some level are charged with dangerous feelings. The adult task is threefold: to provide what Bruce called a ''play area'' in which the adolescent can conduct his risky games; to ensure that the game is played by guiding, clarifying and giving ''feedback'' about behaviour to the boys and girls – in essence, teaching them; and by surviving, i.e. demonstrating that it is possible to stand by one's adult position (e.g. the rules) in the face of the adolescents' attempt to undermine or attack. This demonstrates that it is ''alright'' to be adolescent, and feasible and even desirable to be adult. ''Adults are needed if adolescents are to have life and liveliness'' (Winnicott, 1971). It is not an experiment with hypothetical abstractions: the adolescent is finding out how to assert himself, deal with being anxious, disagree with others, climb down having made a mistake, and so on, without irreparably hurting others or losing self-esteem. To this extent our small group work straddled psychotherapy and social skills training, with the emphasis on the latter.

The central principle for the groups was to provide a safe-enough ''space'' in which disturbed boys and girls could be helped to develop basic skills in inter-personal relationships. We made the assumption that if they did so they would not only develop improved social skills outside the group, and grow in the esteem of their peers, but acquire greater self-esteem and self-confidence. We did not regard these goals as particularly ambitious, but thought them appro-priate for the young people in our unit whom we considered both markedly heterogenous and unwell for an adolescent inpatient population. To this extent we did not see the groups as exactly equivalent to small psychotherapy groups. Rather, they formed part of the unit's wider social matrix, enabling more speci-fic therapeutic and educational methods to operate within.

We made another set of assumptions that influenced the way we worked. It has often been observed that groups can mirror individuals – both individual development and individual deviations. For example, groups have been described as going through anxiety-laden, paranoid and depressive periods, but also as being realistic, setting conscious goals and working towards them (e.g. Bion, 1961; Walton, 1974; Skynner, 1975). The principle of transference suggests, furthermore, that in a therapeutic relationship individual feelings and behaviour can similarly recapitulate earlier feelings and behaviour. On the basis of these fairly fundamental psychotherapeutic notions we developed a set of goals for the groups and the individuals in the groups, based on Erikson's epigenetic model of human development (Erikson, 1963). This epigenetic, ''stepwise'' model (Figure 1) provided a useful framework for a series of succes-sive goals for the groups, and particularly for the individuals. Figure 2 lists a translation of Erikson's ''favourable outcomes'' into what we considered feasible goals. This approach reflected the face-validity or commonsense of Erikson's stages and of our interpretation of them, rather than adherence to a particular hypothetical model.

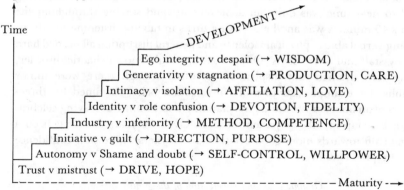

Fig. 1. Schema for Erikson's developmental-epigenetic model of stages in individual emotional development (''favourable outcome'' in brackets)

1. DRIVE, HOPE:	Turning up; turning up on time; Staying; staying until the end.
2. SELF-CONTROL, WILLPOWER:	Behaving reasonably; talking; listening.
3. DIRECTION, PURPOSE:	Participating.
4. METHOD, COMPETENCE:	Planning, experimenting.
5. DEVOTION, FIDELITY:	Belonging to the group.
6. AFFILIATION, LOVE:	Involvement, sharing.
7. PRODUCTION, CARE:	Doing things for and looking after others in the group; and outside it.
8. WISDOM:	Leaving the group; feeling that it had been worth belonging to it; leaving things with the group.

Fig. 2. Adaptation of Erikson's "favourable outcomes" for individual development into operational tasks in the groups

We therefore set our sights to the lowest common denominator we thought could be achieved by a group of young people which might consist of, for example, a 17-year-old boy with autism, a 16-year-old girl with anorexia nervosa, a 15-year-old boy with schizophrenia, two 15-year-olds with severe depression and conduct problems, one highly articulate and the other mildly retarded, and an intelligent 14-year-old with a major obsessive-compulsive disorder. Arrival at a group on time was a big success; for the group to start on time was another; to undertake a task involving most members was a step forward, and involvement of all a major leap forward; remembering last time's group and thinking ahead to next time was quite an achievement; and staying throughout the group's 45 minutes was another. Taking turns in talking, listening to others, avoiding verbal abuse, physical violence and general disruption all needed hard work by staff and adolescents. Often a group would end in chaotic disorder, leaving staff drained and dispirited; yet often enough there were minor triumphs, for example activities or conversation being sustained for three-quarters of an hour, or boys and girls planning a welcoming or leaving celebration for a group member – patient or staff. Over the years there has been a gradual shift towards more good events than disasters, more staff confidence and more predictability.

Organization and supervision of the groups

Another feature of the unit with which planning had to contend was the high proportion of staff in training. As a teaching unit, training is fundamental to its operation; it also means that two-thirds of our staff stay for only three months to a year, about the same length of stay of many children, and shorter than some. We tried to include at least one of the more permanent, senior staff in each group. There were five groups at first, then four when we reduced our bed numbers from 32 to 24. There were usually five or six children in each group, and three staff. They met twice a week for 45 minutes, followed by 15 minutes for the staff alone.

Once a week the staff met together in one of two supervision groups, each taken by two of the more permanent staff members. We had two groups to start with because we wanted to keep each supervision group "small group" size too; this arrangement has persisted despite it now being more feasible to hold a single group. It has provided a useful opportunity to explore staff feelings about competitiveness, curiosity and so on as well as the chance to observe similarities and differences between groups. Every six weeks both supervision groups meet for joint planning and an exchange of ideas and teaching.

The existence and persistence of the groups required help from those not taking part. This help needed to be consistent and, as far as possible, genuine (in Carl Roger's (1961) sense) because adolescents would be expected readily to exploit any ambiguity in the requirement that they should attend the groups; and in any case they would rapidly come to undervalue them if they realized that some staff undervalued them. Young people's acute sensitivity in this respect is a familiar phenomenon. The approach to the staff was threefold, involving education, group experience and direction.

First, seminars and meetings were held to explain and discuss the reasons for introducing group work to the unit; this took place in the more formal administrative meetings too, within the adolescent unit and in the Department as a whole. Doubts, questions and dissent were heard and practical problems responded to. Important practical matters were raised: where could five groups meet in reasonable privacy, since there was competition for such space? When could they meet, since there was the existing ward programme, the school timetable and staff programmes to consider. What would happen during staff leave, and, since nurses wanted to take a major part in the groups, how would they fit into the exigencies of their duty rotas? Was small group work effective? Was it justified to add to the work and timetable of an expensive resource in this way? How would patients be allotted to the groups, and how soon after admission? Immediately, or after an unattached period? Suppose someone would not attend the group? What, if any, symptoms or behaviour would justify exclusion from the group? Might the existence of the groups confuse adolescents already experiencing a very full therapeutic programme, which included other groups, family work and individual work? Might the staff get muddled too? Would the groups "stir things up"?

The introduction of the groups raised all the above issues, and more, in practice as well as hypothetically. But these matters were not special to the groups; questions of attendance, sanctions, inclusion or exclusion, effectiveness and so forth were good questions to ask about everything in the unit's programme. Less overt issues were explored too, particularly in the staff group. Elsewhere (Steinberg, 1986) I have described how this group began as an organization-focused meeting taken by myself, and developed into a staff group taken by an outside consultant (Foskett, 1986), budding off in the process a separate, formal administrative meeting. Issues of authority, control, communication, hope and disappointment, and personal competence (mine, the groups' staff, the unit's staff) were raised, by no means only in relation to the groups; but the groups functioned as a useful focus and catalyst for this sort of discussion. We took care that they did not also become a scapegoat. We learned, therefore, to use group experience to explore many things, including the working of the small groups.

Third, the groups were an exercise in authority too. The senior staff thought the groups were a good idea, their probable advantages (as outlined earlier) outweighing their possible disadvantages, so they took place, without prolonged equivocation.

To return briefly to the question of supervision: at the time group work was introduced to the unit the systematic supervision of clinical work was not well established. In medical circles in particular the supervision of staff in training tends to be confined to the ward round, and detailed, personal supervision of work in progress is the exception rather than the rule. We used the model of psychotherapy supervision in setting up our staff supervision groups, in which the week-by-week progress of the small groups was reviewed using both verbal report and experiential techniques such as role play and sculpting and, with appropriate care and permissions, tape recordings. Problems with videotape and viewing screen facilities have not allowed us to use these in supervision, so far, but such direct observation is valuable and will be introduced.

Progress of the groups

Research

Two colleagues have attempted to develop a simple instrument for recording patterns of behaviour in the small groups with a view to assessing change; Teresa Wilkinson, clinical nurse tutor and one of the group supervisors, and Brian Jacobs, psychiatric registrar, devised a record form to be completed jointly by the small groups' leaders immediately after each meeting. Every six weeks the group leaders did the same exercise separately, to provide a measure of reliability, and in the same week independent measures of the children's functioning were made in the unit's school. Attendance, verbal communication, non-verbal communication, group participation, constructive activity and the amount of intervention required on the part of the group leaders were recorded on five point scales. The study (unpublished) has not gone beyond the pilot stage but Wilkinson and Jacobs felt they had a useful method of assessment which seemed sensitive to changes in group behaviour. A possible use for it would be to test the hypothesis that changes in individual behaviour in the small groups would precede and predict changes in other relationships in the unit and outside. Our impression is that this happens for some young people, particularly in relation to the development of new social skills. However, if this impression were confirmed the question would remain whether the groups produced this change, or whether they were simply the first settings in which the change was expressed or observed.

Undertaking this study proved difficult. The study and the supervision meetings both provided vivid reminders of the vast amount of activity during even a few minutes of a single group, how difficult it is to record observations and experiences while participating in the group, and how elusive the material would be if the observer were not participating.

Effect on the children

The groups have done no harm, and, as mentioned above, we have observed individual improvement taking place in the groups, though without being able to say if the groups were active in bringing it about. Lest this seems a trite observation, it needs to be said that the children in the groups were diagnostically mixed, including young people with psychoses and autism, as well as of both sexes and most intellectual levels from mild mental retardation upwards; moreover, many of our adolescents are seriously disruptive and sometimes aggressive. That the small groups have survived and are settings where improvement takes place and productive work is done very frequently and regularly (games played, activities organized, welcoming and farewell parties held, happiness and sadness shared) has meant for us that they are, on balance, therapeutic.

They have also been accepted by the adolescents; that is to say, reluctance to attend groups has not been strikingly different from reluctance to join in with other therapeutic or educational activities, and it has been treated in the same way, i.e. by insistence that they do. To this extent the groups have become part of the social fabric of the unit, contributing to and reflecting the milieu.

Effect on the staff

Staff too take the groups for granted; they are part of the unit's timetable and help furnish its structure. This was not always the case, and in the first two years staff involved in groups did not always feel that other staff supported them, so that an adolescent found wandering during group time was not invariably confronted. Feelings about taking part, or not taking part, were for a time an important focus of the staff group and were often on the agendas of administrative meetings too.

The groups, always multidisciplinary and always involving nursing staff, have increasingly been a focus for nurses' initiatives; this has been increasingly accepted and recognized by their senior administrators who, in the early days, were inclined to challenge nurses' participation in this sort of activity when "they should be on the wards". The logic of this attitude is not easy to grasp, but has not entirely gone away, and is likely to emerge in times of staff shortages. The clinical nurse has a lot to put up with.

Staff, and again nursing staff in particular, have become enthusiastic about the achievements and methods of groups, and the use of group work, large and small, has increased throughout the unit over the years. Staff taking the groups found them stressful but stimulating from the start. Shortage of participating staff has only been an occasional and transient phenomenon, and most of the time we have had "waiting lists". Feelings of being overstretched by the groups has now become a phenomenon restricted to particular groups at particular times, and dealt with by focused work in the supervision meetings.

Recurring themes, from which we all have learned, include:
(a) Issues of authority and control.
(b) Handling feelings such as helplessness, anxiety and frustration, and understanding the psychological and social dynamics that engender them.
(c) Developing skills in working together, particularly across disciplines and personal styles.
(d) Learning about continuities and discontinuities from the group to outside the group, and with the passage of time; changes, for example, as staff and patients come and go from the unit and the groups.
(e) Learning and clarifying aims and methods in situations that tend towards the chaotic, making useful observations, finding the language to describe and communicate what is going on, setting goals and monitoring progress.
(f) Seeing how adolescents and adults behave together in groups, and finding out how to record and report it.
(g) Seeing how one therapeutic approach functions among many; in the development of the groups, as in the development of the unit as a whole, we have had to work out, and work on, the place of the small groups in an adolescent unit which also uses and teaches family and individual psychotherapy, ward and community group work, behaviour therapy, medication and physical investigation. These and related questions as they apply to the Bethlem unit are discussed by Wilson (1986) and Steinberg (1986).

CONCLUSIONS

The largest question of all concerns how we spend our time. We have no proof that the groups "work" in the sense that would satisfy most scientific enquirers. We do not know enough about how the small groups work to be able to answer such questions as: Does a sense of belonging to a small group reinforce an adolescent patient's sense of belonging to an institution, or does it help the boy or girl orientate towards more natural groups, such as family and friends outside? Does it provide a useful balance between both of these, enabling the patient to use the unit *and* to leave it? If small group work helped provide a way into the unit and a way out it would indeed be useful.

For the unit, the groups have provided a valuable focus for staff training and development. Introduced by a psychiatrist, a teacher and a clinical psychologist (Steinberg, Merry and Collins, 1978), they are now largely run by the nursing staff. They have been a focus for learning about the organization and evaluation of a treatment programme; about approaches to staff training and supervision; and a vehicle for teaching on adolescent and group behaviour, and social dynamic and psychodynamic principles and practice. They have demonstrated the limitations imposed when a teaching unit has to rely on the work of a large number of staff who are in transit; but also the possibilities of this situation. It has, however, proved difficult to evaluate the impact of the groups as systematically as we would have wished. Although we made a start on this, it would have been interesting to have made baseline observations about the unit as well as its patients before the groups started, something I would recommend to any team or organization contemplating introducing them. This is because of a strong impression that whatever the groups have done for the children, they have also achieved a great deal for the unit as a whole.

REFERENCES

Abramowitz, C.V. (1976). The effectiveness of group psychotherapy with children. *Archives of General Psychiatry* **33**, 320–326.

Acton, W.P. (1970). Analytic group therapy with adolescents. Proceedings of the 5th conference of the Association for the Psychiatric Study of Adolescents, pp. 49–59.

Berkowitz, I.H. (Ed.) *Adolescents grow in groups: experiences in adolescent group psychotherapy.* New York: Bruner Mazel.

Bion, W.R. (1961). *Experiences in Groups.* London: Tavistock.

Brittain, C.V. (1968). An exploration of the basis of peer-compliance and parent-compliance in adolescence. *Adolescence* **2**, 445–458.

Brown, D. and Pedder, J. (1979). *Introduction to Psychotherapy. An outline of psychodynamic principles and practice.* London: Tavistock.

Bowlby, J. (1979). *The making and breaking of affectional bonds.* London: Tavistock.

Bruce, T. (1975). Adolescent psychotherapy groups. *Therapeutic Education* **3**, 38–42.

Bruce, T. (1978). Group work with adolescents. *Journal of Adolescence* **1**, 47–54.

Caplan, G. (1970). *The Theory and Practice of Mental Health Consultation*. London: Tavistock.

Coleman, J. (1980). *The Nature of Adolescence*: London: Methuen.

Dare, C. (1985). Family Therapy. In *Child and Adolescent Psychiatry: Modern Approaches*, Rutter, M. and Hersov, L. (Eds), pp. 809–825. London: Blackwell Scientific Publications.

Dare, C. (1986). Family therapy and an adolescent in-patient unit, in *The Adolescent Unit: Work & Teamwork in Adolescent Psychiatry*, Steinberg, D. (Ed.), pp. 83–96. Chichester: John Wiley.

Erikson, E.H. (1963). *Childhood and Society*. New York: W.W. Norton.

Evans, J. (1965). In-patient analytic group therapy of neurotic and delinquent adolescents. *Psychotherapy & Psychosomatics* **13**, 265–270.

Foskett, J. (1986). The staff group. In *The Adolescent Unit: Work & Teamwork in Adolescent Psychiatry*, Steinberg, D. (Ed.), pp. 169–178. Chichester: John Wiley.

Frank, M.G. and Zilbach, J. (1968). Current trends in group therapy with children. *International Journal of Group Psychotherapy* **18**, 447–460.

Kraft, I.A. (1968). An overview of group therapy with adolescents. *International Journal of Group Psychotherapy* **18**, 461–480.

MacLennan, B.W. and Felsenfeld, N. (1968). *Group counselling and psychotherapy with adolescents*. New York: International University Press.

Meeks, J.E. (1974). Adolescent development and group cohesion. In *Adolescent Psychiatry*, Vol. 3, Feinstein, S.C. and Giovacchini, P. (Eds), pp. 289–297. New York: Basic Books.

O'Brian, C., Bruggen, P. and Dunne, C. (1985). Extra meetings: a tool for decisions and therapy. *Journal of Adolescence* **8**, 255–261.

Rogers, C.R. (1961). *On Becoming a Person*. London: Constable.

Sands, D.E. (1953). A special mental hospital unit for the treatment of psychosis and neurosis in juveniles. *Journal of Mental Science* **99**, 123–129.

Skynner, A.C.R. (1975). The large group in training. In *The Large Group*, Kreeger, L. (Ed). London: Constable.

Steinberg, D. (1981). *Using Child Psychiatry*. London: Hodder and Stoughton.

Steinberg, D. (1982). Treatment, training, care or control? The functions of adolescent units. *British Journal of Psychiatry* **141**, 306–309.

Steinberg, D. (1983). *The Clinical Psychiatry of Adolescence*. Chichester: Wiley.

Steinberg, D. (1986). Developments in a Psychiatric Service for Adolescents. In *The Adolescent Unit*, Steinberg, D. (Ed.), pp. 209–221. Chichester: Wiley.

Steinberg, D., Merry, J. and Collins, S. (1978). The introduction of small group work to an adolescent unit. *Journal of Adolescence* **1**, 331–344.

Steinberg, D. and Yule, W. (1985). Consultative Work. In *Child and Adolescent Psychiatry: Modern Approaches*, Rutter, M. and Hersov, L. (Eds), pp. 914–926. London: Blackwell Scientific Publications.

Stranahan, K., Schwartzmann, C., and Atkin, E. (1957). Group therapy for emotionally disturbed and potentially delinquent boys and girls. *American Journal of Orthopsychiatry* **27**, 518–527.

Walton, H. (1974) (Ed.) *Small Group Psychotherapy*. Harmondsworth: Penguin.

Warren, W. (1952). In-patient treatment of adolescents with psychological illnesses. *Lancet* **1**, 147–150.

Wilson, P. (1986). Individual Psychotherapy in a Residential Setting. In *The Adolescent Unit: Work & Teamwork in Adolescent Psychiatry*, Steinberg, D. (Ed.), pp. 97–111.

Winnicott, D.W. (1971). *Playing and Reality*. London: Tavistock.

Wolkind, S. and Rutter, M. (1985). Sociocultural Factors, in *Child and Adolescent Psychiatry: Modern Approaches*, Rutter, M. and Hersov, L. (Eds), pp. 82–100. London: Blackwell Scientific Publications.

7. Boundaries or chaos: psychodrama with adolescents

PAUL HOLMES

J.L. Moreno, in Vienna before World War I, was one of the first clinicians to use groups therapeutically with adolescents (Rachman and Raubolt, 1984). Out of his experiences with the creativities and spontaneity of children playing with him grew his major contribution to the repertoire of psychotherapy: psychodrama (Moreno, 1947). This method, like all the other therapies, has developed a body of techniques and approaches designed both to ensure that the therapy continues for each individual and is helpful (see Blatner, 1973; Leveton, 1977).

Adolescents are not the easiest age group to work with, partially because they are still working on the development of the defences and avoidance techniques they will habitually use as adults. As a consequence they more often feel poorly defended against anxiety and frequently resort to "action defences" rather than developmentally more advanced "psychic defences" (Blos, 1962).

They are constantly, as part of their growth into adulthood, testing and provoking the adults around them with whom they have powerfully ambivalent feelings, wishing both to have a sense of security (through emotional containment) as well as the experience of separateness and freedom. Thus group leaders develop methods of "containing" the anxiety, and setting "boundaries" or "limits" to the potential "acting out".

The parents of many of the adolescents in therapy have been totally unable to meet the developmental needs of their children (either in infancy or later) and at times further tasks fall to the therapists, including those of nurturance, limit

Working with troubled adolescents
ISBN 0–12–179720–1

setting and education (Phelan, 1974). No doubt some of these needs must be met by the therapists in an adult group (Delvey, 1982). However, the urgent (and at times concrete) behaviour of adolescents, coupled with their immaturities, results in a pressure on the therapists to modify their techniques or to incorporate aspects of other therapeutic schools (Rosenberg and Cherbuliez, 1979), requiring a degree of flexibility to reach an integrated effective style.

"Containment" (of feelings) is one aspect of the therapeutic process fundamental to work with children, adolescents/or adults. Bion (1962) developed this concept both in the psychoanalytic setting and in the close relationship of parent and child. By this process, the anxiety of patient (or child) is held within the relationship and made bearable, allowing therapy (or normal emotional growth) to occur.

In psychotherapy, as in life, a complex hierarchical system of containers (with their boundaries) exists. Figure 1 illustrates, in a schematic way, some of the boundaries that we felt were important to the existence of the psychodrama group described in this chapter.

Boundaries may be divided into three categories: those related to interpersonal relationships (including "containment" in Bion's sense); those related to rules and policies, both of the therapeutic technique being used and those specific to a particular therapeutic situation; and boundaries dependent on the physical setting. Within each of these categories a hierarchy exists, from the situation closest to the patient, to those most general and distant from the patient (levels 1 to 5 in figure 1).

In any therapeutic situation (and especially an adolescent group) different boundaries are containing patient and/or staff anxiety at different times. These shifts between boundaries seem to be determined by various factors, for example, by changes in therapeutic policy, by increasing anxiety in the group, or by pressures from outside the group (often out of the control of the therapists). Of course, therapists cannot ever alone maintain control or even awareness of all these factors, but at different times aspects of all these boundaries might intrude into awareness during the running of a group.

This chapter will explore, through the description of one session, some of the stresses that may occur in an adolescent psychodrama group. The techniques used attempted to follow the classical model of Moreno. Other practitioners, working with adolescents, have found it useful to draw more on the theatrical aspects of drama/therapy in an attempt to maintain the group's involvement and to help contain the anxieties roused by the very personal methods of classical psychodrama (Langley, 1983; Shuttleworth, 1983a, 1983b).

Figure 1

FORM OF BOUNDARY OR CONTAINMENT   LEVEL OF BOUNDARY

FORM OF BOUNDARY OR CONTAINMENT	Intrapsychic 1	One-to-One 2	One to Group 3	Group to Group 4	Interagency 5 — Agency to Agency
EMOTIONAL	Patient's own psychic defence mechanisms e.g. denial or projection.	Patient's therapeutic relationship with director or another adult in group. Director's relationship with co-therapist.	Patient's relationship with other adults in group and other group members. Staff support group.	Family sessions. Individual sessions. Liaison with other therapists involved outside the group. Staff supervision.	Contact with schools and referring agencies.
RULES AND PERMISSIONS	Patient's "super-ego" processes.	"Rules" and techniques of psychodrama, e.g. use of technique of "role reversal".	Rules, policies and temperospatial arrangements specific to this group, e.g. coffee to mark start and end of group.	Permission and support from consultant and colleagues. Awareness of group among colleagues in adult psychiatry.	Supervision and control of adolescents by other adults, e.g. school escorts, school staff check child attends, hospital security staff.
PHYSICAL	Patient's defensive use of "action", e.g. nose-picking or head-banging.	Varying physical distance between director and protagonist (therapist and patient) during a psychodrama, altering the protagonist's experience of containment.	Patient's use of favourite chair or curtain as a means of defence.	Consistency of group room and the use of its door as a boundary.	Main hospital front door as a boundary.

A PSYCHODRAMA

The session was attended by five adolescents, and was directed by the author and a co-therapist.

> The afternoon always begins, before any adolescents arrive in the hospital, with my checking with my co-therapist that we have remembered to get coffee and milk. Two early arrivals appear and sit in the waiting room, causing some minor degree of disturbance. We ask our secretary to keep an eye on them.

An essential step before inviting an adolescent to join a group is selection (Kraft, 1961). Psychodrama has been used to help adolescents with a wide range of difficulties (including major conduct disturbances, drug abuse and psychosis). However, in selecting members for an outpatient group it is essential (both for the individual and the group's sake) that some care is taken in deciding which adolescents are suitable (Raubolt, 1983). The potentially explosive and openly needy nature of many disturbed adolescents may precipitate professionals into offering therapeutic help without fully assessing their suitability for the mode of treatment being offered.

Young people must be selected on the basis of a realistic potential for change; a judgement which includes assessment both of their motivation and wish for change and their ability to make relationships (however tentative) with adults and peers. Adolescents should be considered with great caution if:

1. they are so narcissitic they cannot participate in the mutual group process;

2. have such severe personality or conduct disorders that they pose a real threat to the group process (often through ''acting out'');

3. show signs of an active psychotic process;

4. are intellectually retarded so as not to be able to grasp fundamental aspects of the group process;

5. it has also been demonstrated that those adolescents (or their parents) who show a paranoid (or prickly) quality are difficult to engage in an outpatient setting, as the projected anxiety is difficult to contain (Holmes, 1983).

Our experience has shown that other groups of adolescents can benefit from such a group; these include:

1. Isolated, depressed adolescents who benefit from the social aspects of a supportive group (Corder, Whiteside and Haizlip, 1981) and the possibility of feedback from peers.

2. Those adolescents struggling with developmental tasks such as separation from parents, sexual identity and school achievement.

3. Adolescents with intense concern over aggressive feelings, especially when these are confused with issues of dependency on parents.

4. Delinquent adolescents do well, especially when their behaviour appears to relate to inner turmoil and family strife, allowing the development of better ways of dealing with conflict.

There obviously cannot be any rigid guidelines as to which young people might benefit. However, our experience has shown that it is crucial that the adolescent expresses some clear wish for "something to change" in their life, and are able to accept that part of this change *might* have to occur in themselves.

For many adolescents the offer of a psychodrama group will not be their first contact with the helping professions; indeed in our experience many were already patients of the group leaders, a situation that seems to aid engagement in a group (Richmond and Gaines, 1979). It is essential to indicate to the potential group member how the group will differ from their previous experiences (e.g. in school, family therapy or even individual therapy).

The basic "ground rules" of the group must also be made explicit and agreed to by the adolescent in an individual meeting with the group leaders before the adolescent enters the group. Our rules are few and clear:

1. The adolescent must wish to join the group (no parental or legal coercion).

2. The adolescent must *try* to participate, although no one will be forced to be a protagonist.

3. Powerful emotions may be displayed verbally or symbolically but not through direct violence.

4. In times of stress in the group, adolescents must stay in the room (no "running out") and also attempt to come regularly to group meetings.

5. Confidentiality is essential, group members being told they must not talk about *other* members of the psychodrama group outside the sessions. The group leaders must ensure they do not break confidentiality when talking to parents or teachers. Ideally the adolescent should be present when any meetings are arranged between the group leaders and parents or teachers.

It has not been found essential for the group leaders to meet with the parents, as long as some contact exists through some other professional who both gains parental permission for the adolescent to joint the group and carries out any further liaison.

Although developing good relationships with the opposite sex is an essential task of adolescents, we found that in ths group the anxiety, competitiveness and flirtation between the sexes was often very disruptive. Subsequent groups have been run for boys only (with other colleagues running a girls' group), which seems to be a more workable arrangement.

Sarah arrives with the school volunteer who had been escorting her to the group.

This arrangement was organized by her school. It has a particular use on this occasion because Sarah, who could be very provocative, had been in a fight with one of the boys in the group, and as a result was reluctant to leave the group alone at the end. The support of her school (through the availability of an escort) enabled her to feel safer and protected, and to continue to work through the difficulties with the boy.

Five youngsters are now waiting. John and Winston decide to go down to the hospital shop. We remonstrate; we are told the group starts in ten minutes (which is true) and they rush away. By 2.00 p.m. they return, full of excited stories of being picked on by the hospital security staff.

We discovered that although we felt the physical boundary of the group to be the Department of Psychiatry, the adolescents, not surprisingly, felt their outer physical boundary to be the hospital front doors. Within this vast building, the security men become important (and rather unexpected) allies. When the adolescents' anxiety rose too high (as was the case with the two boys on this particular day) and they fled the Department, it was often the security officers (in their rather formal uniforms) who, if trouble ensued, directed the adolescents back to us. Adults unknown to our group seemed, at times, more able to exert authority over them than we did, perhaps because the adolescents were intimidated by strangers. In subsequent groups the other staff members, not involved with the group directly, have fulfilled this role.

We go along to the group room, leaving our secretary to bring along the late-comers. The adolescents are annoyed to find the remains of the food from a lunch time meeting held in the room by another Department. The rubbish is soon moved out into the corridor!

We "borrowed" the group room from adult psychiatry and thus had very little control over this vital "containing" space. Any change in the room provoked increased anxiety in the adolescents (and an associated annoyance and distress in the staff).

PHASE 1 – WARM UP

A general "chat" session starts. This is halted by the arrival of a late-comer, who is teased by the others. I call the group to order and explain that we will start today's session with a guided fantasy exercise.

Classical psychodrama usually starts with "warm-ups", a phase designed partially to increase group cohesiveness, but also to stir up issues in the minds of group members on which they might choose to do some psychodramatic "work" later in the session. "Warm-ups" may be more or less physical or verbal, depending on the leader's assessment of the group's needs that day (Corder, Whitehead and Vogel, 1977; Brandes and Phillips, 1978).

> The youngsters begin to settle. To aid this, the level of lighting is reduced. This, however, at once seems to make Winston more anxious. He gets up, goes over and opens the door, and begins to talk to someone in the corridor beyond.

The door became a very potent boundary for this group. At times, being enclosed in the group room, with all the feelings aroused in there, seemed to produce a sense of "claustrophobia" in the adolescent. Standing half-in and half-out of the room seemed to relieve this tension, complete departure perhaps stirring up other fears. Although, as therapists, we had some control over what happened in the room, once a patient opened the door the room boundary ceased to be the operative container. Now the youngster faced the next level of containment (or lack of it).

The incident with Winston also highlights the need for our group staff to maintain contact and to explain our activities, when possible, to other staff in the Department of Psychiatry, who may have to persuade an adolescent to return to the group room.

> My co-therapist has encouraged Winston to come back into the room, and is now sitting beside him. I begin to start the warm-up.

The co-therapist often accepted the role, for a time, of being a one-to-one "container" of a very anxious or distressed group member, if they would allow this, thus permitting the therapist (or, in psychodramatic terms, the director) to continue with the rest of the group. To focus on the distressed person at once did not always seem appropriate (and, as in the case of Winston, might provide unhelpful secondary gains for the behaviour). On other occasions, when, for example, a group member (not directly involved in a psychodrama) began to cry, an adult might be able to comfort them, by having a quiet talk, while the group continued around them. After a while this contact might help the adolescent share the reasons for their distress with the rest of the group.

> I begin to talk slowly to the whole group, taking them on an imaginary walk from the room we are in, through the hospital, out the front door, across the street (a journey very real to all of us), then through a door and down a long flight of steps to a corridor with several doors leading off it (a place now created uniquely in the mind of each group member). I offer a choice of doors. Each door opens on to a room remembered from the adolescent's real life, past or present.
>
> The group is encouraged in their own minds to explore it and the objects it contains, then to select an object to carry back with them.
>
> I then reverse the journey, until all the group are, in their minds and in reality, back in the group room, still holding, in imagination, their chosen objects.

This guided fantasy, like other psychodrama warm-ups, has a very special relationship to each individual's psychic anxiety. The exercise has apparently rather rigid boundaries offered by the director (in this case the description of the early stages of the journey). Within these safe boundaries, the individual is freed to be creative, again in this case by the choice of rooms and objects.

The choices have a similarity to the free associative process of psychoanalysis (although the psychic significance would not be stressed at this point in a group). It is probable that if a group of disturbed adolescents were to be asked directly to select an object from their past full of emotional significance, more resistance would be aroused and a less pertinent (if any) object would be selected.

> I ask the group, one at a time, to say what object they have returned with, and to talk about it for a few moments. Donna has brought back an old teddy bear, a comfort in her past (and, one suspects, present), while John has brought back an old desk (significantly, the same object was selected by him in a similar exercise some months previous). Slowly the whole group disclose their objects and talk a little about them. In several cases the emotional significance of the object is clear to me (if not, as yet, to the adolescent).
>
> I ask who wishes to do more (*psychodramatic*) work on the object, becoming this afternoon's protagonist ("he who takes the centre of the stage"). Nobody volunteers!

This, in an adolescent group, was not an unusual response. At other times, two or three youngsters might have indicated a desire to "work" on a problem highlighted in their minds by the warm-up. When this occurred, the whole group would be involved in deciding which individual (and thus problem) they wished to see worked on that afternoon. Such decisions could be made through a group discussion or, when no clear choice arose, through some form of vote (perhaps by the group members moving to stand by the person they wished to see as the protagonist). Thus the group take some responsibility for which individual will become protagonist for the next phase of the session.

The process of making a group choice not only increases the chance that the psychodrama will have some relevance to several (if not all) group members, but also increases the protagonist's sense that he has the permission (and thus the support) for his psychodrama. If, however, no protagonist emerged, we would continue the group with less threatening work, sometimes involving the adolescents in more warm-ups, or moving them, perhaps into sub-groups, into the production and presentation of short, improvised sketches, moving closer in techniques to drama/therapy.

This movement away from intrapsychic conflicts reduced the adolescent's anxiety and allowed the group to continue; indeed the dramas produced may well have some less direct symbolic significance for the group members. If, later that afternoon, an individual did seem ready to "work", a psychodrama might well be undertaken (if time allowed).

PHASE 2 - PSYCHODRAMA

I feel John is ready to work, being somehow more open in the group than of late,
and I remind him of his past choice of the same subject. He agrees to "work", but
I sense his mounting anxiety. At this point I move closer to John, giving him
support in his anxiety by my physical presence.

With an adult protagonist some limited physical contact may very usefully
increase the sense of containment (a hand laid lightly on a shoulder or arm).
However, such contact seems, usually, more risky with an adolescent who may
experience it as intrusive, flirtatious or provocative.

It is always crucial that the protagonist agrees to "work". This clearly
verbalized "man-to-man" contract with the director helps to ensure a working
alliance which will act to contain later anxiety in the sessions and avoid a regression in which the protagonist's reality testing of his relationship may become
very strained (i.e. the director moves from a "real" position in which "containment" can be offered to one suffused with projections).

We start with John agreeing to play the desk. I interview the desk standing close to
John, talking to him as if he were the desk.
Me: What sort of desk are you?
J: An old desk, no use to anyone.
Me: How do you know that?
J: I am being thrown away.
Me: By whom?
J: A young woman. She has a better desk now and doesn't need me.
Me: Have you anything special to offer her, better than the younger, newer
        desk?
J: Yes, I've a secret drawer.
Me: (I use my therapeutic alliance to talk to John as John): Is there anyone in the
        group who could play the woman?
J: Yes, Clare (the co-therapist).
        Clare agrees to take on this "auxiliary ego" role for John. A dialogue now
        begins between the "old desk" and the "young woman". At the point at
        which the desk asks again why it is being thrown out, I tell John and Clare to
        reverse roles and Clare, now playing the desk, to repeat the last question,
        which John has now to answer as the young woman.

Role reversal, in which the protagonist changes role with the auxiliary ego, is a
central technique in psychodrama, and is one process that separates it from
some other "active" therapies (e.g. drama therapy or role play).

The experience for a protagonist of playing "the important other" in his life
can be profound. Role reversal is a technique that can be seen to have several
functions:

   1. It helps the director and the group member playing the auxiliary ego
   gain further information about the other person, both as "historical" fact
   and as they are experienced as an inner psychic person in the protagonist's
   mind.

2. It seems to be a potentially mutative experience for a patient to play a person important in their psychic world and to experience themselves, outside, played by the other group member.

3. It also has a profound ability to control excessive regression or extreme affect on the part of the patient. For example, a protagonist may move from being his child self, screaming at mother, to being the mother being screamed at.

As this dialogue continues, John now back playing the desk, it becomes clear that the "young woman" represents his mother, and that the desk is symbolic for a fused image of his father, stepfather and himself. Both the men in his life have been "thrown out" by his mother. I feel that John has a strong psychic connection with his father (whom he has not seen for 12 years) and is tending to "act out" the family myth that this man was and is a no-good thief and gambler through stealing money from his mother and spending it on fruit machines.

As director I feel now that it would be most productive to help John separate himself from his father, having established that he fears that his mother is about to throw him, like his father, out of the family home (a threat often made). I suggest to John that he might like to talk to his father.

Such a move, following some professional intuition, can allow a director and protagonist to move rapidly into new, important areas of psychic work. As always, such a move should only be made with the protagonist's agreement (in the therapeutic alliance).

John readily agrees. He chooses Dave to play father. The scene now continues with father and son talking. John plays his own father for a considerable part of this phase.

It allows him to find, within himself, a "family identity", but also to verbalize for the first time fantasies about why his father left, what part he had in this, and how this related to his mother. With John back as himself an attempt was made to close the scene by bringing John close to an available and supportive father figure (through the group member playing his father). In psychodrama such a move into "surplus reality" can be used to explore events that never happened in the past, and indeed may never be able to happen in the future.

It seems that individuals are somehow driven to repeat situations in their life which reflect early traumatic relationships (the repetition-compulsion of Freud: Laplanche and Pontalis, 1973). This "act-hunger" may be worked with in psychodrama through initially enacting a "repetition-compulsive" situation, then progressing on, through the psychodrama, to a new level of emotional expression (blocked in the previous repetitions), while also exploring a different way of resolving the conflict. Clinical experience shows that such a process may not only increase insight into the individual's need to repeat, but also free them to seek more productive solutions to their internal conflicts.

The techniques of psychodrama, and the containment and relative safety of the setting, seems to make such moves possible.

Winston, who until now has been watching the psychodrama with rapt attention, moves over and hides behind a curtain in the room. He is allowed to stay there. His father is also a very absent figure in his life, and John's psychodrama seems to have stirred up powerful feelings in him.

Within the room, the adolescents had the chance to withdraw (when psychic pain became intolerable) by hiding (as Winston did behind the curtain). Alternatively, this anxiety could be contained by involving the group member more actively in the psychodrama. Winston might have been asked to "double" John (that is to stand by him and add his comments, from his own understanding) in the psychodrama, or he might have, at an earlier stage in this psychodrama, been chosen to play the father. (See Blatner (1973) for more detailed descriptions of this technique.)

It was apparent in this group (and similar observations have been made by me in adult psychodrama groups) that it was those not directly involved (through active participation) who become more disruptive (through their mounting anxiety at watching someone else's psychodrama). Ideally, especially with adolescents, as many as possible of the group should be involved in an active way (through playing auxiliary egos, crowds, or even more concrete "props" like trees or walls).

John, as his father, begins to express some of his feelings towards his son, and to offer some explanations as to why his marriage had broken down so many years previously. No one exists alone and such powerful psychodrama clearly will have repercussions with others outside the group (family, friends, especially adolescents and other professionals involved in the care and education of the child) and, of course, other group members.

One of the reasons adolescents were placed in this group was that difficulties had been experienced in engaging their families in therapy (see Holmes, 1983). It became apparent that even if not many of these families could be worked with in family therapy, regular contact was essential, both to help the families accept change in their adolescents (and thus to continue to support their attendance at the group), but also to take up and work with family issues raised in the context of the group.

When we forgot that the adolescent lived in a family system, we found that we courted disaster. In fact, far from reducing the time spent on therapeutic work (through the process of group treatment), we found we increased it, as a proportion of families asked for, and received, further meetings. Some of these were carried out by the staff of the group. Others, for historical reasons, by therapists not directly involved in the psychodrama group.

The involvement of these other colleagues clearly raises another central issue of containment. When the group was first proposed to the other members of the department, it became apparent that no one had actually experienced a psychodrama group. A demonstration workshop was held for all the staff who might have adolescents in the group. It was, of course, essential to keep those colleagues who had patients in the group informed of progress (or lack of it). This was especially necessary when we felt any psychodrama work might, for instance, increase the adolescents' "acting out".

PHASE 3 – SHARING

The group all move into a circle. I ask if anyone has anything to share with the protagonist.

The sharing is the third part of a classical psychodrama. It allows all the group to express feelings and thoughts stirred up about themselves. The director has the task to ensure they do not attempt to "interpret" the protagonist. A group sharing should be a very supportive process, helping the protagonist who may be (as is the case today) feeling very lost, upset and unique in his distress.

Today the sharing becomes an especially powerful process. Dave tells us that he too had difficulties not unlike John's and that playing John's father (and John through "reversals") had been a very powerful experience for him too.

It often happens that a protagonist selects a group member to play an auxiliary ego for whom the role has some special significance. Sometimes the choice is made as a result of known, shared, information about each other's lives; at other times, less tangible processes seem to be at work. Indeed this process, allowing some degree of vicarious experience, seems to be therapeutic (Brabender, Albrecht, Silliti, Cooper and Kramer, 1983). Psychodrama raises the crucial issue of how much of themselves, and their own difficulties, the adults should share with the adolescents, and how, when strongly identified with group members, the staff could still remain in control. As psychodrama does not use the process of "transference" fundamental to individual and group analytical therapy, there is no therapeutic reason why any individual (director included) should not share with the group any relevant personal experiences. Indeed some degree of self revelation (of facts and feelings) by the adults seems to facilitate the group process (Hurst, Stein, Korchin and Soskin, 1978), especially when linked to an obviously caring atmosphere.

The adults offer themselves not only as more appropriate role models, through demonstrating ways of coping with life events, but also as objects for deeper identifications (Corder, Whitehead and Vogel, 1977). However, after discussion among the staff, we felt that our containing and authority role involved issues of how the adolescents saw us. Too many disclosures about the chaos in our lives outside the group might, we felt, reduce our ability to help the adolescents. I think we feared loss of "face" with a subsequent loss of ability to maintain control. However, we did feel that self-disclosure from our own pasts (childhood and adolescence), was appropriate when a particular psychodrama raised pertinent points.

We found, at times, that the discussion in the "sharing" needed more active leading than usually occurs in an adult psychodrama group. Indeed we often make links between the session and known events in the adolescent's life. However, deep or intrusive interpretations should be avoided, as such intervention may not only distress the individual concerned, but disturb the whole group (Kraft, 1961).

> Eventually, it was clear that no more group members had things they wished to share. As its director, I made a mental survey to check, as far as possible, that no one was sitting on major distress. The group is now formally closed, and we all settle down to coffee and biscuits before the adolescents depart.

The whole group needed to be aware that the session had a beginning and (perhaps more crucially) an end, marked by the coffee period. This final stage, after the formal period of sharing, not only allowed the adolescents to socialize but also to regain their composure if they had been upset during the group. We learned that at times adolescents were able to talk about problems in this atmosphere that they had felt unable to owing to the more intense atmosphere of the group. The food also allowed the adults to demonstrate caring and nurturance in a concrete way for often very deprived adolescents.

> Today, John seems fairly relaxed, as do other group members. However, as usual, an enormous number of biscuits seem to get eaten.

After other groups, we had felt it necessary to offer some additional emotional support to an adolescent and, on one occasion, to contact a school to warn them that an adolescent might be a little more distressed and difficult than usual in the week following a particularly stressful group. Because we could not predict what might happen during the group, one staff member always allowed enough time to sort out any problems that did arise.

Finally, the group leaders collapse in the staff room over yet another coffee, aware that it has been a long, intense group and to ponder what the implications (short- and long-term) will be of John's psychodrama.

OVERVIEW

Implicit in the therapeutic technique of psychodrama is the belief that behaviour in the present (be it "satisfactory" or "problematic") is governed by past events, often from early childhood, which are crucial factors in the development of an adult personality. In psychodrama this "inner world" of the protagonist is portrayed dramatically using a theatrical format directed by the therapist, as illustrated in this chapter. The resulting dramas must not be seen as in any way an objective reflection of past situations or relationships in the protagonist's life. The characters upon the psychodramatic stage are externalizations of the protagonist's inner world. The stories being enacted represent dramatizations of the private fantasies of the patient (Isaacs, 1948). The process of "role reversal" ensures that the characters eventually portrayed by the "auxiliary egos" (other group members) reflect closely the psychological reality of the protagonist.

In the early stages of a psychodrama, when the protagonist is describing and enacting a scene from the very recent past (say a confrontation that day with a school teacher), perhaps a degree of objectivity exists, depending, of course, on the adolescent's ability to "test reality". However, as the psychodrama progresses and events from earlier experiences are staged (say a confrontation between son and father), the "others" portrayed become increasingly aspects of the protagonist's own psychological world (i.e. a son's experience of father, *not* an objective historical representation). Thus the character on stage (especially when portrayed by a protagonist in role reversal) may be considered (in psychoanalytic terms) to be an externalization of an "inner object", the drama involving aspects of the internal (conscious or unconscious) fantasies that govern his daily existence.

In individual and group analytic therapies these aspects of inner object relationships are played out through the "transference" between patient and therapist (and other group members) (Foulkes 1975; Walton 1971). In psychodrama a similar process occurs more explicitly between the protagonist and his "auxiliary ego", played, for the duration of the psychodrama only, by another group member. As a consequence at other times group therapists (and other group members) can be more open within the group setting, allowing for a more relaxed style of relationship. Indeed friendships can develop that might be disapproved of as counter-productive to the therapeutic process in those other group therapies that also work at the level of the unconscious. Such friendships can be very important (especially for the more isolated and lonely group member).

A psychodrama will often start with a "here and now" situation in an adolescent's life (say, a confrontation with a teacher). This scene is enacted, the protagonist reliving some of the emotions associated with this relationship. As the drama progresses the director seeks to understand (aided by empathy and intuition) the earlier relationships that might be fuelling the feelings in the present crisis. He may ask the protagonist: "when have you had these feelings before?" or if the emotions being expressed in the psychodrama seem rather regressed, "how old are you now?" "Here and now" scenes are stopped and historically earlier scenes started (say, father-son). This process can continue right back to infancy, when the protagonist's earliest object relationships may be enacted (say, mother and infant). Thus the present sense of persecution by teachers can be explored through an experience (in the psychodrama) of the earlier frustrations of an infant with its mother (see Goldman and Morrison, 1984). However, no psychodramatist should leave the protagonist there. The drama should return to the original drama, which is repeated, now informed by both the emotional and cognitive aspects of the previous scenes. The director can encourage the protagonist to try new, more satisfactory ways of dealing with situations. This process ("role rehearsal") helps ensure that an integration occurs between the deepest aspects of the inner world and the vital issues of everyday life (say, confrontations with teachers), allowing the adolescent to explore and rehearse more satisfactory ways of relating to the world.

This chapter has illustrated the use of classical Morenion techniques of psychodrama, used with an adolescent group. An attempt has been made to demonstrate how the "containment" of anxiety (through a variety of psychological and practical measures) can help reduce potentially destructive "acting out" among group members. It is suggested that the anxiety levels of both group members and staff must be held at a fairly low level if creative and therapeutic work is to occur in a group setting (as, of course, is also true in individual therapy). However, it must be acknowledged that adolescents as a client group are not easy to work with, and it may become necessary to modify techniques if groups are to be run successfully (especially in outpatient settings). Moreno expounds the central role of "creativity" in the therapeutic process. Psychodrama groups with adolescents require, at times, that the director's own creativity is called upon to devise ways of ensuring the therapeutic group process is allowed to continue and flourish. However, to allow such creativity on the behalf of the director to flourish, training (as with all therapeutic techniques) is essential.

Details can be obtained from: The American Society for Group Psychotherapy and Psychodrama, 116 East 27th Street, 11th Floor, New York 10016, USA; The Federation of Trainers and Training Programs in Psychodrama, 2050 Laurel Canyon Boulevarde, Los Angeles, California 90046, U.S.A.; The Holwell Centre for Psychodrama and Sociodrama, East Down, Barnstaple, North Devon EX31 4NZ, England.

The author wishes to acknowledge the great assistance given to him by his various co-therapists who have run groups with him.

REFERENCES

Bion, W.R. (1962). *Learning with Experience*. London: Heinemann.
Blatner, H.A. (1973). *Acting In. Practical Applications of Psychodrama Methods*. New York: Springer Publishing.
Blos, Peter (1962). *On Adolescence. A Psychodrama Interpretation*. New York: The Free Press.
Brabender, V.A., Albrecht, E., Silliti J., Cooper J. and Kramer, E. (1983). A study of

curative factors in short-term group psychotherapy. *Hospital and Community Psychiatry* **34(7)**, 643–644.

Brandes D. and Phillips H. (1978). *Gamesters Handbook. 140 Games for Teachers and Group Leaders*. London: Hutchinson.

Corder, B.F., Whiteside R. and Vogel, M. (1977). A therapeutic game for structuring and facilitating group psychotherapy with adolescents. *Adolescence* **12(46)**, 261–268

Corder, B.F., Whiteside, L. and Haizlip, T.M. (1981). A study of curative factors in group psychotherapy with adolescents. *International Journal of Group Psychotherapy* **31(3)**, 345–354.

Delvey, J. (1982). Parenting errors and their correction in group psychotherapy. *American Journal of Psychotherapy* **36(4)**, 523–535.

Foulkes, S.H. (1975). *Group-Analytic Psychotherapy. Methods and Principles*. London: Gordon and Breach.

Geldman E.E. and Morrison, D.J. (1984). *Psychodrama: Experience and Process*. Dubuque, Iowa: Kendall/Hunt.

Hollander, C. (1978). *The Warm-up Box*. Denver: Snow Lion Press.

Holmes, Paul (1983). 'Dropping Out' from an adolescent group. A study of factors in the patients and their parents that might influence this process. *Journal Adolescence* **6**, 333–346.

Hurst, A.G., Stein, K.B., Korchin, S.J. and Soskin, W.F. (1978). Leadership style determinants of cohesiveness in adolescent groups. *International Journal of Group Psychotherapy* **28**, 263–277.

Isaacs, S., (1948). The nature and function of phantasy. *International Journal of Psycho-Analysis* **29**.

Kraft, I.A. (1961). Some special considerations in adolescent group psychotherapy. *International Journal Group Psychotherapy* **11**, 196–203.

Langley, D.M. (1983). *Drama therapy and Psychiatry*. London: Croom Helm.

Laplanche, J. and Pontalis, J.B. (1973). *The Language of Psychoanalysis*. London: Hogarth Press.

Leveton, E. (1977). *Psychodrama for the Timid Clinician*. New York: Springer Publishing.

Moreno, J.L. (1947). Theatre of spontaneity: an introduction to psychodrama. *Monograph* **22**. New York: Beacon House Press (1973).

Phelan, J.R.M. (1974). Parent, teacher or analyst: the adolescent group therapist's trilemma. *International Journal of Group Psychotherapy* **24**, 238–244.

Rachmann, A.W. and Raubolt, R.R. (1984). The pioneers of adolescent group psychotherapy. *International Journal of Group Psychotherapy* **34(3)**, 387–413.

Raubolt, R.R. (1983). Brief, problem-focussed, group psychotherapy with adolescents. *American Journal of Orthopsychiatry* **53(1)**, 157–165.

Richmond, L.H. and Gaines, T. (1979). Factors influencing attendance in group psychotherapy with adolescents. *Adolescence* **14**, 715–720.

Rosenberg, J. and Cherbuliez, T. (1979). In-patient group therapy for older children and pre-adolescents. *International Journal of Group Psychotherapy* **29**, 393–405.

Shuttleworth, R. (1983a). Psychodrama with disturbed adolescents in creative therapy. Jennings, S. (Ed.). Banbury, Oxon: Kemble Press.

Shuttleworth, R. (1983b). Group work in educating children with behaviour problems. Upton, G. (Ed.). Cardiff: Faculty of Education, University College, Cardiff.

Walton, H. (1971), Ed. *Small Group Psychotherapy*. London: Penguin Books.

8. Social skills training with adolescents

WILLIAM R. LINDSAY

INTRODUCTION

Social Skills Training (SST) has been recently established as a treatment option with adolescents who have interpersonal and social difficulties. The work of social psychologists such as Argyle (1969) has helped to delineate the area and establish a framework for treatment. Argyle outlined elements of social behaviour which could be readily analysed and trained, and also illustrated the way in which these skills and behaviours should be co-ordinated for successful social interaction. Argyle, Trower and Bryant (1974) were among the first to extend this work into the development of therapeutic techniques for training social skills. The first applications were with adult subjects and much of the SST literature and therapy was directed towards time limited programmes which covered the range of social skills and social situations experienced by adults.

Although some early work had been done to promote the social abilities of adolescents (Sarason and Ganzer, 1973; Bailey, Timbers, Phillips and Wolf, 1971), the emergence of SST as a discrete treatment encouraged many therapists and researchers to develop and evaluate the approach for this client group. Trower (1978) argued that SST would be an appropriate treatment approach for adolescents who have difficulties with authority figures and peer relationships. By assessing non-problem teenagers Minkin *et al* (1976) established question asking, positive feedback and proportion of time spent talking as important conversational skills. They then trained four predelinquent teenage girls in these skills and the girls achieved a standard which was higher than their

Working with troubled adolescents
ISBN 0-12-179720-1

non-problem peers. Spence and Marzillier (1981) found some success using SST with young offenders, but note that the institution can occasionally obstruct change, despite the enthusiasm of staff. Many similar studies have shown that SST can be successful, at least in the short-term in various settings.

The author has taken a somewhat different approach to SST, partly because he has worked mainly in an outpatient setting and also because the programme formats developed for adults have not always been appropriate for adolescents. In particular, the tight structure and time limited nature of a "social skills package" provided a setting which the teenagers found difficult (Symons and Lindsay, 1978). The adolescents were not relaxed with the format, they found it difficult to get to know each other and they remained somewhat inhibited. It was found that providing some less structured time, playing games, drinking coffee, etc., established a more effective atmosphere for organizing an SST programme (Lindsay, Symons and Sweet, 1979). Working independently, Jackson and Marzillier (1982) came to similar conclusions and Jackson (1984) coined the appropriate phrase "social skills training youth club" to describe the setting.

While these authors have found this an effective way to proceed, the methods of training and training situations which are presented in this chapter are basic to all forms of SST with adolescents which have been used by various therapists. Therefore, while some aspects of an SST youth club shall be described, the principles of SST reported here would be the same for all other therapeutic situations.

There are some advantages to working in this way with adolescents:

1. The youth club provides a natural setting for observing the adolescents' social difficulties. This is an invaluable source of material for the therapist to work on later during the formal SST sessions.

2. Because the group know each other fairly well, they are able to take part in the role plays and are less self-conscious about being video-taped.

3. The teenagers get to know each other and the therapist, so when the group turns to more personally intrusive social material they are able to be more open about their difficulties.

4. Difficulties inevitably arise during these youth club sessions, because everyone is aware of the methods of SST, the "club" can be stopped and the SST can begin immediately. We can look at what led up to the incident, how the various group members dealt with it and how it proceeded. We can then investigate how else it might have been conducted. For example, if there is a fight, we can determine what led up to the fight and which pieces of interaction contributed to it. Then alternative ways of interacting can be role-played to show how the fight could have been avoided. This can be a very powerful illustration of how SST can be used to alter the outcome of a social exchange.

5. The skills which have been learned can be used in these unstructured sessions. The therapists are aware of each teenager's difficulties and can encourage them to use their skills in this very realistic setting. One hopes that this would foster generalization, although later in the programme sessions are held in community facilities which are designed to promote generalization of skills.

Another advantage of holding such a group seems to be the continued attendance of the teenagers. The attendance rates in the groups reported by Jackson and Marzillier (1983) and Lindsay et al. (1979) are high.

Standard features of the format are that sessions last a whole afternoon or evening. Two or three sessions at the beginning of the programme are spent getting to know each other. The therapy room may have table tennis, snooker, darts, records, table games, a sitting room and a kitchen. Football, tennis and larger games are less useful because people do not talk and socialize when they are playing. The most useful games are those which require a reasonable proximity to allow social interaction. Finally, an hour is laid aside in the middle of the session for formal training. It should be remembered that although this format has been found useful by the present author it is not the only way to approach SST with adolescents; the principles and methods of training will be the same no matter which therapeutic setting is chosen.

METHODS OF TRAINING

(1) Didactic teaching

Generally the groups would have a number of initial sessions to teach the teenagers about social skills. This can be done through handouts or simple verbal presentations, which contain the information to be taught. This method is fairly straightforward and the content of these sessions is outlined later on.

(2) Modelling

Modelling is an extremely important technique for training social skills and can be organized in several ways. The essential aspect of modelling is that we can demonstrate particular behaviours, skills or coping strategies without going into confusing or tedious explanations. It can be done via pre-recorded videotapes, which show the teenagers how to respond to set situations. Here we might enlist the help of adolescents who are good at performing in a particular social situation. Their performance is video-taped to take back to the group as an example of a reasonable way of coping in that situation. The technique can also be immediate to the training situation. For example, the group leader may demonstrate a particular aspect of training covered on that day or he may get one member of the group who is good at a particular skill to show the others his way of doing it. Therefore when a role play situation arises within the group, one member would show the rest how to cope in this setting.

Alternatively, modelling can be used to show ineffective ways of dealing with the situation. If group members find this threatening the therapist can do the role play and allow members to criticize the performance. Building on the modelling and discussion of "what not to do", the group can then role play more effective ways of dealing with the social situation.

(3) Role playing

The value of role playing during treatment is that it provides a situation which is similar in salient respects to the real situation. Therefore the teenager can learn to respond to some of the stimuli which he or she will meet in the real situation. The fact that it is within therapist control means that (a) failure is less important since the adolescent can practise several times; (b) he can practise small pieces of the whole sequence of skill before putting it together; (c) anxiety provoking aspects can be introduced as the therapist judges, according to the therapeutic demands; and (d) the situation can be very realistic or contain only a couple of relevant stimuli depending on the demands of training.

Normally, role playing would go hand in hand with modelling in that someone would model effective or ineffective ways of dealing with a situation and then the group would role play their own responses. Clearly these role play sessions are not time limited and the group can go back to the situation again and again until everyone is satisfied that the skills being used are reasonable for coping in that situation. Therefore role playing is another important aspect of training and again is a flexible technique which can be adapted to suit individual needs.

(4) Behavioural techniques

Although the behavioural techniques of skills training are not extensively used, one or two of the methods are useful in the context of role playing and modelling and probably warrant a separate mention. Prompting may be used extensively in the initial phases of role playing. The prompts would be very explicit. For example, if someone were trying to start a conversation with a member of the opposite sex and when confronted with the role played situation genuinely could not think of anything to say, the therapist might give the direct prompt, "Say 'Would you like to go up to the café with me?' " If someone was having difficulty breaking into a conversation group the therapist might physically guide them to an appropriate place in the group and prompt them to break into the conversation at a certain time. Obviously it is important to fade out the therapist's presence from the beginning of the therapeutic technique, so that the adolescent is soon performing by himself or herself. Other behavioural techniques such as reinforcement, time out from reinforcement, shaping and cueing may be used occasionally where appropriate.

(5) Cognitive techniques

One of the striking aspects of many of the adolescents referred is their lack of confidence in the abilities they possess. A person who is quite socially skilled may never talk to strangers or someone of the opposite sex because they lack the confidence. With several colleagues the author has been trying to develop some methods to assess and treat these cognitive difficulties (Lindsay and Kasprowicz, in press, Lindsay, 1986). One relevant approach is the cognitive behaviour therapy of Meichenbaum (1974, 1977; see also Chapter 12). It can be used at a fairly basic level, which has an attractive and practical simplicity eminently suited for use with adolescent groups. The essential aspect of the treatment is that anxieties and performance difficulties are maintained by negative self-statements which people say to themselves before and during a sequence of interaction or behaviour. The approach does not assume that the teenagers are aware of their self-statements and many may not even have formed the thoughts linguistically. Nevertheless they are part of the person's approach to the situation and if the therapist asks about them, they can be elicited. Furthermore, positive self-statements can be used during SST whether or not the adolescent has used them beforehand. The main approach is that during the role play sessions the therapist asks about, elicits and comments on various self-statements that the person has in relation to the ongoing conversation. By challenging the elicited self-statements the therapist increases their importance to a level where the adolescent may be able to use them in developing their confidence and ability to cope with the interaction. The techniques are especially important where the adolescent may have the skills to carry out certain social interactions, but lack of confidence and negative self-statements prevent them from using these skills effectively.

A PROGRAMME FOR SOCIAL SKILLS TRAINING

This programme is organized in sections which are loosely sequenced together. Each section is worked through week by week until everyone in the group feels it is completed. The sections on conversation and heterosexual interaction take about a couple of months each. The sections dealing with situations requiring assertion (general assertion skills, keeping out of trouble and dealing with authority figures) may take about a month each. Interview training tends to be the shortest section, since it is the most discrete and the situation is standard. The first three sections also tend to be quite short, lasting perhaps a couple of weeks each. They set the style of the group and the framework for the later sections.

1. Non-verbal communication

This would usually be the first section of SST. There is more didactic teaching about social skills in the first three sections than there is later. It is unusual to have a group member who has any knowledge of social skills and so all the various aspects of communication should be covered. Although we use and indeed depend on these skills all the time, it is novel to have them analysed in this way and many adolescents will be extremely self-conscious at first. Argyle (1969) outlines the various skills used in social interaction and it is fairly easy for the therapist to explain social skills to the group according to this analysis. However, from the first, therapists should emphasize the importance of having confidence to use the skill the group members already possess. Although it is useful to know what the various skills are, they may not have any need to learn new social skills. Instead it would help their relationships to organize their skills more effectively and have the confidence to use them in different settings. The non-verbal skills for this section have been set out extensively elsewhere (Argyle, 1969; Trower, Bryant and Argyle, 1978). These include facial expression, posture, gesturing, gaze direction, proximity, body movements, clothing and hygiene. The section would be introduced to the teenagers under the headings of "What can you tell about people by the way they look?" and "What can you tell about people by what they do?"

From the very first it is essential to begin role play. In this section there are simple charades where group members are told to convey a message to the group without speaking, e.g. someone may be given the task of asking someone else to come and sit beside them, or someone may have to convey emotion such as happiness, sadness, anxiety, etc. The group then analyse what it is about the non-verbal expression which suggests the emotion.

(2) Non-verbal aspects of speech

This topic would be introduced under the heading "What can you tell about people by the way they sound?", to establish social skills such as tone of voice, volume, pitch, clarity, speech errors, pace and length of speech. The role play involves having the teenagers say neutral phrases in different ways to convey either a different meaning or a different emotion, e.g. "What are you doing today?" or "What were you doing last night?" These simple statements can convey a range of meaning and emotion depending on how they are said.

(3) Verbal aspects of speech

In this section the group begins to talk about what you actually say to others. It is less difficult to understand and can be introduced simply under the heading

"What you say is important". The role playing is more straightforward, with practice of various forms of speech, e.g. question asking, question answering, expressing opinions, giving information about yourself and getting information from other people. The group can analyse the different reactions you get when you give rude or polite answers, long or short answers, happy or sad answers, etc.

Summary of social skills

The therapist should summarize each section as it is completed, but it can be useful to have a formal session after the first three in which all the various aspects of social skill are summarized. Here it would be emphasized that different people co-ordinate their skills differently, and it is important the individual does what feels most comfortable rather than something he finds awkward. If the teenager feels very strange interacting in a certain new way, then this could undermine his confidence to the extent that he will not socialize at all. Given that the performance is broadly acceptable, it is better the adolescent feels at ease even if others may feel it is not quite right. Therefore in this section we would look at different ways of organizing the various skills, pointing out that they should be loosely co-ordinated together.

With certain client groups the first three sessions on social skills can be less helpful or indeed confusing. The concept of social skill is fairly complex and with teenagers who are mildly mentally handicapped or even of borderline intelligence, it is sometimes confusing and boring to go through the elements of social skill. Some of these adolescents have a double difficulty in that they may have some intellectual handicap and a poor attention span. If they feel they are not understanding the sections on social skill, they could get dejected and their attention can start to wander (quite quickly). To avoid this, immediately begin role playing "real" situations rather than spending time on these hypothetical exercises. The elements of social skill would be brought up in the context of more realistic problems and any teaching about individual skills would be incorporated into the role plays on conversations, assertion or whatever.

(4) Initiating conversations

Many of the adolescents are very shy or awkward when approaching others to begin social contact. Others can be aggressive or intimidating in the same situation. There are several situations in which teenagers begin social interaction with others and many of them are dealt with in later sections of this programme. This section covers two basic aspects of initiating conversations – with strangers and with friends.

(a) Strangers. Sessions would always begin with a discussion about the topic, in this case starting a conversation with a stranger. Attempts should be made to

elicit situations where the teenagers have actually talked to strangers, so that some reasonably realistic situations may be used in the role plays. However, some set situations for talking to strangers can also be used in the role play sessions. For example, the therapist might play a stranger in the street and the adolescent has to draw his attention and ask directions. Here the first important aspect is how to gain someone's attention without being rude, by using a phrase such as "Excuse me. Could you tell me the way to . . .?" and finishing by thanking the person. Many of our teenagers abruptly say "Where is High Street?" or "How do I get to the Leisure Centre?" With this role played scene, as with other similar situations, when one is receiving instructions it is important to listen to and understand what the other person is saying. Therefore as an extension to the role play the group can analyse how one responds to a confusing or complicated answer. There are several similar situations which could be role played under this heading, for example asking a stranger in a supermarket where certain goods are, asking where the changing areas are in a sports centre or swimming pool, etc.

A second type of situation where one would meet a stranger would be at a party, an outing or some gathering where the type of interaction is less obvious. Here the group can discuss the skills to use to get the other person to talk, e.g. begin with a question after having said "Hello". Questions are a good way to start a conversation because the other person will always respond. It is also better to use open questions which cannot be answered "Yes" or "No". For example, we might role play meeting someone on a school outing to a museum. Here we might encourage the teenagers to ask a few set questions after having said "Hello", e.g. "Have you been here before? What is the best thing to do here? Have you seen anything decent here?" From the answer the other person may reveal some information which can be used to continue the conversation.

After a session practising how to talk to strangers we would ask a couple of strangers along to the group. These would be both adults and adolescents and would give the teenagers in the group the opportunity to practise their skills in a real setting.

(b) *Friends.* In general, the teenagers find it easier to initiate conversation with friends. The principles are the same in that we still have to attract someone's attention and begin the interaction. The adolescent can be encouraged to practise with a topic of common interest, e.g. a television programme or a sports match, etc. Once again, a question about the topic is the easiest way to begin.

(5) Continuing conversations

Having started the conversation some teenagers may find it quite easy to continue the interaction. However, many teenagers would have as much difficulty in keeping things going as they have in starting the conversation.

Perhaps the main skill here would be how to answer someone else's question. We would practise long answers which do not effectively cut the other person off. Many of the teenagers would generally answer with "Yes" or "No" statements or some other short reply. This may be because they do not have the skill to continue in any other way, or it could be that they feel antagonistic towards the conversation and do not wish to encourage it. A common example is if someone opens the conversation by saying "What have you been doing today?"; most of our teenagers would reply "Nothing!" It is important to spend some time helping them to think about some answer which would foster the conversation rather than end it.

Another way to continue the conversation is to reveal information about yourself. Simple pieces of factual information such as "I was at school today" can lead to developments in a conversation. Expressing feelings and opinions about yourself or things you have been doing can be even better ways to continue a conversation, e.g. "I was at the football yesterday and it was rubbish!", because this would invite the other person to enquire about the reasons for the opinion and feelings.

When continuing conversations it is extremely important to listen to the other person. Often the adolescents do not actually listen to what is being said in the conversation and cannot continue the talk in a relevant way. Therefore the group can practise listening to what is being said and selecting a piece of information to carry on the conversation.

Some of the teenagers are over-talkative and intrusive rather than withdrawn or shy. This sort of person may try to develop a conversation with constant interruptions. Here the teenagers should consider whether or not it is better to wait for a lull in the conversation before you begin to talk. If they feel that what they have to say is important and interesting, then the same is true for other people and they should let them finish before speaking.

(6) Breaking into conversation groups

This is very similar to the previous two sections, although it is better to deal with it separately since some adolescents feel even more intimidated when there is a group of people to whom they wish to talk. It is probably more common for adolescents to talk in groups than in pairs, which is another reason for dealing with conversation groups as a topic by itself. Here we would role play the various situations where adolescents get together in groups. Again the skills for starting and continuing a conversation are similar to those in the previous conversation sections, the main difference is situational.

One of the main role played situations is breaking into a conversational group in the school playground. Here a number of adolescents would be talking in a circle and the teenager has to break into the group physically before he can begin the conversation. Some shy teenagers may have to be guided physically into the group by the therapist before they can begin the conversation. The therapist should then quickly fade out the physical prompt.

(7) Assertion

This section deals mainly with the establishment of the person's rights in the situation where someone else attempts to impose his or her will. The point is made that there are degrees of vehemence in assertion and that we should respond in order to be effective and at the same time cause minimum offence. Two main responses are typical of the teenagers.

(a) Under-assertiveness. Here the person is generally quiet and withdrawn and tends to be picked on by others or pushed aside by others. The kind of situations are: when a teacher blames you for something you have not done; when someone barges in front of you in a bus queue; or when your parents tell you to do something else when you are watching something interesting on TV. It is important to realize that for the most part these role played scenes have been gathered from the adolescents themselves. Therefore while we as therapist may feel that responding to something like parental request is more important than watching TV, the adolescents may consider it an imposition on an activity they have been looking forward to. The essential point is that such a confrontation should be dealt with reasonably.

(b) Over-assertiveness. Here the person tends to become very angry when a polite refusal or mere statement of fact would be enough. When a teacher blames you for something you have not done, the under-assertive teenager might merely accept the punishment, although they know they have not committed the misdemeanour. The over-assertive person rants and raves, accusing the teacher of picking on him, blaming others, generally becoming inappropriately excited and possibly causing a major incident when a simple and positive statement of innocence would have diffused the situation.

During this section we would pay particular attention to the social skills involved. The person should defend themselves appropriately. It is no use sitting in an awkward or sullen silence.

In situations calling for assertion it is sometimes useful not to say too much, but to state the facts, be reasonable and not too over-bearing and vehement. It is important to be polite and not abusive. Assertion also calls for a particularly careful use of non-verbal skills. The person should keep their voice quality strong, clear and even. It is usually appropriate to have high levels of eye contact. Some teenagers will have particular difficulty in keeping both their voice quality and non-verbal skills appropriate.

(c) Positive assertion. In general, the teenagers with whom the author has contact do not feel that positive assertion is important. This would include things

like praising and encouraging other people or offering compliments and congratulations to others. In the group we would certainly mention it and perhaps have a session talking about it, but the group members are often indifferent to the appropriateness of such skill. The main reason for this is probably because of the difference in value systems between the adult therapists and teenage group members. Within their peer group it is rarely appropriate to congratulate or compliment anyone. That is not to say the same would be true in other communities. It may be that an adolescent SST Group in another culture would spend much more time on positive assertion. If this were the case then the principles of training would be the same as in the other sections. The therapist should try to gather role play situations from the teenagers themselves which would be appropriate to their circumstances.

(8) Keeping out of trouble

This section would usually follow on from assertion, because many of the skills are similar. Often adolescents are referred to us because they have been in trouble at school, at home or with the police. The particular relevance of SST is that in certain situations the reason for the incident can be traced, to some extent, to a lack of social skill on the part of the teenager. One obvious example is where a quiet and unassertive person is led into trouble by an aggressive peer.

A withdrawn boy can be persuaded to set off a fire-alarm in school by being very unassertive to those who were making him do it. Sometimes more immature adolescents are encouraged to steal sweets for their friends. These situations lend themselves readily to role play and the quiet individuals can learn assertive skills which will help them avoid this sort of trouble.

The second example is the kind already mentioned, where the teenager might over-react to a teacher or a policeman enquiring about an incident. Some adolescents seem to mistake an enquiry about an incident for an accusation of guilt. They may then become over-assertive in their own defence which immediately makes the other person suspicious that they are in fact guilty of the offence. Here again, the situations lend themselves to role playing a more even-tempered and reasonable response. Clearly over-assertion is as bad as under-assertion.

(9) Dealing with adults and authority figures

Once again this section would develop from the last one. From keeping out of trouble with the police and teachers the programme follows on to other situations with authority figures. Some of the simplest problems happen in fairly standard settings, which we would role play, e.g. talking to a guidance teacher, a policeman, a doctor, school nurse, etc. In many of these cases, the purpose of the social exchange is to convey certain pieces of information; in order to do so the adolescent should not become over-anxious or antagonistic.

Occasionally it is necessary to teach the teenagers how to deal with difficult situations with adults. One example is when an authority figure is being sarcastic or in some way provocative with the individuals or groups of teenagers. The teenagers should remain calm and polite. In any such situation, about the worst thing you could do is become equally sarcastic. Unfortunately, some of the people who are referred would have developed a reputation for aggressiveness or antisocial behaviour and this reputation seems to invite a provocative approach from some adults. During role play we would always encourage the teenagers to be appropriately assertive rather than aggressive.

Another set of role played situations with authority figures is pertinent in this section. That is, making approaches to authority figures in less standard settings, such as talking to a teacher at a bus stop. When most adolescents talk to people in authority, it is when there is a problem. By organizing more positive settings it gives the teenagers a chance to have a more reasonable interaction and to establish another form of relationship. While there have been some striking successes with this section of the SST programme, it should be said that on occasion the adult has been quite unable to cope with this less formal setting. Therefore, when the teenagers try to talk to their teachers outside school, a few teachers have been either unable or unwilling to enter into the social contact. Generally, however, the various adults seem to welcome more positive contact initiated by the adolescents.

In addition to these different types of social interaction we would spend some time discussing and role playing contact with parents, relatives and neighbours. This part of the programme generally elicits a number of problem situations which the teenagers have experienced or are going to be introduced to. Therefore these situations can be actual experiences or problems which the adolescents are worrying about. For example, visiting a relative whom they have not seen for some time; a problem which happened recently when a neighbour asked for some help with his garden; or simply an incident with parents in the house. These can be easily role played and rehearsed with other members of the group taking the part of parents, neighbours or teenagers themselves.

(10) Interviewing skills

This is perhaps the most discrete part of an SST programme. Several studies have looked at interviewing training alone, (Kelly, Wildman and Berler, 1980; Hood, Lindsay and Brooks, 1982) and it has certain characteristics which set it aside from other sections of an SST programme. The main difference is that it is a very unusual social situation where the rules are standard. The interviewer will have a set of questions he wishes to ask and the interviewee should disclose certain relevant facts as well as finding out about the job. However, it is necessary to deal with interviewing because inevitably during the course of an SST programme some of the teenagers will begin to worry about going for job interviews, even for part-time jobs, and it is appropriate to do interview training when it is mentioned.

Training includes the usual methods of modelling, role playing and discussing aspects of the interviews. Role plays would include reacting to easy and difficult interviewers and a range of different jobs as well as the one in which the teenager was interested. If the interview training was to be a planned part of the programme (this would be necessary if most of the group were about to leave school), then an experienced interviewer who was unknown to the group would be asked along to role play some interviews. Then the group could receive realistic feedback and instruction from this interviewer.

(11) Interaction with members of the opposite sex

Some of the most embarrassing and difficult problems are dealt with in this section of the programme and so it would usually be placed towards the end of the programme. This gives the adolescents time to get to know each other and the therapist, so that when sensitive information is discussed it will be in a more trusting atmosphere. Some of the teenagers have never talked to a person of the opposite sex outside normal requests in the classroom, and it is acutely anxiety provoking to role play this sort of interaction.

We would begin by simply starting a conversation with a person of the opposite sex. The teenagers will already have done this in previous sections but it does no harm to return to some skills already covered. Then the group can move onto talking to girls or boys in a café, at a disco or in other social settings such as bowling or skating. The next step would be to actually go skating, bowling and to a café to practise these skills within the group. Although these outings require some organization, they are well worth it from a number of points of view: (a) they give the adolescents a chance to practise in the real setting skills learned during role plays; (b) the outings give the therapists an idea of how well the adolescents are progressing in real social situations; (c) since training is now being conducted in real social situations the prospects of the teenagers' new social strategies generalizing to these situations at other times of the week becomes greater; and (d) the outings are also good fun. Finally, we would have a party or disco to which we invite some teenagers from another home or establishment so that there are some peers and strangers to talk to and interact with.

SUMMARY AND CONCLUSIONS

The organization of an SST group has been presented. The methods described were didactic teaching, modelling, role playing, behavioural techniques and cognitive techniques. The programme outline has covered non-verbal communication, non-verbal aspects of speech, verbal aspects of speech, initiating conversations, continuing conversations, breaking into a conversation group, assertiveness, avoiding trouble, dealing with adults and authority figures, interviewing skills and interaction with the opposite sex. Although the author would often proceed within a less structured "Social Skills Youth Club", the methods have been used in various outpatient and inpatient settings.

While this chapter provides some details on how to set up and conduct an SST group, there has not been sufficient space to describe assessments for such a group. The reader should turn to Bellack (1979), Jackson (1983), Spence (1983) and Lindsay and Lindsay (1982) for descriptions of relevant assessment techniques.

SST seems a promising approach to adolescent social difficulties. Studies have reported reasonable short-term improvements both within subjects (Lindsay et al., 1979; Minkin et al., 1976) and in comparisons with other forms of treatment and waiting list controls (Spence and Marzillier, 1981; Jackson and Marzillier, 1983). However, these authors have found that improvements do not maintain to longer term follow-up assessments. (Spence and Marzillier, 1981; Jackson and Marzillier, 1983.)

It has been argued (Shepherd, 1980) that SST will be more successful when treatments are directed at and maintained by existing social networks. Therefore the clients would incorporate any social approaches into their existing social contacts. Lindsay and Kasprowicz (unpublished) have recently found instances where clients have maintained or even increased their conversational abilities and social contacts at six month follow-up when they have been in residential settings which fostered and encouraged their social skills. This certainly seems a valuable area of study so that the possibilities of maintaining better social abilities may be established.

Another area of concern with adolescent SST groups is that of social validation of the skills being taught. The author has found that difficulties can arise in the group because of differences between therapists' social values and the teenagers' peer group values. Once alerted to these differences it is reasonably easy to deal with obvious instances in a group. In these cases the teenagers themselves would set their own targets for training, given that they were broadly acceptable to society in general and their peer group in particular. However, it is much harder to estimate how pervasive are these value differences when they are less obvious. At worst it may be that there is a constant subtle clash of social values which undermines the effectiveness of a group. A possible solution to this would be a body of knowledge concerning the social values and attitudes of adolescents which would serve as a background for running groups and setting targets for treatment. Until this is available it is important for the therapist to be aware that value differences may be a problem when running SST groups for adolescents.

There is much to be done in the development of social training for adolescents, but the organized structure of SST and the enthusiasm of the teenagers themselves would indicate that it is a worthwhile treatment to pursue.

The author would like to thank Nancy Thomson and Ruth Symons for establishing the service in which it was possible to develop this work.

REFERENCES

Argyle, M. (1969). *Social interaction*. London: Methuen.

Argyle, M. (1975). *Bodily communication*. London: Methuen.

Argyle, M., Trower, P. and Bryant. (1974). Explorations in the treatment of personality disorders and neurosis by social skills training. *British Journal of Medical Psychology* **47**, 63–72.

Bellack, A.S. (1979). Behavioural assessment of social skills. In *Research and Practice in Social Skills Training*, Bellack, A.S. and Hersen, M. (Eds). New York and London: Plenum Press.

Bailey, J.S., Timbers, G.D., Phillips, E.L. and Wolf, M.M. (1971). Modification of articulation errors of pre-delinquents by their peers. *Journal of Applied Behaviour Analysis* **4**, 265–281.

Hood, E.M., Lindsay, W.R. and Brooks, N. (1982). Interview training with adolescents – a controlled group study incorporating generalisation and social validation. *Behaviour Research and Therapy* **20**, 581–592.

Jackson, M. (1983) Social skills training with adolescent psychiatric out-patients. In *Developments in Social Skills Training*, Spence, S. and Shepherd, G. (Eds.), pp. 193–217. London: Academic Press.

Jackson, M.F. and Marzillier, J.S. (1982). The youth club project: a community based intervention for shy adolescents. *Behavioural Psychotherapy* **10**, 87–100.

Jackson, M.F. and Marzillier, J.S. (1983). An investigation of the treatment of adolescent social difficulty in a community based setting. *Behavioural Psychotherapy* **11**, 302–319.

Kelly, J.A., Wildman B.G. and Berler, E.S. (1980). Small group behavioural training to improve the job interview skills repertoire of mildly retarded adolescents. *Journal of Applied Behaviour Analysis* **13**, 461–471.

Lindsay, W.R. (1986). Cognitive changes after social skills training with young mildly mentally handicapped adults. *Journal of Mental Deficiency Research* **30**, 81–88.

Lindsay, W.R. and Kasprowicz, M. (In Press). Challenging cognitions with young mildly mentally handicapped adults. *Mental Handicap*.

Lindsay, W.R. and Kasprowicz, M. (Unpublished). Social skills training within an existing social network – one year follow-up.

Lindsay, W.R. and Lindsay, I.S. (1982). A self report questionnaire about social difficulty for adolescents. *Journal of Adolescence* **5**, 63–69.

Lindsay, W.R., Symons, R.S. and Sweet, T. (1979). A programme for teaching social skills to socially inept adolescents: description and evaluation. *Journal of Adolescence* **2**, 215–228.

Meichenbaum, D. (1974). *Therapies manual for cognitive behaviour modification*. University of Waterloo: Unpublished manuscript.

Meichenbaum, D. (1977). *Cognitive behaviour modification: an integrative approach.* New York: Plenum Press.

Minkin, N., Braukmann, C., Minkin, B., Timbers, G., Timbers, B., Fixsen, D., Phillips, E. and Wolf, M. (1976). The social validation in training of conversation skills. *Journal of Applied Behaviour Analysis* **9**, 127–139.

Sarason, I.G. and Ganzer, U.J. (1973). Modelling and group discussion in rehabilitation of juvenile delinquents. *Journal of Counselling Psychology* **5**, 442–449.

Shepherd, G. (1980). The treatment of social difficulties in special environments. In *Psychological Problems: The Social Context*, Feldman, P. and Orford, J. (Eds.). New York: Wiley.

Spence, S. (1983). *Social skills training with children and adolescents.* N.F.E.R. Nelson: Windsor.

Spence, S. and Marzillier, J.S. (1979). Social skills training with adolescent male offenders – I short term effects. *Behaviour Research and Therapy* **17**, 7–16.

Spence, S. and Marzillier, J.S. (1981). Social skills training with adolescent male offenders – II short term, long term and generalised effects. *Behaviour Research and Therapy* **19**, 349–368.

Symons, R.S. and Lindsay, W.R. (1978). Some problems in social skills training with young adolescents. Paper presented to the Scottish Association for Behaviour Modification.

Trower, P. (1978). Skills training for adolescent social problems: a viable treatment alternative. *Journal of Adolescence* **1**, 319–329.

Trower, P., Bryant, B.M. and Argyle, M. (1978). *Social skills and mental health.* London: Methuen.

9. Cognitive behaviour therapy: a therapy for the troubled adolescent

ELSPETH K. McADAM

Introduction

Adolescence is a time of great change, when individuals are in transition. They are in a state of flux, all the developmental changes – physiological, emotional, cognitive and moral – spurring them onto adulthood and yet there is the wistful yearning for the security and lack of responsibility experienced in childhood. The complexity of this developmental growth, the struggles of adaptation and acceptance of the changes can be very daunting and confusing for adolescents and for those working with them. This paper argues that cognitive psychotherapies as developed by Ellis (1962) and Beck (1963) for the treatment of emotional disorders in adults can be adapted helpfully to work with adolescents.

History

Attitudes considered by cognitive therapists can be traced back to the philosophical writings of ancient Greece, where Epictetus suggested that it is not "things" themselves which disturb us but the view we take of them. Kelly (1955) and subsequently Ellis (1962) and Beck (1963) developed techniques enabling therapists to analyse an individual's internal cognitive constructs which laid the foundations for cognitive therapy for emotional disorders. Changes in behaviour therapy, with a shift of interest by behaviourists towards covert cognitive processes (Mahoney, 1974), have fuelled a rapid advance in popularity and application of cognitive therapy. Thus, cognitive behaviour

Working with troubled adolescents
ISBN 0 – 12 – 179720 – 1

therapy (CBT) represents a set of procedures which includes to a greater or lesser extent both cognitive and behavioural techniques.

The next part of the paper will summarize the theory and practice of cognitive behavioural psychotherapy as outlined by Beck (1976). This form of therapy has been shown to be effective in the treatment of depression in adults (Rush, Beck, Kovacs and Hollow, 1977; Kovacs, Rush, Beck, and Hollow, 1981; Blackburn, Bishop, Glen, Walley and Christie, 1984). Very little has been written about the use of this technique with adolescents (Young, 1984; McAdam and Gilbert, 1985). The difficulties of working with adolescents will be discussed and the ways in which CBT could overcome some of these difficulties is put forward.

Theory

Inherent in the cognitive approach is the notion that individuals are not passive recipients of stimuli but active interpreters of their world according to their own sets of values, beliefs, expectations and attitudes. These interpretations colour the view they have of themselves in their world. This view significantly influences mood and behaviour. To understand ''the view'' a person takes of events, the therapist explores the idiosyncratic styles of appraisal and interpretation which may predispose to maladaptive emotions and behaviour. Hence, cognitive therapists would argue that cognitive interpretation influences the individual's physiological response to a situation and his behaviour and emotions within that situation. For example, if you hear a noise in the middle of the night and you think it is a burglar, you are frightened, your heart pounds, and you may hide under the bedcovers! If, on the other hand, you believe it is the cat knocking over the saucepans, then you may swear and go back to sleep.

The principles of CBT rest on uncovering and changing those aspects which influence cognitive interpretation in maladaptive ways. Beck has introduced the idea that people continually evaluate themselves in relation to their performances and to other people's opinion of them. This stream of inferences Beck has called automatic thoughts. Negative evaluation of these automatic thoughts will give rise to negative emotions.

Automatic thoughts often occur as habitual responses to specific events and arise from underlying predispositions to construct the world in negative ways when presented with ambiguous cues. These underlying ''predispositions'' are often called cognitive constructs or **base schema**. Beck (1976) suggests that common primary beliefs or schema which predispose people to depression have to do with achievement and with ''loveability'' or acceptance. Beck argues that these primary schema lie at the core of an individual's personality. They determine his behaviour and the way he responds to people and how he interprets others' responses to him.

Beck regards the individual's *belief* in these negative thoughts as a central issue in depression; these thoughts will give rise to changes in the person's physiology, motivational levels, cognitive attitudes and ability to experience pleasure. This can be illustrated by looking at the predictions that follow specific negative ideas. For example, if a person believes nothing he does will work out, he feels hopeless; consequently he will be unmotivated to try anything and thus will lose the opportunity to enjoy any activity.

When a person is depressed, his thoughts are self-defeating. These negative thoughts result from **cognitive errors** which distort the evidence, so that the individual develops a negative and gloomy view of himself, his world, and his future (the negative cognitive triad – Beck, 1976). When a depressed patient talks of his experiences and his interpretations of these, the type of cognitive error he makes becomes apparent. There are a number of cognitive errors described. Three examples are given below.

1. Minimization. Distorting the evidence so that a positive achievement is not fully recognized. Example: "So I got eight A grade O-levels – anyone could if he worked as hard as I did."

2. Personalization. Blaming oneself for someone else's behaviour when there is no justification to do so. Example: "The reason my parents separated is all because of me."

3. Dichotomous, absolute thinking. All experiences are placed in one of two opposite categories – "black or white" – and the extreme negative view is taken. Example: "My girlfriend ditched me . . . I will never find another."

Hence it can be seen that exploration of both beliefs/ base schema and styles of thinking (cognitive errors) are of importance if we are to help the person operate in a less maladaptive way.

COGNITIVE THERAPY IN PRACTICE

As with other psychotherapies, unconditional positive regard, genuineness and empathy are regarded as essential therapeutic qualities for cognitive therapy. Cognitive therapy is, however, different from many of the traditional psychotherapies in that the therapist takes a much more active role in the therapeutic session. The cognitive approach involves active participation by the therapist in asking questions, summarizing, getting feedback and promoting alternative responses. As a result, silences, which often make teenagers uncomfortable and self-conscious, are avoided.

The neutral collaborative empiricist stance (see below) taken by the therapist is a useful way of maintaining unconditional positive regard, since many adolescents express beliefs such as "emotions are silly" or that their own thoughts are silly. Adolescents may find it difficult to talk, particularly about emotions. The emotions are new and more intense than those of childhood, and they emerge with the physical, physiological, psychological and cognitive changes that occur in adolescence. The techniques allow their beliefs to be examined in a neutral way. There is, therefore, an acceptance of their perspective of reality regardless of how distorted or limited it may appear to be.

1. Agenda. An agenda is set with a clear understanding of the range of problems a patient has. Then a hierarchy of these problems is established so that only one problem is worked on at a time. The patient is discouraged from jumping from one problem to another and is guided back to work on the agenda he has set. This is often helpful as adolescents seem to have numerous problems and have difficulty differentiating them.

2. Identifying the target problems. Here the therapist needs to be specific and inquiring. As far as possible, the therapist should understand the patient's view of himself and his surroundings. Questions, summaries and feedback are crucial at this stage. These are useful techniques in helping separate out the interwoven problems and clarifying the problems as they are perceived.

3. Gathering data. The therapist asks questions, encouraging the patient to be specific about the problems, and breaking the problem down (as is done in behaviour therapy) so that the details are fully understood by both the patient and the therapist.

4. Summarizing the problem. The therapist summarizes the problem, using the patient's own words and emphasizing certain words, thereby attempting to bring out the cognitive errors the patient makes, e.g. "As I understand it, you think that you must always . . . Is that how it is?" This helps the therapist to understand clearly how the patient construes his world.

5. Feedback. The therapist asks the patient if each summary is accurate. Summarizing and feedback should occur frequently to enable the patient to correct misinterpretations and to give the therapist an opportunity to reframe the problem.

Using the above techniques patients are helped to: (a) monitor automatic thoughts; (b) substitute alternative interpretations for the event which provoked the automatic thoughts; (c) examine the evidence for and against distorted automatic thoughts; (d) recognize the connections between these thoughts, mood and behaviour; and (e) learn to identify and alter the deep-seated beliefs which predispose him to distort his experiences, and to recognize the cognitive errors he tends to use.

6. Setting of homework. Homework is an important part of the therapy as it ensures the patient has learned the techniques of coping with distress and can manage on his own, taking control of his emotions. The patient is encouraged to use these forms (see Appendix 1) when he experiences painful events between the therapy sessions and when therapy has ended. There is a strength in encouraging the young person to understand the theory behind the therapy and to do homework, as it acknowledges the adolescent quest for independence, the ability to cope alone and not to succumb to any kind of control by an authority figure. The homework is an important part of the educational aspect of CBT as it can pinpoint difficulties the patient is having in sorting out his distress. The process of writing down is not as alien and distancing as might at first appear; some view it as an easier way of communicating, others see it as playing games, and in addition it is reasonably common for adolescents to write diaries. The process of doing homework allows young persons to sort out their own difficulties and unhappinesses, so that they feel in control and independent of authority figures.

THE THERAPEUTIC PROCESS

In order to understand the appplication of these techniques, there is a need to look in more detail at the five strategies used in the therapeutic process.

1. Monitoring of automatic thoughts (ATs)
As stated earlier, these are the self-evaluative thoughts. The negative thoughts produce dysphoria and are to do with loveability, self-worth and competence. They are, therefore, the ones in which the therapist is primarily interested. The superficial ATs that are first presented need to be explored further. This is done using a technique of inference chaining, which means asking questions like "What happens then? What does that make you feel about yourself? What do you think others think about you?" This needs to continue until the base schema are reached and the dysphoric emotion previously experienced is re-experienced. By reinvoking the intensity of the emotion, experienced generalization should occur with a spread of state-dependent learning. Situation-dependent learning also takes place as the patient experiences emotionally provoking events and is not devastated by them.

Automatic thoughts can be elicited in a number of ways:

(a) ATs experienced in therapy are often to do with "transference". For example, if the therapist is early, the patient is worried that the therapist thinks his is a serious case. If however the therapist is on time, the patient thinks he is only doing a job and doesn't really care. And if he is late then he is not taking the patient's problems seriously enough. If the patient does feel this way, he needs to be made aware that these are his thoughts; and he should test their validity by looking for other reasons as to why the therapist might be early, late or on time before he believes his original conclusion. These inferences are often very useful and powerful ways of demonstrating how cognitive errors and base schema produce dysphoria.

If there appears to be a change in affect during a session, questions should be asked like "What was going through your mind? Is it to do with material being discussed or is it because you think I am bored or fed up with you?". Transference and counter-transference are treated in a matter-of-fact way as sources of data.

(b) Using techniques of imagery. The patient is asked to go back to the situation which produced the dysphoric mood: "Tell me in detail . . . and what happened next . . . and what did that make you think about . . . and what do you think others thought of you . . . ?"

(c) Role play. The patient is asked to act out the scene in an attempt to evoke the ATs originally present.

(d) The use of a similar but less-anxiety-provoking situation. For example, "Has this ever happened to you before?" Very often it is easier to recall the automatic thoughts of a past event as there is less anxiety and emotion surrounding it than a more recent painful event.

2. Generation of alternative ideas

It is at this stage of generating alternative ideas that adolescents are so constructive and productive. This can be attributed to cognitive maturation. According to Piaget's (1984) theory, the adolescent shifts from the stage of concrete operations, which characterizes thinking during middle and late childhood, to the stage of formal operations. With the advent of formal operations, the adolescent gains a number of important new capabilities: "he can take his own thoughts as an object and reason about it" (Elkind, 1968). He can consider not merely one possible answer to a problem, or explanation to a situation, but many possible alternatives. This is different from the younger child, who is likely to adopt the first possible solution as fact, rather than appreciate the arbitrariness of his solution (Owens, 1953). The ability to generate hypotheses systematically and to test them against the evidence, i.e. to think scientifically and objectively, greatly increases the adolescent's capacity to deal with himself and the world around him. Adolescent thinking becomes more abstract: more general and metaphorical and less related to personal, immediate experience.

In paraphrase, Elkind (1968) suggests that it is perhaps the development of the capacity for formal operational thought that makes the adolescent aware of the discrepancy between how things are and how they might be at home, at school, and with themselves – which probably underlines many of the recurrent adolescent feelings of dissatisfaction, rebellion and depression. He is always comparing the actual with the possible and discovering that the actual falls very short.

Several methods can be used to generate alternative ideas:

(a) Distancing. Stand back and take a more objective view. Are there any other possible explanations for the behaviour?

(b) Role Reversal. It can be useful actively to encourage role reversal by asking questions like "What would you have felt if someone had interpreted your comment that way? How might you have meant it?" Or the therapist acts as the patient and generates alternative conclusions.

(c) Depersonalization. Very often people will apply one standard of judgement to themselves and another to everyone else. Asking them what others might feel in the same situation can help them to see how harsh they are being on themselves.

(d) Collaborative empiricism. The patient's belief is made into a hypothesis. Then a list of pros and cons is drawn up to prove or disprove the hypothesis. Some of the items on the list might need testing, so an experiment might be set up to test their validity. For example, the following list might be derived from case history 1:

Hypothesis: "My mother does not care about me."
List of items:

True	False
1. She puts me down a lot.	1. She comforts me when I am miserable.
2. She is disappointed I don't have a job.	2. She does occasionally give me a cuddle.
3. She hates my clothes.	3. She does my washing.
4. She disapproves of my friends.	4. She cooks for me and my friends.

Using this approach, patients can evaluate their beliefs rationally and if necessary test them out. This young lad was encouraged to ask his mother about her view of his friends and what she felt about his being unemployed so that he felt he could more rationally evaluate the information feeding into his automatic thoughts.

Elkind (1967), in discussing adolescent egocentrism, argues that as the young adolescent is undergoing a physiological metamorphosis, his concern is primarily with himself. Accordingly, since he fails to differentiate what others are thinking about from his own mental preoccupations, he assumes that other people are as obsessed with his behaviour and appearance as he is himself. The young person, therefore, anticipates the reaction of other people to himself.

This obvious cognitive distortion is amenable to evaluation using cognitive techniques.

Case example 2: A young girl who had previously taken an overdose of tablets – an act of which she was very ashamed – believed that when she met new people they would know she had done such an irresponsible thing and would not want to be friends with her. Cognitive therapy, and in particular the technique of collaborative empiricism, encouraged the adolescent to sort out the evidence supporting her belief.

CBT also helps adolescents distinguish among the options they are offering (i.e. the inferences they are making about a situation) and their evaluation of these. The inferences which cause pain are usually the result of cognitive errors, and the most common error made by adolescents is one of dichotomous, black-and-white thinking. The evaluation of the inference they believe in, when in distress, is negative. The process of collaborative empiricism encourages the adolescent to explore alternatives to their black-or-white view, and even if they still believe their view to be the right one, they can be helped to appreciate that their evaluation is more catastrophically negative than need be. The whole process of encouraging young people to view themselves and their world from other perspectives is rewarding. Adolescence is a time when they are receptive to this approach as young people are discovering the arbitrariness of their own mental constructions and learning to differentiate them from perceptual reality.

Children who have been deprived in their childhood of parental care and attention may enter adolescence with a rigid, concrete interpretation of their past, thus feeling rejected, unloved and often angry. When faced with depressing events in the present, they will often "recruit in" these painful childhood memories (Gilbert, 1984). These memories then become available to the same therapeutic scrutiny. The adolescent can be helped to reinterpret the experience of rejection and, even if it is "real", to learn to accept it without the catastrophic evaluations they have been making.

Case example 3: A young man of 16 had taken multiple overdoses in serious attempts to end his life. His mother had devoted herself to a demanding fundamentalist religion when he was seven. There was a great deal of marital strife, for which he felt responsible, as well as financial stress. He felt he had lost his mother, she did not love him, always put him down, and if his mother did not love him how could anyone else? He was helped to see that probably the marriage had gone wrong before or around the time his mother became religious and that his mother was a sad person who had a lot of needs of her own. The fact that she was unable to give to him did not necessarily reflect on him as an individual (see CBT form, Appendix 1). Once he accepted this, he became much less angry and was more gentle with his mother, allowing her to give more to him. Further behavioural techniques were employed to encourage him to meet his lost school friends, to socialize and reinforce his feelings of acceptability. His self-esteem improved to the extent of finding himself a job and a girlfriend.

Once patients are skilled at identifying their ATs and can generate alternative rational thoughts, they are encouraged to keep a daily record of these using Beck's recording form for dysfunctional thoughts (see above case history). As the patient gets more experienced in recognizing his automatic thoughts, these can be explored further until the base schema are reached. In adolescents these are not deeply entrenched and so are easy to evoke, question and modify.

It is helpful to get the patient to evaluate his belief in both his automatic thoughts as well as his rational responses by writing percentages on these forms to indicate how strongly the patient rates his belief in these thoughts (see Appendix 1). In this way both patient and therapist can monitor improvement and, in addition, the activity gives the patient positive reinforcement as he progresses.

3. Recognizing the connection between automatic thoughts, affect and behaviour

It is useful here to get the patient to predict what inevitable consequences in behaviour and emotion arise from belief in automatic thoughts and then later in alternative ideas (see Appendix 1). There is often scope for humour and a realization of how passive or how much of a "victim" the youngster has been making himself. By also looking at the rational responses, the adolescent can see how he can start to take control of his feelings and actions. The addition of behavioural consequence columns to the CBT forms demonstrates clearly the impact of thoughts on emotions and behaviour.

4. Modifying base schema and cognitive errors

It is necessary to make the patient aware of the cognitive errors he has been utilizing, i.e. why is everything he does worthless, whereas everything anyone else does is of value.

The patient's awareness can be activated first through neutrality – which means never contradicting or belittling beliefs, but simply accepting them so that it is not necessary for the patient to defend them; secondly, through humour, gently teasing the patient as he begins to feel more confident and the recurrent nature of cognitive errors and base schema become evident; thirdly, while using the technique of collaborative empiricism, the global or pervasive appraisals being used by the patient should be pointed out.

Probably the most difficult part of CBT is trying to help patients see how beliefs in their base schema result in their feeling and behaving in certain maladaptive and ineffective ways. The recurring nature of these themes becomes evident on the forms when they have been worked to a deeper level. Patients can then see that the reasons for maladaptive behaviour tend to stem from their belief in their base schema. It is necessary to explore these to produce permanent mood and behavioural changes. Experimentation is a useful way of confronting and testing a fundamental belief in loveability or achievement.

ISSUES ARISING IN THE USE OF COGNITIVE PSYCHOTHERAPY WITH ADOLESCENTS

As Bower (1974) and Donaldson (1978) have clearly demonstrated, cognitive development is not as age related as previously thought, thus the ability to think operationally is not confined to adolescence. Many younger children have developed the ability to think in an operational way and are therefore well able to benefit from this approach. Donaldson (1978) has argued that young children can think this way when the information makes "human sense" to the child, but they have difficulties with problems of a more abstract and formal nature. Maturation of this cognitive process and the ability to cope with more complex problems is necessary for the successful use of CBT. Children who have not developed some degree of sophistication in their thinking processes do not do well using the techniques outlined above. It is, therefore, important that when assessing a child's suitability for CBT one must ensure that they have the ability to think operationally. This is done during the assessment interview when the young person is asked about his anxieties and thoughts about attending the interview. The ease with which he is able to entertain alternative hypotheses is investigated.

Adolescents' morality is also in transition. The moral attitudes of younger children are determined by authority figures and unquestioningly maintain a stated social stability and order. Concepts of morality based on individual or personal values or judgements have not yet developed in the younger child. It is to this stage that the adolescent evolves. Now there is an emphasis on procedural rules for reaching a consensus and a concern with establishing and maintaining individual rights, equality and liberty (Kohlberg, 1969; Turiel, 1974). In the process of adolescent moral development, there is a change and development of a stronger sense of self, where they have to sort out their own political, sexual and religious values. Up until this point they have accepted the values of their parents; now they have to make choices for themselves. There is the potential for flexibility and fluidity in adolescent thought processes which allows them the freedom to accept other evaluations and interpretations. Their values are not deeply entrenched and are therefore more easily shifted than those of adults.

Authority and self-control are important issues in adolescent emotions. The educative aspect of CBT, where patients are taught to "tune in" to dysphoric emotion and the automatic thoughts producing them and to treat these as a source of data (the validity of which can be proved or disproved), allows patients to take control of their emotions and respects their need for privacy and independence. The process of doing homework reinforces this by allowing them to sort out their difficulties and unhappinesses outside the therapeutic relationship.

Many adolescents are brought in by their parents, who are registering the complaint and asking for help for their child. The therapeutic relationship is therefore precarious as adolescents often have not come for therapy of their own free will. The therapist is often seen as an authority figure; therefore, unconditional positive regard and respect for the adolescent as an individual are all the more important. Questions should be asked that can easily be answered. Initially, the questions should be neutral and also be about areas of life that are going well, so that the youngsters' self-esteem can be boosted. Most authority figures in their lives are likely to have been concentrating on the negative aspects of their behaviour and will often see only negative aspects of hobbies (e.g. pop music). The positive regard shown for these areas in their lives will often engender trust and facilitate communication. If parents have brought their child along, it is important to make all members of the family aware that the information being given to the therapist is accepted neutrally and as their valid personal perspective, other perspectives being explored but no moral judgements being made. (The technique is similar to that used in Milan Family Therapy (Palazzoli Selvini, Boscolo, Cecchin and Prata, 1980).) This is important as one has to engage both the adolescent and his parents if therapy is to be succesful. Parents may feel discriminated against and alienated, as well as feeling jealous of and threatened by the therapist's relationship with their child.

It is necessary to be sensitive to their need to talk, giving them plenty of time to talk if they want to and yet avoiding silences. This can be done by summarizing and clarifying what they have been saying. The cognitive therapies involve active participation by the therapist in asking questions, summarizing, getting feedback and promoting alternative responses.

Adolescence is a time of transition where the youngster is on a bridge looking wistfully over his shoulder at his childhood and looking ahead at the future with trepidation and excitement. There is a progressive striving towards autonomy that in the end hopefully outweighs the pull towards passivity (Wilson, 1981). Prolonged intensive psychotherapy may lead to regressive behaviour and emotion and encourage dependency which may interfere with the developmental transition. Peer-group relationships and acceptibility are of great importance at this stage of development as it is a time when attachment is transferred from parents to peer groups (Blos, 1962, 1979). Thus rejection or ridicule by peers could increase their state of confusion and conflict over where their loyalties lie and threaten the safety of natural development. CBT is an outward looking approach so encouraging peer group interaction, the latter often being used to test the validity of hypotheses. CBT deals with the present and is problem-oriented. Past traumas are worked through in the same way, with the alternate

APPENDIX 1 – MODIFIED CBT FORM FOR CASE HISTORY 1

WHAT HAPPENED?	EMOTIONS	AUTOMATIC THOUGHTS	BEHAVIOUR RESULTING FROM AUTOMATIC THOUGHTS	ALTERNATIVE THOUGHTS/ COPING THOUGHTS	BEHAVIOUR RESULTING FROM ALTERNATIVE THOUGHTS	HOW DO I FEEL NOW
What made you upset? Event or Daydream	Be precise about what you are feeling, sad/anxious/angry. How do you feel it. (1–100)	Write down the thoughts that came immediately before these feelings. How much do you believe these automatic thoughts? (1–100)		Write down your alternative/coping thoughts in response to automatic thoughts. Rate belief 1–100	What plan of action will I now make?	1. Rerate Emotion 2. Rerate belief in AT
Asked mother a question, she ignored me.	Rejected Hurt Despondent 80%	1. She never listens to me. 2. No one listens to me. 3. I'm so boring and uninteresting. 4. No wonder I am unemployed. 5. I'll never achieve anything.	I don't bother to talk to her, or have the confidence to talk to anyone. Don't go to Job Centre. If jobs in paper, won't telephone, as too frightened.	1. She was busy in the kitchen cooking. Maybe she didn't hear me. 2. When I used to meet my friends they seemed to find me interesting and amusing.	1. Make sure when I talk to Mum she's in the room and not busy. 2. Make more effort to go and meet my friends. 3. Go and badger Careers Advice and Job Centre again. Look in	1. Sad 20% Rejected 10% 2. 30%

newspapers more regularly.

3. I doubt whether that is the reason I am employed. The unemployment figures are so high. It's probably very little to do with me.

4. Achievement isn't the only road to happiness, although I want to do something with my life 80%

6. I'm a failure. 98%
....
Note:
Cognitive Errors
never –
generalization
no one –
magnification.
Base scheme –
I'm a failure.

perceptions or interpretations being discussed. Reinterpretation and acceptance without the catastrophizing of childhood memories help the child come to
terms with their life experiences.

Conclusion

CBT with adolescents can be seen as a useful form of psychotherapy utilizing
the natural development of cognitive skills in adolescence. As with all psychotherapies, it has its shortcomings and drawbacks, but for many young people it
is helpful. In assessing who to take on for CBT it is very important to ensure that
the ability to consider alternative hypotheses is well developed, as it is the exis-
tential question on the arbitrariness of the nature of reality that forms the basis
of cognitive psychotherapy.

REFERENCES

Beck, A.T. (1963). Thinking and depression: 1. Idiosyncratic content and cognitive dis-
    tortions. *Archives of General Psychiatry* **9**, 324–333.
Beck, A.T. (1976). *Cognitive Therapy and the Emotional Disorders*. New York: International
    Universities Press.
Beck, A.T., Rush, A.J., Shaw, B.F., & Emerg, G. (1979). *Cognitive Therapy of Depression*.
    New York: J. Wiley and Sons.
Blackburn, I.M., Bishop, S., Glen, A.I.M., Walley , L.J. and Christie, J.E. (1981).
    The efficacy of cognitive therapy in depressions: A treatment trial using cognitive
    therapy and pharmacotherapy, each alone and in combination. *British Journal of
    Psychiatry* **139**, 181–189.
Blos, P. (1962). *On Adolescence: A Psychoanalytic Interpretation*. New York: The Free Press of
    Glencoe Inc.
Blos, P. (1979). *The Adolescent Passage: Developmental Issues*. New York: International
    Universities Press.
Bower, T.G.R. (1974). *Development in Infancy*. San Francisco: W.H. Freeman and
    Company.
Elkind, D. (1967). Egocentriscm in adolescents. *Child Development* **38**, 1025–34.
Elkind, D. (1968). Cognitive development in adolescents. In *Understanding Adolescents*,
    Adams, J.F. (Ed.). Boston: Allyn and Bacon, pp. 128–158.
Ellis, A. (1962). *Reason and Emotion in Psychotherapy*. New York: Lyle Stuart.
Ellis, A. and Grieger (Eds.) (1977). *Handbook of Rational Emotive Therapy*. New York:
    Springer.
Donaldson, M. (1978). *Children's Minds*. London: Fontana Paperbacks.
Gilbert, P. (1984). *Depression: From Psychology to Brain State*. London: Lawrence Erlbaum
    Associates.
Kelly, G. (1955). *The Psychology of Personal Constructs*. New York: Norton and Co.
Kohlberg, L. (1969). Stage and sequence: the cognitive developmental approach to
    socialization. In *Handbook of socialization theory and research*, Goslin, D. (Ed.).
    Chicago: Rand McNally.
Kovacs, M., Rush, A.J., Beck, A.T. and Hollow, S.D. (1981). Depressed outpatients
    treated with cognitive therapy or pharmacotherapy: A one year follow up. *Archives
    of General Psychiatry* **38**, 33–39.

Mahoney, M.J. (1974). *Cognition and Behaviour Modification.* Cambridge, Mass: Ballinger.

McAdam, E.K. and Gilbert, P. (1985). Cognitive Behavioural therapy as a psychotherapy for mood disturbance in child, adolescent and family psychiatry. Newsletter of the *ACPP* Vol. 7,1, 19–27.

Owens W.A. Jr. (1953). Age and mental abilities: a longtitudinal study. *Genet. Pyschol. Monograph* **48**, 3–54.

Palazzoli Selvini, M., Boscolo, L., Cecchin, G. and Prata, G. Hypothesising-Circularity-Neutrality: Three Guidelines for the Conductor of the Session. *Family Process* Vol. 19 no. 1, pp. 3–12.

Piaget, J. (1954). *The Construction of Reality in the Child.* New York: Basic Books.

Rush, A.J., Beck, A.T., Kovacs, M. and Hollow, S.D. (1977). Comparative efficacy of cognitive therapy and pharmacotherapy in the treatment of depressed outpatients. *Cognitive Therapy and Research* **1**, 17–37.

Turiel, E. (1974). Conflict and transition in adolescent moral development. *Child Development* **45**, 14–29.

Wilson, P. (1981). Short-term intervention with adolescents. Unpublished.

Young, H.S. (1984). Counselling strategies with working class adolescents. *British Journal of Cognitive Psychotherapy* Vol. 2, 2, 21–32.

10. Behavioural approaches to working with adolescents in trouble

BARRIE BROWN

INTRODUCTION

Over the years, practitioners working with young offenders have not enjoyed much in the way of success. The literature on treatment of delinquents is littered with failures. In the 1950s the Cambridge Somerville Project could find no significant differences between treatment by psychotherapy and no treatment at all (McCord, McCord and Zola, 1959), and psychiatric treatment was reported to have no ameliorative effect on the number of subsequent convictions of young offenders (Teuber and Powers, 1951). By the end of the 1960s criticisms were being voiced throughout the Western world about the lack of effectiveness of attempts to rehabilitate young offenders (see, for example, Menninger, 1968 in the U.S.A. and Taylor, Walton and Young, 1973 in the U.K.).

Common to these criticisms was the charge that psychiatry was imprecise and oversimplistic in the way it defined delinquency. Psychiatric formulations ignored the stigmatizing effect of the criminal justice process itself and failed to account for the fact that, far from being a preserve of the pathological minority, delinquency is a commonplace and temporary condition of the majority.

In this country, until the 1970s, young offenders were placed in approved schools but these too were found to be relatively impotent in coping effectively with young people in trouble (Cornish and Clarke, 1975). Revisions of services for young people in trouble arising out of the Children and Young Persons Act,

1969, (which established a comprehensive care system for all children, with community homes with education on the premises for some of the most disturbed youngsters in care) led to provisions which were found to be no more effective than the approved schools they replaced (Tutt, 1982).

By the time Taylor, Cornish and Clarke and Tutt had joined it, the bandwagon of criticism of residential and custodial responses to juvenile delinquency was rolling very quickly indeed. By the early 1980s many residential programmes were being closed in the United Kingdom.

This revolution in practice stemmed not only from the empirical research quoted above but also from a growing realization of the importance of the environmental circumstances in which the young people in the cities in Great Britain are reared today. Practitioners generally had largely failed to incorporate this realization into their day-to-day practice. It was, however, this same realization which led many to seek to develop a range of practical alternatives to custody or care, including interventions based on the behavioural model.

THE BEHAVIOURAL MODEL

The behavioural model offers a conceptual framework for understanding and changing the behaviour of adolescents in trouble. The core principle of the model is that "abnormal" behaviour in children and adolescents does not differ from normal behaviour in the way it develops, persists or is modified (Herbert, 1974). The adolescents' behaviour is learned, maintained and regulated by its effects upon the environment as well as by the feedback received with regard to the consequences of that behaviour. How the adolescent behaves, in other words, can be understood as the outcome of a two-way transaction between the person (that is, the inborn and acquired strengths and weaknesses) and that person's acting and reacting on (and to) the environment.

The behavioural model seems to offer a relevant theoretical approach to the treatment of a wide range of problems with adolescents (Herbert, 1978). A number of practice methods have now been derived from this model. Whatever the precise approach employed, assessment of the need for and the planning of any intervention tends to contain several stages:

1. The adolescent's behaviour is described in as specific a way as possible and problems for the young person, parents, teachers and other significant people identified. This identification involves specifying the consequences of the behaviour – the system of reinforcers and punishers which surround it – as well as pinpointing the behavioural problems themselves.

In carrying out this preliminary task, the behavioural practitioner is concerned not with *why* the behaviour is as it is, nor what *underlies* the behaviour or *how* it came to be that way, but *what* is the adolescent doing, under *what* conditions are the pinpointed behaviours emitted, *what* are the consequences of these behaviours and *what* behaviours can be encouraged in their place? The initial objective is the identification of the repertoire of the skills of the adolescent and the surrounding circumstances which are currently present. In essence this first stage involves establishing a baseline.

The longer term objective of the approach is to broaden the adolescent's repertoire of skills using intervention methods derived directly from the learning processes which account for how both problem and skilled behaviours are acquired. A number of principles underlie these processes: behaviour resulting in reinforcement is likely to become better established or to occur more frequently; behaviour leading to punishment is likely to be weakened or to occur less frequently; learning is sometimes enhanced, diminished or distorted by intra-individual emotional, cognitive and physiological processes; learning may occur as a result of the observation of others being reinforced or punished or through the influence of models or under conditions of interpersonal persuasion. Most behavioural approaches are essentially practical elaborations of a combination of these processes.

2. The second practical step is to assess what resources are available for bringing about appropriate change in the adolescent's behaviour using the processes described above. Are parents capable of coping with an intervention programme? How realistic are the teachers' expectations of the adolescent's performance in the classroom and so on?

3. The third step is to identify the goals of intervention with the adolescent. In what direction should the change of behaviour go and how far?

Having completed these three assessment and planning steps, a practical behavioural intervention programme can now be implemented.

The remainder of this chapter describes a number of examples of behavioural approaches to working with adolescents in trouble at Orchard Lodge. Examples have been selected of practical applications of behavioural approaches that are relevant to a variety of practice settings in which adolescents in trouble are cared for, educated or treated. Orchard Lodge is a resource centre for the assessment and treatment of juvenile delinquents placed into the care of local authorities in South East London. Residential facilities at the Centre are offered in large family-style houses located together in the heart of the local community, with consultant support from psychologists and psychiatrists.

A GROUP BEHAVIOURAL PROGRAMME

The first example is Unit One, a behavioural programme located at Orchard Lodge. Unit One was intended to replicate Achievement Place (Kirigin, Wolf,

Braukmann, Fixsen and Phillips, 1979), a model behavioural approach to working with small groups of young offenders in residential settings located in the community. The approach used in Achievement Place contains three essential elements:

(a) the use of a flexible motivation system based on the adolescent's earning points and on contractual agreements between the adolescents and child care staff. These motivation systems are gradually and systematically replaced by

(b) the use of intensive social reinforcement programmes and

(c) the development of the adolescent's self-government through the use of contracts and peer involvement techniques.

In the original Achievement Place model programmes, two "teaching parents" (in the U.S.A., psychologists or child care workers who received specialized training for the job) design and carry out treatment programmes incorporating the three approaches identified above, in order to correct problems as they occur in the group home. The "teaching parents" supervise the activities of young people in the home, at school and in the local community. They also liaise with the youth's own home, social service departments and other community and voluntary agents. The term "teaching parent" derives from the focus adopted in the model programmes on the teaching of new skills as the primary task.

Unit One was designed to provide a community-orientated alternative, similar to Achievement Place, for young offenders who would otherwise have been placed in institutional or custodial settings because of the seriousness of their involvement in criminal behaviour.

Unit One is the most recent of a number of attempts in the U.K. to implement a behavioural programme with young offenders. The token economy component of the model has been introduced at Aycliffe (Hoghughi, 1979), in a programme which focused on personal targets and peer group reinforcement. Cullen and Seddon (1980) also introduced the token economy component for older adolescents in a Borstal (now called a Youth Custody Centre). This experimental programme employed an incentive scheme using points as a currency with a group of 12 older adolescents presenting with a variety of severe behaviour disturbances.

In neither programme has there been a published attempt to establish a comprehensive replication of the model Achievement Place programme other than the token economy component. Another omission is the absence of any replication in a community setting.

The only two community-based projects employing an approach based on the Achievement Place model are the SHAPE project (Ostapuik, 1982) and the BAY project (McGivern, 1980), both located in Birmingham, England. These projects have developed a variety of approaches, including a token economy and contracts with young people in the community. Unfortunately, neither has attempted to carry out any analysis of the effectiveness of the programme.

Unit One attempted to incorporate as many components of the original Achievement Place model as possible but differed from the original in one staffing policy. In the original Achievement Place model the staffing consisted of a professional teaching parent couple who lived in the houses with a "family" of six to eight young people. In Unit One, staffing had to be adapted to the conditions of service laid down by employers and trade unions in the United Kingdom. Instead of a couple, the "family" of about seven to 12 youths in Unit One had a team of eight care workers led by a group leader. At any one time only two or three of these staff were on duty in the house.

The programme

The Unit One programme comprises a token economy, a school programme, teaching interactions and self-government. The token economy provided a firm structure during the period immediately after the youth's admission, but was arranged so as to transfer the youth from external points reinforcers to social and self-controlled reinforcement. This was achieved by using sequential stages.

Youths could be admitted to any stage, but usually started on the first and most basic, Stage A. All that was required at this stage was that the youth kept to eight basic rules of the house. Points earned were written on the card by the youth and counter-signed by a care worker.

Failure to keep to the rules was dealt with by the use of another component of the programme, a *teaching interaction*. The teaching-interaction was defined as a one-to-one direct teaching session in which the care worker taught the component skills involved in succeeding at a skill, giving an opportunity for the youth to practise in either role play or in video, and giving social reinforcement and/or points for co-operation.

Where this procedure failed to produce a correct response, a *subsystem* was used. Earning a subsystem in Unit One meant that the youth was suspended from earning any privileges, or indeed consuming any, until he had completed two tasks so designed as to help him avoid earning the subsystem again. For example, if a youth lost his temper in an argument and smashed a window, this would constitute breaking one of the eight house rules – everyone in the house must look after fixtures and fittings. A typical subsystem would be that he should complete all the arrangements for the glass to be measured, cut and fitted by a glazier, pay the bill, and practise with his keyworker for 30 minutes how to "stay cool" in an argument.

The youths also carried around a points card on Stage B. They were able to write points on the card, not only for adhering to the basic rules as in Stage A, but also for achieving personal targets. These targets – usually not more than four or five, were derived from a careful behavioural assessment of the youth's assets, deficits and excesses during a pre-admission assessment period.

The assessment listed a menu of skills the programme could teach in order for the youth to achieve success in returning to his home and community. What characterized Stage B was that *all* personal targets had methods which involved earning points on the points cards. In Stages A and B the youth was able to take his card at the end of the day (usually after tea in the late afternoon) to his key-worker to cash in the points and order back-up reinforcers for the next day. Typical back-ups included sweets and extra food, access to audio and video-tapes, trips to watch football, ice skating and extra late TV.

Unlike the Achievement Place programme, however, points were not taken away. Recent research at Orchard Lodge (Scherer and Brown, 1984) has shown that the use of a response-cost programme similar to the Unit One Subsystem was not only more effective than taking points away in reducing negative and disruptive behaviours, it also significantly reduced the frequency of the use of an exclusion-time-out procedure in a behavioural programme in a secure unit containing very violent and disturbed adolescent offenders.

Stages C and D, again in contrast to the Achievement Place programme, did not so much wean the youth from point earning by extending the delay between point earning and consumption of reinforcement as by progressive introduction of more self-governed agreements. Stage C involved at least one target which used a contracting method rather than points reinforcers. Stage C was completed when *all* the four or five personal targets were contracted. Stage D was usually employed in the final days of a youth's stay in Unit One, when he was spending only a few hours each week in the programme. The stage simply involved verbal agreements between the youth and the care workers.

The orientation in this programme of self-control through gradual introduction of contractual agreements, first written, then verbal, arose out of an earlier attempt in the U.K. to replicate the daily-weekly-merit progression employed in the model Achievement Place programmes. This earlier programme experienced particular problems in the transfer from the weekly points stage to the non-points merit stage (Brown, Beddow, Merker, Spense, Leheay and Christie, 1978).

The school programme was also adapted from the original teaching-family model. Some of the youths attended the educational centre available on the Orchard Lodge campus, but some either remained at their own school, or returned there after a few months. In either case, arrangements were made for the youth to take his points/contract card into class with him, and for the teacher to continue any relevant aspects of the programme there using the same methods and principles.

The adolescents in Unit One

In its first year, Unit One received eight young people from residential assessment centres or long-term residential care who were deemed suitable for placement only in long-term institutional care by virtue of the severity and frequency of their previous offending. The oldest youth was 17 years and the youngest 13 years on admission, with an average age of 14.47 years.

All the youths came from families living within five miles of Unit One, although one of the youths had been rejected by his parents and had lived in a group home for over 10 years. A second youth had rejected opportunities to live with his father in another part of London, and a third was unable to return to live with his mother because of her long-term hospitalization with a chronic psychiatric illness. Only two of the youths had intact original two-parent families. All eight had long-term histories of offending, two of them with several convictions for violent sexual crime.

Results

Placement

Five of the youths were placed either at home after discharge or in an alternative community-based setting. Thus, one youth was placed in a flat and in employment, and a second returned to a family-group home in the community. Only three of the youths were discharged from Unit One to long-term institutional or custodial care.

Although comparison with other programmes must be made with caution (because of the very small size of the sample and the fact that there was no opportunity to place the youths in Unit One by random allocation) these results provide some cause for optimism in the effectiveness of the programme. Recent evaluations of custodial and residential institutional care have shown much less positive outcomes (Tutt, 1982).

Offending

The results for offending are particularly encouraging. Five youths avoided further offending, during the programme and throughout a one year follow-up period, the same five who were returned ''successfully'' to their own or a surrogate home. In contrast, the three ''unsuccessful'' youths committed a further five offences during the programme and two more during the follow-up (by one youth).

Length of stay

The unsuccessful youths (i.e. those not returned home) stayed on average 10 weeks less in Unit One than successful youths, and a return to their own homes and communities was usually possible within about seven months. Successful youths were also more likely to receive social skills training as part of their programme, and to have close involvement by family members.

General outcome
In spite of the very small numbers involved in this preliminary analysis, early indications of success can be found in the process of delivering the Unit One programme to individual youths. The majority of the youths co-operated with intensive individual work, and parents were able to involve themselves with the programme staff in extending the token economy, skills training and teaching interaction elements to the youth's own home.

Attrition in the programme was minimal. Only one of the eight youths dropped out of the programme before a planned discharge took place.

BEHAVIOURAL CONSULTATION

Unit One is an example of the application of a package of behavioural approaches to providing amelioration in a community setting with adolescents in trouble. A second practice context in which behavioural approaches have been developed has been with individuals or groups using behavioural consultation of various kinds. For example, in an attempt to help young people experiencing catastrophic reactions as a result of family crises, Dutton (1981) developed and evaluated a behavioural programme for police trainees to help them through crises in family settings. Although the target trainees improved their crisis intervention skills, subsequent evaluation showed that, in the absence of encouragement through promotion for these new policing skills, their use declined rapidly in frequency as the trainees became fully-fledged police officers. This example of indirect intervention demonstrates a common feature of this kind of behavioural approach: the failure to incorporate comprehensive evaluation of the outcomes of the consultation in the real world outside the intervention setting itself.

A similar problematic feature is evident in a second approach to developing behavioural consultation – direct preventive intervention with groups of clients. For example, Stumphauser, Veyoz and Aiken (1979) carried out a series of analyses of the behaviour of members of a gang on the streets of Los Angeles. The objective of the project was to establish a lower rate of violent behaviour amongst gang members. The analysis led to the establishment of an escort service provided by gang members for the elderly in local communities. As with the policing skills programme above, success of the programme has been established only in the short-term. Nevertheless, both of these examples of behavioural consultation work in the United States demonstrate how the extent and range of behavioural approaches can be extended beyond one-to-one therapy, and how important it is to plan for maintenance of the interventions in the real world of practice.

In the United Kingdom, the use of consultation by behavioural practitioners has offered a relatively recent area for development in work with adolescents. The following examples demonstrate behavioural consultation approaches with care and teaching staff at Orchard Lodge.

Violence in the classroom

At the same time as the Unit One programmes were being developed, staff working elsewhere at Orchard Lodge were having to cope with apparently unprovoked and unpredictable violent behaviour in some of the adolescents resident in the centre. In time, it became clear that an analysis of violence at Orchard Lodge was a necessary prerequisite to identifying how care and teaching staff could reduce the frequency of violent behaviours.

This analysis (Brown and Drinkwater, 1984) was able to show that physical assaults on care staff in the resource were closely associated with attempts by the staff to obtain compliance from the adolescents. In a study of 140 such episodes over a period of six months, more than half the incidents were preceded by a demand for compliance by the care worker. A similar proportion of the episodes included refusal by the adolescents to accept the compliance demand.

This surprising finding was discussed with the care workers. After a series of staff meetings, it was decided to proceed to a second stage of the intervention. The consultant would now examine and provide advice on the way in which care staff used compliance demand in that setting. Thus, Abbott (1984) examined the use by teaching staff of compliance demands.

Her data showed that staff used a limited range of methods of asking the adolescents to comply. Each worker had a recognizable style of compliance bidding. Thus, some made frequent demands, others hardly any at all, some signalled they were about to ask for compliance and waited until the adolescent looked towards them before completing the request, others inserted a compliance bid without waiting for the young person to turn towards them. Some workers did not wait for the young person to comply before intruding in some way into the young person's response. Others made their compliance bid and then did not intrude.

Abbott (1984) found that how frequently the non-compliant responses were presented by young people in the classrooms at Orchard Lodge depended on the style employed by teachers when asking for their compliance. Higher levels of compliance amongst the pupils were obtained by teachers who made less frequent demands for compliance. Teachers who failed to wait for the young person to comply before intruding and/or did not wait until the adolescent looked towards them before completing a compliance request, obtained lower rates of compliance by the pupils in the classes. These differential responses were not evident to the teachers themselves.

These results were in turn discussed with the team of care workers. A wide-ranging debate concerning the relationship between the worker's behaviour and young people's non-compliance ensued. To illustrate the point in the discussion, data were shown demonstrating the precise links between the worker's behaviour and non-compliance. This discussion and these data then made it possible for the group of workers to resolve for themselves how to organize relevant aspects of the environment of the community-home.

Developing basic child-care skills

Earlier in the development of Unit One, the need to improve the use of social reinforcement by care workers became apparent. One member of the consulting team (Carr, 1982) thus developed a measure of teacher interaction skills, having first thoroughly researched the development of evaluation techniques in the original model Achievement Place group homes. The purpose of this measure was to assess how many positive qualities of interaction were used by individual care-staff during the training course in both role play and *in vivo* practice. Carr (1982) piloted a reliable and cross-situationally stable measure of the number of teaching interaction elements used by care workers in naturalistic settings by means of a structured observation schedule. She also developed a role play test of the use of teaching interaction elements which could be used to evaluate the impact of training during the training sessions themselves.

In a study examining the usefulness of these measures in the Unit One programme, Carr (1982) was able to show that role play scores increased significantly for all components of the teaching interaction, but that *in vivo* measures showed improvements only in the area of giving rationales to the young people in the family group home. These results suggested some practical ways of overcoming the difficulties of generalizing skills learnt in a training course to *in vivo* practice, which were subsequently used in the Unit One staff training programmes.

DISCUSSION

Although the Unit One programme was planned originally as an attempt to replicate the Achievement Place model programme (Kirigin *et al.*, 1979), the development of behavioural approaches to working with adolescents in trouble discussed here has been descriptive rather than experimental. One of the practical problems in replicating a model such as Achievement Place is the extent to which professional, occupational and cultural factors require modification of the original model. In the case of Unit One, two particular influences have necessitated abandonment of certain features of the original model. These are the rejection by professional staff and the clients of much of their peer-manager programme in the original model and the disparity between the conditions of work experienced by the teaching parent couple in the typical Achievement Place group home in the U.S.A. and the conditions of work required by employer and trade union agreements in this country. The former problem is probably culturally-determined and has proved impossible to overcome. The initiation of prefects or trusties has negative connotations.

Elsewhere in Europe (Yule and Brown, 1986) the solution to the latter problem has been to set up Achievement Place model homes in collaboration with voluntary charitable bodies, albeit with financial support from central government. In the U.K. most voluntary organizations providing services for adolescents in trouble are likely to offer similar conditions of employment as central and local government social service practice settings. Again, solutions are not readily apparent to deal with this problem.

A third major problem for practitioners wishing to develop behavioural approaches with adolescents in trouble is the lack of statutory responsibility on local or voluntary bodies for resourcing evaluation of innovatory practice. The development of behavioural consultation at Orchard Lodge, valuable though it has proved in providing feedback to practitioners in that setting, has been possible only because of the availability of postgraduate clinical psychology students with an interest in carrying out data-based projects as a part of their training, and by a small number of care staff with both energy and a commitment to evaluative research. Resources for research are difficult to justify in a climate of economic restraint in public welfare. In a contemporary climate of professional opinion in which welfare models, behaviourally-based or otherwise, are seen as irrelevant when compared with the need to treat, decriminalize and decarcerate young offenders (Tutt, 1982), the justification is even more difficult.

In spite of these problems, early indications of success in the use of behavioural approaches with adolescents in trouble in Unit One has provided further encouragement for the development of innovative behavioural approaches at Orchard Lodge to working with adolescents in trouble. Behavioural consultation has been valuable in helping to improve the content and effectiveness of training and has subsequently improved intervention practice.

Nevertheless, a fourth issue emerges clearly from the experience gained at Orchard Lodge in the development of behavioural approaches. It is the lack of facilities for intensive and continuing training. Training is necessary to expand the development of behavioural work beyond the limited number of isolated initiatives that have been reported in the U.K. in the last five years.

The pioneering work of the original Achievement Place team at Lawrence, Kansas (Kirigan et al., 1979) has had a considerable impact on the thinking of practitioners working with young offenders throughout the world. Early reports of the successful use of simple token economy approaches paved the way for rapid growth in the use of behavioural techniques (Kazdin, 1977), but by the end of the 1970s many practitioners were reporting difficulties with the simple behavioural approach (Brown and Christie, 1980). For example, the latter authors list as significant problems to be dealt with: the cost of training and support of staff, the resistance of some young people to the model, misuse of the token economy by some clients and difficulties in achieving generalization of newly acquired behavioural changes outside the treatment setting.

The multi-component approach pioneered by Achievement Place has gone a long way to dealing with each of these problems. The social learning basis of the approach encourages the use of cognitive methods, in particular modelling and direct teaching by the teaching parents, and the involvement of the clients themselves in developing the rules and operating them in the clinical setting reduces their resistance and misuse of the techniques. Generalization is also enhanced by using cognitive methods, although there is much research and exploration to be carried out to identify what works, with whom and why. Certainly the broader social learning theory basis for modern behavioural approaches to working with adolescents is now beginning to emerge as a powerful approach.

REFERENCES

Abbott, K. (1984). The antecedents of compliance and non-compliance in adolescents in residential care. Unpublished M. Phil. thesis. Institute of Psychiatry, University of London.

Brown, B.J., Beddow, J., Merker, A., Spence, S., Leheay, C. and Christie, M.M. (1978). The Gilbey token economy management system for delinquent boys in residential care: a review of the first year. Tennal School, Birmingham, England, unpublished internal review document.

Brown, B.J. and Christie, N.N. (1981). *Social Learning Practice in Residential Child Care.* Oxford: Pergamon.

Brown, B.J. and Drinkwater, J. (1984). A method of recording violent episodes in residential care using behavioural analysis. *Orchard Lodge Studies of Deviancy* 3, 136–151.

Carr, S.J. (1982). Some aspects of the use of "teaching interactions" in a residential setting for young male offenders. Unpublished M. Phil. thesis, Institute of Psychiatry, University of London.

Cornish, D.B. and Clarke, R.V.G. (1975). *Residential Treatment and its Effects on Delinquency.* H.M.S.O., No. 32.

Dutton, D.S. (1981). Training police officers to intervene in domestic violence. In *Violent Behaviour: Social Learning Approaches to Prediction, Management and Treatment,* Stuart, R.B. (Ed.). New York: Brunner/Mazel.

Herbert, M. (1974). *Emotional Problems of Development in Children.* New York: Academic Press.

Herbert, M. (1978). *Conduct Disorders of Childhood and Adolescence.* London: Wiley.

Hoghughi, M.S. (1979). The Aycliffe token economy. *British Journal of Criminology* 19, 384–399.

Kazdin, A.E. (1977). *The token economy*. New York: Plenum Press.

Kirigin, K.A., Wolf, M.M., Braukmann, C.J., Fixsen, D.L. and Phillips, E.L. (1979). Achievement Place: A preliminary outcome evaluation. In *Progress in Behavior Therapy with Delinquents*, Stumphauser, J.S. (Ed.). pp. 118–145. Springfield, Ill.: Charles C. Thomas.

McCord, W., McCord, J. and Zola, I. (1959). *Origins of Crime*. New York: Columbia University Press.

McGivern, M.A. (1980). Intermediate Treatment - the development and assessment of an approach to community care. Paper read at the 1980 World Congress on Behavior Therapy, Jerusalem.

Menninger, K. (1968). *The Crime of Punishment*. New York: Viking Press.

Ostapuik, E.B. (1982). Strategies for community intervention in offender rehabilitation: An overview. In *Developments in the Study of Criminal Behaviour* Vol. 1, Feldman, M.P. (Ed.), pp. 135–166. Wiley: Chichester.

Scherer, M. and Brown, B.J. (1984). Time Out - An alternative to rooms. Paper presented at the ABAC Annual Conference, Bulmershe College, July.

Stumphauser, J.S., Veyoz, E.V. and Aiken, T.W. (1979). East Side Story: Behavioral Analysis of a high juvenile crime community. In: J.S. Stumphauser (Ed.) *Progress in Behavior Therapy with Delinquents*. Springfield, Ill.: Charles C. Thomas.

Taylor, L., Walton, P. and Young, J. (1973). *The New Criminology: For a Social Theory of Deviance*. London: Routledge & Kegan Paul.

Teuber, H. and Powers, D. (1951). The effects of treatment of delinquents. Research Publications of the Association of Neural and Mental Disorders, 31, 139–147.

Tutt, N. (1982). An overview of intervention with young offenders: The political and legal contexts. In *Developments in the Study of Criminal Behaviour*, P. Feldman (Ed.) Vol. 1, pp. 1–26. Chichester: Wiley.

Yule, W. and Brown, B.J. (1986). International Applications. In *Behavioral Approaches to Crime and Delinquency*, Morris E.K. and Braukmann C.J. (Eds.). New York: Plenum.

11. Helping adolescents improve their ego-identity

RAY R. BUSS AND ROBERT D. ENRIGHT

How often has a clinician diagnosed an identity disorder in a youth, but has no adequate treatment model? Virtually all the published literature on ego identity enhancement involves case study applications which often tend to be idiosyncratic to the given case. One exception to this case study approach is a programme proposed by Rachman (1974) which requires adolescents to make choices by asking such questions as, "With whom do I identify?", and then make commitments based on their responses. The major drawback to this approach is that it is not based on a theory of ego formation. In fact, the lack of ego identity intervention procedures may ultimately reflect the fact that until very recently no clear model of identity formation had emerged in the literature.

In this chapter, we present a recently articulated model of identity formation (Enright and Deist, 1979; Enright, Ganiere, Buss, Lapsley and Olson, 1983; Enright, Olson, Ganiere, Lapsley and Buss, 1984), which offers insights about plausible intervention procedures, and data from several empirical studies in which we tested the validity of the model and the utility of such interventions (Enright et al., 1983; 1984). The social cognitive developmental identity formation model proposed in the chapter is a refinement of the one proposed by Erikson (1968) and it incorporates recent evidence that the development of social perspective-taking, understanding the world from other people's viewpoints, is both a necessary and sufficient ability which is crucial in identity formation (see Enright et al., 1983; 1984).

Working with troubled adolescents
ISBN 0-12-179720-1

A SOCIAL PERSPECTIVE-TAKING MODEL OF IDENTITY FORMATION

Before describing the model in detail, we will lay the foundation for the model by briefly discussing (a) relevant material related to Erikson's theory about identity formation, and (b) Selman's and Kohlberg's social perspective-taking models.

Erikson's perspectives on identity formation

Erikson (1968), the primary spokesman for the construct, indicates that identity consists of three subconstructs: a self, an ego and formal operational abilities. The self is the content of one's thoughts as the person reflects on one's own body image, personality or behavioural role(s). According to Erikson (1968, p. 208), when an individual possesses an identity, the self will include "a conscious sense of individual uniqueness" *and* a sense of "solidarity with a group's ideals". Gallatin (1975) elaborates on this notion and characterizes self as the person's awareness of how he or she is like *all* other people, like *some* other people and like *no* other people. Moreover, until very recently, most ego identity researchers had focused on the self component of identity, while ignoring the formation process (Baker, 1971; Marcia, 1966; Stark and Traxler, 1974; cf. Enright *et al.*, 1983; 1984).

According to Erikson (1968), the content of the self is the direct result of two formative processes. One of these is the ego which screens and synthesizes incoming information. The other is formal operational abilities first discussed by Inhelder and Piaget (1958). Formal operations are qualitatively advanced ways of thinking which first develop during adolescence. Generally, formal operations are the abilities to think abstractly. More specifically, they are a group of abilities including hypothetico-deductive reasoning, propositional logic and the awareness of all possible variables and their interrelations in solving a problem. It is this latter ability which is particularly germane in the current context because it allows the adolescent to synthesize cognitively material from his or her environment to aid identity formation (see Erikson, 1968, p. 245). Specifically, Erikson suggests the formal operational ability of being aware of all possibilities as the important component of identity formation. In identity formation, the awareness of all possibilities is primarily an awareness of social rather than non-social possibilities as seen above in Erikson's and Gallatin's description of the self. Thus, if the adolescent is to have a clear understanding of the self, he or she must consider all the ways in which the self is unique, as well as all those ways in which there are shared commonalities with other societal members.

Selman's and Kohlberg's social perspective-taking models

Enright and Deist (1979) have recently clarified and expanded Erikson's theoretical notion of identity formation. While acknowledging the importance, or perhaps even the necessity, of formal operational abilities for the development of ego identity, Enright and Deist point out that formal operations *per se* may not be sufficient without the more specific cognitive acquisition of advanced social perspective-taking skills. Thus, social perspective-taking skills are viewed as a component of Piaget's formal operational stage which allow the adolescent to engage in abstract thought about social input from the environment. In general, social perspective-taking represents the ability to understand the world from the viewpoint of others. Both Kohlberg (1976) and Selman (1976, 1980), in inferring these underlying structures from clinical interviews, describe the developmental progression in the following way.

Level 1. In Kohlberg's and Selman's models, the young child can understand one other person's viewpoint besides the self's. This is done sequentially rather than simultaneously (i.e. self's perspective or the other's at any one time).

Level 2. In both models, the child can take a reciprocal perspective, the self's and the other's, at the same time. Selman's model includes the ability to reflect upon the self from the other's viewpoint. Thus, the person can see how the self's reactions are similar to or different from the other's reactions.

Level 3. In both models, the child can take a "third party" perspective, or understand the social world from the group's viewpoint. Again, the Selman model suggests that the person can reflect on the self from this viewpoint, thus seeing similarities and differences between the group and the self.

Level 4. In both models, the adolescent co-ordinates group perspectives to form a societal perspective. This perspective allows the individual to understand society, and in Selman's model, allows the adolescent to see similarities and differences between the self and society.

These stage progressions are assumed to be integrative and hierarchical (Kohlberg, 1976; Selman, 1976; 1980). As the person progresses, he or she retains earlier developments while establishing more complex structures. At the highest level, an adolescent who demonstrates level 4 social perspective-taking would be able to understand, integrate, and synthesize information about (a) various social groups, (b) similarities of the individual to those social groups, and (c) differences of the individual from those social groups. Therefore, an adolescent, presumably in level 4, should be capable of understanding one other person, various groups such as family and peer groups, and society, as well as how the self is similar to and different from these social entities. For example, Selman has described the adolescent who is in level 4 as being capable of reflecting on the self from one other individual's viewpoint (e.g. we get along because we're both considerate), from the group's viewpoint (e.g. they seem to like me because we have the same values), and from society's viewpoint (e.g. I seem to fit into society because I follow laws and generally co-operate). Through such self reflection , the individual might be able to understand how he or she fits into the dyadic friendship, the family, the peer group, and the larger society, thus realizing solidarity with several group ideals at once.

On the other hand, as we noted above, a second aspect involved in identity formation as it relates to social perspective-taking is an awareness of one's individual uniqueness or an understanding of how the self is like no other person(s) (Erikson, 1968; Gallatin, 1975). Again, an adolescent, presumably in level 4, would be able to ''step outside the self into another's shoes'' and reflect on how the self differs from one's friends, the family, the peer group, and the society as a whole. This ability to reflect on differences would lead to an understanding of one's own uniqueness relative to several groups at the same time.

While social perspective-taking ability as described by Kohlberg and Selman may enhance identity formation, it also may be a causative factor in identity confusion or diffusion. For example, Erikson (1968, pp. 245-246) describes a way in which formal operations may lead to identity confusion when he states:

> The sense of identity, then, becomes more necessary (and more problematical) whenever a wide range of possible identities is envisaged . . . We have described the prime danger of this age . . . as identity confusion, which can express itself . . . with sudden choices.

Thus, complex cognitive strategies may make the identity search easier or more difficult. This is all the more reason to incorporate systematically such cognitive strategies in intervention procedures.

A MODEL OF IDENTITY FORMATION AND ENHANCEMENT

Few programmes have been described to help adolescents reduce identity confusion. Rachman (1974) suggested a programme which was designed to enhance development of identity by asking adolescents to respond to questions like ''With whom do I identify?'' Based on his or her response, the adolescent is then encouraged to make commitments in order to enhance identity formation. However, no guidelines are specified for the adolescent to use in cognitively searching (the formal operations component of identity formation) the environment for people with whom he or she can identify. If possibilities are indiscriminately considered, by the therapist and adolescent, the result may be too many possibilities and choices resulting in identity confusion. The social perspective-taking model of identity formation proposed by Enright and Deist (1979), on the other hand, can serve as a blueprint to guide the therapist in enhancing identity formation.

Before considering the specifics of such a blueprint, we briefly review some of the basic concepts that we have discussed in the chapter. These concepts form a set of basic assumptions which are central to the social perspective-taking model of identity formation proposed by Enright and Deist. Enright and Deist's model makes the following assumptions: (a) identity formation starts with an understanding of others; (b) only when the person understands those others is he or she capable of understanding the self in relation to those others; (c) the understanding of self in relation to others must take into account perceived similarities and differences of the self as compared with others. An exclusive focus on the understanding of others would lead to rigid conformity, not identity, while an exclusive focus on the differences between oneself and others would lead to adolescent egocentrism where the person distorts the self, thinking he or she is totally special and unique (Elkind, 1967); and (d) identity forms when social perspectives are taken so that the individual minimizes confusion. By helping the adolescent focus on the perspectives required at each subsequent level in the perspective-taking sequence (see below), that is by starting with the more simple level 2 perspectives and working up to level 4, the therapist will be assisting the adolescent to get a clearer sense of his or her uniqueness and commonality with others. This sense of uniqueness and commonality constitutes an achieved ego identity (Erikson, 1968; Gallatin, 1975).

Enright et al. (1983; 1984) developed a procedure, based on the assumptions of the model presented above, which allowed high school seniors and college students to work their way through the various levels of the perspective-taking sequence in order to enhance identity formation. In these studies, perspective-taking interventions were employed to reduce the confusion that is characteristic of persons forming an identity and to increase the clarity and organization of thought necessary for identity achievement. The present model utilized a cognitive strategy based on perspective-taking considerations to enhance identity for those engaging in the strategy and thus to minimize identity confusion brought on by the emergence of formal operations. It is important to note here that a clear distinction must be made between a cognitive *structure* and a cognitive *strategy*. The *levels* which we discussed earlier in the section on social perspective-taking define *structures*. *How* one uses these structures to solve particular problems defines *strategy*. It is assumed that if adolescents can use their current social perspective-taking structures in conjunction with particular strategies described in the next paragraph (and in the Procedure section) then their level of ego identity will improve.

A general intervention procedure

At this point, we wish to provide the reader with a general description of the strategy which our high school and college subjects used in several experiments to examine whether the Enright and Deist model could be successfully used to enhance ego identity development. The essence of the strategy was to guide subjects through the various levels of social perspective-taking (i.e. one other, groups of others, and society) while simultaneously requiring the subjects to

think about similarities and differences which they may perceive between themselves and the social others. The general description follows.

First, Enright *et al.* (1983; 1984) had individual subjects think about one
friend and how the self is like and unlike that friend. This exercises level 2
perspective-taking strategies. Next, the subjects tried to understand their
nuclear family and how the self is like and unlike that family. This exercises
level 3 social perspective-taking, in which a group perspective is taken. Next, an
opposite-sex peer group was considered. Again, this involves a level 3
perspective-taking strategy. The subjects next thought about their society and
how they were like and unlike that community and its norms. This is a level 4
strategy. Finally, taking all of the above perspectives the person thought about
how he/she was like all others, some others, and no others in formulating a self-
philosophy. We used this general description to guide our thinking as we
designed three experiments to test the utility of the Enright and Deist model to
enhance identity formation in high school and college adolescents.

EMPIRICAL DATA

Experiment 1

Subjects and instrument

In the first experiment (Enright *et al.*, 1983), 43 high school seniors (22 experimental and 21 control subjects split at the median to determine if intervention would be successful only with low identity status subjects) completed
Rasmussen's (1964, undated) Ego Identity Scale (EIS) twice – at a pre-test and
a post-test. The EIS is a 72-item forced-choice measure in which a person either
agrees or disagrees with each statement. The Rasmussen EIS, consisting of six
subscales, operationalizes conflicts from Erikson's first six stages of psychosocial development with 12 items per subscale. A total score for the six subscales
is obtained and it is interpreted as the degree of psychological health exhibited
by the individual. The scale has been shown to be reliable and valid as a measure of ego identity (Rasmussen, 1964; Bach and Verdile, 1975; Rothman,
1978).

Procedure

Both groups met for one hour a day, three days a week for two weeks. The EIS
was administered to both groups on days 1 and 6. On the other four days, both
groups met together in the same room and went through a paper-and-pencil
intervention on an individual basis. A paper-and-pencil intervention was
chosen to more precisely standardize the treatment of both groups.

The experimental group was asked to go through a series of questions in writing that operationalized the Enright and Deist (1979) model of identity formation. On day 2 (the first day of intervention), they were asked to think about one same-sex friend and how the self was like and unlike that person (level 2 perspective-taking abilities). On day 3, they considered their families (level 3), on day 4 they considered an opposite-sex peer group (level 3). A same-sex group was not used because, during pilot testing, it was observed that there was too much repetition between the same-sex friend and group. On day 5, they considered society (level 4). A summary of the day 2 intervention with the same-sex friend is as follows:

1. In three sentences describe someone around your age and your same sex who you like pretty well.
2. From what you have observed:
(a) what does your friend talk about most?
(b) what does your friend spend his or her time on?
(Other probes were also asked.)
3. From what you can infer:
(a) what does your friend think about a lot?
(b) what kinds of emotions occupy him or her most of the time – or, in other words, what is his or her approach to the world – or his or her "style"?
(Other probes were included.)
4. Summarize your friend in three sentences.
5. In three sentences, describe yourself as compared with your friend.
6. (a) If there were someone else looking at and comparing you with your friend how would they see you as similar to your friend:
(i) in what you talk about?
(ii) in what you spend your time doing?
(Other probes were included.)
(b) If there were someone else looking at and comparing you with your friend, how would they see you as different from you friend?
(The same probes as 6a were used.)
7. (a) From what you know about yourself and can infer about this person you like, how are you similar to your friend:
(i) in the things you think about?
(ii) in the emotions that occupy you?
(b) From what you know about yourself and can infer about this person you like, how are you different from your friend?
(The same probes as 7a were used.)
8. Summarize yourself as compared with your friend.

The purpose of the questions was to first develop an understanding of the other and then, from that vantage point, to consider the self's similarities and differences. Understanding the other and the self involved the consideration of behaviours (e.g. questions 2 and 6) and thoughts and feelings (e.g. questions 3 and 7). A similar procedure was followed for the family, peer group and society. On day 5, following the societal intervention, subjects were asked the following:

Summarize yourself from all of the comparisons with your friend, family, opposite-sex group and society. Indicate what you have in common with them, the points in which you are unique, and what you are and what you hope to be.

The control group was asked to solve two logical reasoning problems each day. For example, one problem asked them to consider all the possible sets that can be made with the numbers 1, 2, 3, 4, 5. This procedure should lead to enhanced ego identity if the formal operational structure of considering all possibilities is the critical component of identity formation as Erikson (1968) states.

Results and discussion

Results from a three-way (treatment condition × initial high or low identity status × pre-test/post-test as the repeated measure) mixed ANOVA indicated that the interaction of treatment × pre-test/post-test score was significant, favouring the experimental group, $F(1, 39) = 4.44, p < .05$. The mean change for the experimental group was 6.32 points and for the control group it was 2.62. The results of this test of an identity intervention model suggests that social perspective-taking as an organizing strategy can lead to a more integrated identity in adolescents. Experimental subjects showed greater gains in identity than did control subjects, according to Rasmussen's (1964), Erikson's (1968) and Hauser's (1971) interpretation of identity. Hence the Enright and Deist model shows promise as being an effective intervention procedure to foster identity development in adolescence.

We conducted two additional experiments to, first, replicate the findings from our initial study with an older group of youth, and secondly, to examine the results in a follow-up to assess degree of maintenance of the newly acquired abilities (Enright *et al.*, 1984). After all, maintenance is critical to any therapy programme.

Experiment 2

Subjects and instrument

Twenty-eight college students (14 experimental subjects and 14 control subjects), predominantly sophomores and juniors, from a large mid-western university volunteered for the intervention programme. Based on the pre-test identity scores, the sample was split at the median to determine whether the intervention would be successful only with low identity status subjects. The instrument was Rasmussen's (1964, undated) Ego Identity Scale (EIS), the same measure used in Experiment 1.

Procedure

The same procedure used in Experiment 1 was used in this experiment.

Results and discussion

A three-way (treatment condition × initial high or low identity status × pre-test/post-test as the repeated measure) mixed ANOVA was performed for both the total score and the identity subscale score. The major test of interest is the interaction between treatment (experimental or control) and the pre-test to post-test gain. For the Rasmussen total score, the treatment × pre-test/post-test interaction test statistic approached, but did not reach significance, $F(1, 24)$ = 3.30, $p < .08$. The mean change from pre-test to post-test for the experimental group was 4.79 and for the control group it was 0.50. No other effects for the Rasmussen score were significant. The identity subscale score showed a significant treatment × pre-test/post-test interaction, $F(1, 24)$ = 8.66, $p < .007$. The mean change, based on 12 items, for the experimental group was 1.57, and for the control goup it was -0.28. No other effects were statistically significant.

This experiment showed an upward change on the Rasmussen identity subscale for the experimental group following the intervention programme. The question of maintenance of this change over time, however, remained to be answered. Therefore, we designed a third experiment which included a follow-up to examine whether the change is temporary or stable over time. We also thought it was desirable to examine the outcomes with a refined dependent measure to show that a different measurement format can lead to similar results.

Experiment 3

Subjects and instrument

Thirty-one experimental and 28 control subjects (college sophomores and juniors) were randomly assigned to two treatment conditions. To refine the identity measure, we used Hauser's procedure (Hauser, 1971; Hauser and Shapiro, 1972) of asking subjects to respond in two ways: "How I feel now" (about the item statement) and "How I will feel in the future". Hauser interprets a high discrepancy score between now and future statements as indicative of a greater flexibility in identity, and lower discrepancy as indicative of rigidity.

Since the use of the original 72 items would have meant 144 responses (two for each item), the original measure was reduced to 36 and included the original 12 identity subscale items, 12 additional identity subscale items in Rasmussen's manual (undated), and 12 identity items devised by the authors. Four distractor items were also included. Examples of items in the new scale follow.

> My way of doing things is apt to be misunderstood by others.
> (This item is from Rasmussen's original scale.)
> I generally am liked by most people who know me.
> (This item is from Rasmussen's manual.)

I find it hard to figure out why there are differences in life styles between my parents and me.

(This item is a new one developed by the authors.)

Each item, both "now" and "future", was constructed with a six-point Likert-type scale ranging from "strongly agree" to "strongly disagree" to allow for more subtle judgements by the subject than the previous agree/disagree format of the Rasmussen scale. The maximum score for either now or future composite score was 216. We subtracted the now score from the future score to obtain a discrepancy score, the dependent variable in this experiment.

Procedure
The procedure which was used previously was followed for pre-test, intervention and post-test. The follow-up test was administered a month following the post-test.

Results and discussion
The reliability of the 36-item ego identity scale calculated by Cronbach's alpha was 0.80. A three-way (treatment condition × sex × post-test/follow-up as the repeated measure) mixed ANCOVA on the discrepancy scores (i.e. future minus now scores) was done with the pre-test as a covariate because of unequal pre-test discrepancy means for the experimental and control groups. The results showed significant difference between scores for the experimental and control groups, favouring the former group, $F(1, 54) = 4.58, p < .04$. No other main effects or interactions were significant. This higher discrepancy score for the experimental group was the result of an increase in future scores and a slight downward shift in now scores for the experimental group, while the control group remained relatively stable. In effect, there was increased discrepancy with a progressive identity improvement when looking toward the future for the experimental group. This result is consistent with Hauser's (1971) conception of identity achievement. Moreover, a lack of interaction effects for discrepancy scores across post-test and follow-up indicates that the experimental group maintained their post-test profile at the follow-up one month later. Again, the utility of the Enright and Deist model for understanding and enhancing identity formation was demonstrated in these two experiments.

GENERAL DISCUSSION AND IMPLICATIONS FOR INTERVENTION

Adolescent ego identity can be improved in a systematic way in a relatively short period of time. Social perspective-taking strategies in which the individuals start with the more simple perspectives (i.e. only one other person) and gradually progress to more complex perspectives (i.e. an entire society) fosters identity improvement.

A key to the improvement seems to be the way the students relate their understanding of others to the self. In each experiment, the participants carefully thought about ways in which the self is like and unlike others. This relative information gathered about the self may be the necessary ingredient for change to occur, but only future research will indicate whether this is the case. It also seems important, in addition to being consistent with identity theory, that the participants have a summation period at the end in which they can synthesize all of their perspectives into a coherent, whole view of the self.

The series of experiments here is important for the message it gives the clinician about the identity formation process. Although identity itself may be construed as a complex combination of affective variables such as thoughts, feelings and behaviours, identity forms, at least in the cases here, by cognitive strategies primarily. The experiments suggest that if an individual can organize his/her experiences by careful thought, then identity may change. Simple thoughts (i.e. level 2 perspective-taking) which can be expanded to more complex ones (i.e. level 4) probably aid in this organization and help the person clarify his/her identity. Further, the clinician should be aware that these experiments suggest that identity emerges only after other people are understood. Identity should not be characterized as some isolated activity in which there is an exclusive focus on the self. Instead, identity grows out of one's ability to cognitively comprehend others.

Clinicians should also be aware that a programme such as the one proposed here does not work only with those initially low on ego identity. As the results of Experiments 1 and 2 indicate, those initially high grew at an equivalent rate to those who were initially low. Therefore, such a programme need not be reserved for remediation only, but can be used in a preventive way as well. Further, as the results of the third experiment imply, experimental subjects seem to view their future more positively relative to their pre-test identity level when compared with the control subjects. An unexpected finding in the last experiment was that the increase in future-now discrepancy scores at post-test by the experimental group was accounted for not only by a gain in future scores, but also by a slight drop in now scores. It appears that the intervention allowed the experimental group to exercise a more critical view of themselves at the present time relative to their future expectations. Moreover, the gain in future scores suggests an improvement in future identity by the experimental group. This higher discrepancy by experimental subjects relative to present identity achievements indicates psychological health according to Hauser (1971).

As in most intervention programmes, changes can be recommended. For instance, the scientific intervention programmes described here were necessarily more ''artificial'' when compared to actual therapy sessions. The artificiality (i.e. the paper-and-pencil intervention) was necessary for the initial experiments to increase scientific precision as much as possible, since standardization was necessary to eliminate competing hypotheses. Thus, the intervention programme used here may be viewed as a conservative intervention procedure. For those interested primarily in practice, we suggest far more flexibility in the procedures. For instance, spending more time on the intervention questions, small group interaction, or one-on-one discussions between therapist and client may prove to be worthwhile. In fact, it would seem that the artificial nature of the procedure would have actually attenuated treatment effects and held scores down because there were time constraints and no verbal interaction between students and the experimenters.

Up to this point, we have primarily discussed the utility of the intervention procedure for use with both older and normal adolescents who demonstrate fairly well developed level 4 social perspective-taking abilities. This may first appear to be a severe limitation to those therapists who work with either younger adolescents or those with social cognitive deficits. For example, some adolescents cannot take a societal perspective (see Kohlberg, 1976; Selman, 1976, 1980). Are those individuals, then, incapable of benefiting from the identity intervention programme described here? Obviously not, for in theory they are quite capable of benefiting from such an intervention programme.

Because the intervention programme is based on cognitive developmental theory, the therapist must merely gear the intervention to the particular social perspective-taking level of the adolescent in question. That is, the therapist must develop a programme suited to the adolescent's current perspective-taking level. If an adolescent is in level 3 perspective-taking, i.e. viewing the world from the group's perspective, then the programme would include the following: (a) focus on one friend and how the self is like and unlike the friend; (b) focus on the family and how the self is similar and different; (c) focus on the peer group and how the self is like and unlike the peer group. The only aspect of the identity intervention programme that is missing is a focus on the society with its attendant norms and rules and how the person is similar to and different from the society. Thus, all but the final level is included. Although knowledge of friends and groups relative to the self provides for incomplete identity development, it is a valuable first step. After all, identity seems to develop gradually through the adolescent years (Erikson, 1968). Even if an adolescent seems incapable of level 3 perspective-taking, the intervention programme can begin with highly concrete material; having the adolescent think about a friend and how the self is like and unlike that friend (i.e. level 2 perspective-taking). Only gradually would the therapist move to group and then societal perspectives.

Approaches such as the ones suggested above could be tried with adolescents or youth who are having a particularly difficult time achieving an identity.

Delinquents, for example, who lag in their social cognitive abilities (e.g. Jurkovic, 1980) may benefit from an intervention programme such as the one outlined in this chapter if the therapist focuses on the lower levels of perspective-taking only. Making the intervention procedure more flexible, lengthening the time of the procedure, and encouraging therapist-client interaction may also prove to be worthwhile to those in need of a stronger sense of identity.

REFERENCES

Bach, T., and Verdile, R. (1975). A comparison of two measures of ego identity in high school adolescents. *Journal of Psychology* **90**, 269–274.

Baker, F. (1971). Measures of ego identity: A multitrait multimethods validation. *Educational and Psychological Measurement* **31**, 165–173.

Elkind, D. (1967). Egocentrism in adolescence. *Child Development* **38**, 1024–1038.

Enright, R.D., and Deist, S.H. (1979). Social perspective-taking as a component of identity formation. *Adolescence* **14**, 517–522.

Enright, R.D., Ganiere, D.M., Buss, R.R., Lapsley, D.K., and Olson, L. M. (1983). Promoting identity development in adolescents. *Journal of Early Adolescence* **3**, 247–255.

Enright, R.D., Olson, L. M., Ganiere, D.M., Lapsley, D. K., and Buss, R. R. (1984). A clinical model for enhancing ego identity. *Journal of Adolescence* **7**, 119–130.

Erikson, E. H. (1968). *Identity: Youth and crisis*. New York: Norton.

Gallatin, J. E. (1975). *Adolescence and individuality*. New York: Harper & Row.

Hauser, S. (1971). *Black and white identity formation*. New York: Wiley.

Hauser, S., and Shapiro, R. (1972). Dimensions of adolescent self-images. *Journal of Youth and Adolescence* **1**, 339–353.

Inhelder, B., and Piaget, J. (1958). *The growth of logical thinking from childhood to adolescence*. New York: Basic Books.

Jurkovic, G. (1980). The juvenile delinquent as a moral philosopher: A structural-developmental perspective. *Psychological Bulletin* **88**, 709–727.

Kohlberg, L. (1976). Moral stages and moralization. In *Moral development and behavior: Theory, research, and social issues*, Lickona, T. (Ed.), pp. 31–53. New York: Holt, Rinehart, & Winston.

Marcia, J. (1966). Development and validation of ego-identity status. *Journal of Personality and Social Psychology* **3**, 551–558.

Rachman, A. (1974). Identity group psychotherapy with adolescents. In *Clinical child psychology*, Williams, G. and Gordon, S. (Eds). New York: Behavioral Publications.

Rasmussen, J. (undated). *Pretest data for ego identity scale*. (Available from the author: Battelle Human Affairs Research Centers, 4000 N. E. 41st Street, P.O. Box C-5395, Seattle, WA 98105.)

Rasmussen, J. (1964). Relationship of ego identity to psychosocial effectiveness. *Psychological Reports* **15**, 815–825.

Rothman, K. (1978). Multivariate analysis of the relationship of psychosocial crisis variables to ego identity status. *Journal of Youth and Adolescence* **7**, 93–106.

Selman, R. L. (1976). Toward a structural analysis of developing interpersonal relationship concepts: Research with normal and disturbed preadolescent boys. In

Minnesota symposia on child psychology Vol. 10, Pick, A. (Ed.), pp. 156–200.
Selman, R. L. (1980). *The growth of interpersonal understanding; Developmental and clinical analyses*. New York: Academic Press.
Stark, P., and Traxler, A. (1974). Empirical validation of Erikson's theory of identity crisis in late adolescence. *Journal of Psychology* **86**, 25–53.

Part II
Problem oriented approaches

12. Psychoses in adolescence

ELENA GARRALDA AND
PATRICIA AINSWORTH

THE CONCEPT OF PSYCHOSIS IN CHILDREN AND ADOLESCENTS

The International Classification of Diseases, 9th edition (ICD-9), defines psychoses as mental disorders in which impairment of mental function has developed to a degree that interferes grossly with insight, ability to meet some ordinary demands of life and adequate contact with reality. Though the differentiation between neuroses and psychoses in adults can be difficult and remains a subject of debate, the use of the term psychoses to designate problems as defined above remains in wide usage (WHO, 1978). As applied to children, the distinction between psychotic states and other disorders of children, such as neurotic, conduct and emotional disorders, is useful to designate problems qualitatively different from normal behavioural changes.

The psychotic states of childhood require a different conceptual understanding from that applied to other childhood psychiatric disorders and without a good grasp of their nature, adequate handling is not possible. We will therefore describe the condition in some detail.

HISTORICAL DEVELOPMENT

Conditions fulfilling the psychotic definition in children and adolescents have long been recognized. The term "demence praecoce" was said to have been used for the first time by Morel in 1860, as applied to a 13-year-old who developed an acute psychotic type state leading to stupor, "the end result of heredi- tary insanity" since both his mother and grandfather had been insane (Bender, 1969). Henry Maudsley (1867) wrote at some length about the different manifestations of childhood insanity. At the turn of the century, Sante de Sanctis and Heller described schizophrenic and dementing type processes in children, akin to those in adults (Sanctis, 1969; Heller, 1969). Following these initial single-case studies, a number of authors outlined, from group comparisons, the main characteristics of the psychotic states of childhood: namely self-absorption, affective and regressive changes, abnormalities in speech (mutism, incoherence), in thought (non-reality based, hallucinations, incoherence, poverty) and in motor behaviour (hypoactivity, mannerisms, bizarre behaviour) (Bradley, 1942).

These features have survived the passage of time remarkably well and remain the basic symptoms of the psychotic states of children in adolescence. They indicate an altered contact with reality in a subjectively disturbed world, leading to unusual behaviour.

A crucial conceptual advance in the understanding of psychotic states of children and adolescents was derived from descriptions of conditions which differed from those of adults because of a start in early childhood: these were autism and autistic psychopathy or Asperger's syndrome (Kanner, 1943; Asperger, 1944).

Many of the basic psychotic features described by Bradley in his review of childhood psychotic symptomatology in 1942 were present both in the adult-type psychoses described earlier, and in the more specific childhood states recognized later. However, differences between early and late onset conditions in symptomatology and in aetiological and prognostic factors have been identified subsequently. Rutter, Greenfield and Lockyer (1967) in their follow-up study of autistic children failed to find definite delusions and hallucinations such as those seen in the adult-type psychoses. Kolvin and his colleagues (Kolvin, 1971) showed differences in symptomatology, developmental and family history in autistic subjects when compared with late-onset or adult-type psychotic children, though when Green *et al.* (1984) compared pre-pubertal autistics with late-onset psychotic children of comparable age and intelligence levels, few significant differences in symptomatology emerged between the two groups. The differentiation between early-onset and late-onset clinical pictures can therefore present difficulties in some pre-pubertal children.

CLASSIFICATION OF THE PSYCHOSES

In recent times, a classification of different psychotic states according to age of onset has gained increasing recognition, in line with the considerations made before. They include: (1) *psychoses of early onset*, starting before three years of age; i.e. early infantile autism and autistic psychopathy (or Asperger's syndrome/ schizoid personality disorder); (2) *psychoses starting after three years* of age: disintegrative psychoses (or Heller's syndrome); and (3) *late-onset psychoses* starting after five years of age, though rarely diagnosed before age seven: i.e. adult-type psychoses, notably schizophrenia, and, less commonly, manic-depressive psychoses, mixed pictures (schizoaffective or reactive psychoses) and organic psychoses.

The above sub-categories are variously represented in the current international (ICD-9) and American (DSM-III) disease classification systems (WHO, 1978; APA, 1980). In ICD-9, early onset psychoses come under the category of "psychoses with origin specific to childhood" which also include disintegrative psychoses. In DSM-III they are classified under "pervasive developmental disorders". In both systems, late-onset psychoses are classified with their adult counterpart conditions.

The psychoses of adolescence

Most of the psychoses presenting in adolescents are the psychoses of late onset in the above classification and these conditions will be considered in some detail here.

The psychoses of adolescence are uncommon. Accurate figures as to their prevalence are not forthcoming. Such figures as exist are usually based on youngsters who have presented to psychiatric services, and uniform criteria for the presence of psychosis are not always used, so that adolescents with a prior history of early-onset psychoses or those with toxic psychoses may or may not be included. Moreover, a close adherence to DSM-III criteria for schizophrenia will lead to the inclusion of some children whose sole psychotic manifestation is the presence of persistent hallucinations. In addition, the age range studied is not always identical, and this is relevant as the risk for psychoses seems to increase substantially in the older teenagers. As a result there is variation in the figures in different estimates, though they all find that psychotic states are not frequent.

Vrono (1974) in a Russian population gave rates of 0.54 per 1000 population of 15 to 18-year-olds. Rates computed from data on younger adolescents admitted to our regional adolescent unit suggest a yearly incidence of 0.2 per 1000 12 to 16-year-olds, but this figure is an under-estimate as it does not include youngsters admitted to units for children and adults. Gillberg, Wahlstrom, Forsman, Hellgren and Gillberg, (1985) using a broader age range (13 to 19 years) estimated a total teenage risk for psychoses in a Swedish population of 0.54%.

As regards the relative frequency of psychotic states amongst children attending adolescent psychiatric services which take responsibility for the broad spectrum of psychiatric disorders (some units exclude psychotic youngsters for admission), rates for initial or ongoing outpatients vary between 8% and 15% (Steinberg, Galhenage and Robinson, 1981; Masterson, 1967), whereas those for in-patients appear generally higher (38%, Warren, 1949; 12%, Warren, 1965; 22%, Ainsworth, 1984).

THE PSYCHOSES OF LATE ONSET IN ADOLESCENCE

Main clinical features

The following account is largely based on two British descriptive studies to validate the non-organic psychoses of late onset against other psychiatric conditions. Though in a number of subjects in each survey the condition had started earlier, at the time of the study most children were teenagers. Kolvin, Ounsted, Humphrey, *et al.* (1971) validated the syndrome against autism and Garralda (1985) compared psychoses of late onset with other severe but non-psychotic psychiatric disorders of childhood and adolescence. The account will also draw on the German follow-up study by Eggers (1967, 1973, 1978).

There are indications that, as opposed to the psychoses of early onset which are more common in boys, those of late onset are equally frequent in both sexes and may be slightly more common in girls. Some of the children show pre-morbid psychological problems, the main traits being shyness, diffidence, withdrawal, timidity and sensitivity. Though in some youngsters the onset is acute, insidious beginnings are common. Comparison of the data from Kolvin *et al.* (1971), Green *et al.* (1984) and Garralda (1985) suggests that pre-morbid oddities and insidious onset may be more frequent in pre-adolescent than in adolescent onset of the illness. Organic and developmental symptoms may also be particulary common in these younger children (Nunn, Lask and Cohen, 1985; Steinberg, 1985).

There are no symptoms pathognomonic of the late-onset psychoses, but some are characteristic of the conditions because they are present in most subjects, but are rarely found in other diagnostic categories. These are delusions, hallucinations, abnormalities in the production of language, inappropriate affect, bizarre behaviour, social withdrawal and hypoactivity (Garralda, 1985). We will outline these in some detail, since only a good understanding of the distorted internal world of the child can lead to adequately sensitive and focused handling.

Delusions and hallucinations are present in most psychotic children but are not usually elicited in children younger than seven years, most likely because a certain level in intellectual or thought development is necessary for children to be able to express these abnormal phenomena.

Delusions are abnormal beliefs which cannot be explained on cultural or intellectual grounds. The younger the children, the less well structured are their delusions. For example, children under 10 tend to express abnormal ideas about identity changes through identifications with inanimate objects or animals, or have irrational fears of a cosmic content or transitory paranoid delusions (Eggers, 1967). In pre-pubertal and pubertal children delusions become progressively more persistent and complex, with paranoid and hypochondriacal ideas, and later with depressive and religious themes.

By adolescence, the most common themes tend to be paranoid or persecutory in content. Youngsters become preoccupied that people are poisoning them, or putting drugs into their food, or that they are being followed. Delusions of false identities, hypochondriacal delusions and delusions of reference are also relatively common, whereas guilt or grandiose themes seem to be rare (Garralda, 1985).

Delusions of false identities are manifested by youngsters who think that their parents are not their real parents but strangers disguised as such. Hypochondriacal delusions can be bizarre, such as in a youngster who thought that his brain was affected by either having cancer or being empty, and that when he breathed, air came out of his stomach and perhaps through his facial muscles. Delusions of being infested, of pregnancy or of sexual changes are some of the themes expressed. As for delusions of reference, youngsters become preoccupied that people look at them in a special and unusual way and listen to them through the radio, or that comments on television refer to them in a veiled way.

It is not uncommon for delusions to focus on family members (for example, a belief that parents are putting drugs or poison in their food) or on the youngster's own health. Because of this, removal to a medical psychiatric environment often alleviates the difficult family relationships and the associated distress in the patient, and contains the hypochondriacal beliefs. However, if the admission is prolonged and new relationships are formed, delusional beliefs can be focused on unit members, and an awareness of and appropriate response to this is necessary.

Hallucinations or perceptions without the corresponding external stimuli are present in most psychotic children (three-quarters or over). In most cases they are auditory, though in about half, visual and less commonly olfactory or bodily phenomena are also present. Auditory hallucinations usually consist of voices heard inside the child's head talking to the patient and telling him to do something, often something "bad". The voices are as likely to be attributed to familiar people such as parents or teachers, as to be attributed to supernatural beings (God, the devil) or to be non-specific. It is important to note that in a substantial minority of children these voices incite to suicide, and though the youngsters often resist this command, in some cases they may be driven to act on them. As with delusions, the hallucinations may be denied even when they appear to be present, as in youngsters who suddenly seem to become self-absorbed and to listen intently when no sound is perceived by others.

As with the rest of the psychotic symptoms described here, it is important to emphasize that hallucinations can occur as isolated psychotic phenomena in non-psychotic youngsters with conduct and emotional disorders. They tend to be linked in them to environmental stresses such as dramatic or difficult bereavements and to depressive symptoms, and they have been shown not to predict later psychotic episodes. In some youngsters they occur alongside non-epileptic episodic disturbances of awareness and other phenomena such as perceptual distortions, or experiences of depersonalisation (Garralda, 1984*a*, 1984*b*).

Behaviour abnormalities, notably social withdrawal, hypoactivity, silly or inappropriate giggling, bizarre behaviour (e.g. walking in odd postures, stopping in the middle of a sentence and starting to sing, or giving saliva to people) and mannerisms are present in most psychotics.

Whereas the above symptoms are very frequent in psychotics, *other less common psychotic manifestations* can be prominent (Garralda, 1985). They are mutism or incoherence of language (i.e. vague, disconnected, fragmented, "Ophelia" like), flat or incongruous affect (i.e. inappropriately laughing while recounting sad events or situations), perplexity, psychotic disorientation or confusion for time, space and persons, aimless wandering and catatonic symptoms (automatic behaviour, rigidity, excessive compliance). These symptoms do not appear to carry an eventual poor prognosis, but they indicate at the time of illness a particularly severe breakdown in personality functioning, affecting thought and speech, mood, the integration of these faculties and, in some cases, even the loss of the ability to care for the simplest needs such as feeding, dressing or toileting.

Other symptoms common in psychotics are akin to those found in other severely disturbed youngsters with emotional or conduct disorders. Though not specific to psychotic states, they can be disturbing. They include irritability, obsessional symptoms, school refusal, somatic symptoms and problems in relationships between the youngster and family members. Symptoms of distress and depression are probably more common in psychotics than in non-psychotic disturbed youngsters, and the converse is true for anti-social symptoms. Though an aggressive attitude is not infrequent in psychotics, frank acts of violence are rare.

Differential diagnosis between psychotic and severely disturbed, but non-psychotic, adolescents may be difficult in inarticulate youngsters with erratic, impulsive behaviour, and odd, unusual ideas (Steinberg, 1985) or in some histrionically elaborated clinical states (Garralda, 1985). In some of these cases, admission for close observation will be necessary to clarify the clinical picture and to establish the evidence for loss of contact with reality and profound breakdown in personality functioning characteristic of psychotic states.

Course of the psychoses of late onset

The work of Eggers (1973, 1978) indicates a varied course of the condition. Recurrent episodes are far more common than an early decay into chronicity, though a chronic course is more likely to be found if the illness starts before 11 years of age. Overall, about 20% of youngsters may be expected to recover completely, 50% to improve, though with the risk of later relapses, and the rest will remain chronically ill. In Egger's study a good premorbid personality, good social relationships and higher intelligence were linked to good prognosis, whilst a family history of schizophrenia and disturbed family relationships did not have prognostic value. Depressive and euphoric symptoms seemed to be common in later episodes of illness, but they were not associated with a better prognosis. Other authors have shown an association between good prognosis and good intelligence and premorbid personality, with psychotic disorientation and with preserved congruence between emotions and thinking during the illness (Carter, 1942; Annesley, 1961).

It must be noted, however, that, though the immediate prognosis for psychotics following hospitalizations is relatively good (cure or marked improvements on discharge range from about a third (Warren, 1965) to nearly half (Ainsworth, 1984), presumably depending on the severity of the problems at intake and length of stay), further deterioration is sometimes seen at follow-up (Pyne, Morrison and Ainsworth, 1985), and suicidal attempts occur in later stages of the illness, particularly in children with paranoid hallucinatory conditions.

There have been reports of children dying during psychotic episodes. Ainsworth (In Press) has described a fatal outcome in a 14-year-old girl with a picture of "lethal catatonia", and this emphasizes the need to monitor the progress of the condition closely in its acute phase.

Aetiological issues

An increased prevalence of psychoses is found in the families of youngsters with late-onset psychoses (Kallmann and Roth, 1956; Kolvin et al., 1971; Garralda, 1985), but families may need to know that genetic factors play only a relatively minor part in the transmission of the disease. Early neurodevelopmental deficits such as clumsiness and learning difficulties are not uncommon and may increase the vulnerability to develop psychoses (Lloyd and Ainsworth, unpublished; Nunn et al., 1985).

Rarely, the illness may be a forerunner for a disintegrative psychosis and a degenerative neurological condition (Corbett, Harris, Taylor and Trimble, 1977). Somewhat more commonly, the start of illness will coincide with a somatic condition such as a viral illness, Sydenham's chorea or a brain tumour. Though the psychotic state then tends to follow an independent course of the initially contemporary somatic illness, this may not be always the case. Nunn et al., (1985) have recently described one child with severe psychotic episodes always associated with herpetic infections for whom appropriate anti-viral medication may have had an anti-psychotic effect.

Acute organic psychoses, phenomenologically very similar to those seen in functional non-organic psychoses, are seen after ingestion of certain drugs, such as amphetamines, or in acute toxic delirious states in the course of severe systemic physical illness. There is often associated clouding of consciousness and subsequent total recovery.

There is to date only indirect evidence for supposing that stressful life events make an overall contribution to the psychoses of late onset. Precipitants of illness are commonly given in some surveys of adolescent psychoses (Garralda, 1984c), whilst work in adults with schizophrenia suggests that stressful life-events may precede the onset of the condition (Birley and Brown, 1970) and that stressful attitudes in the family increase the risk of relapses (Leff and Vaughan, 1981). Certainly, in some cases the start of the illness is so closely linked to stressful events that, as in adults, the term "reactive psychoses" has been used (Warren and Cameron, 1950). Clinically, recurrences of illness at times of stress are observed, as for example before exams.

LATE ONSET OR BASED ON AN EARLY-ONSET PSYCHOSES?

The differentiation between early and late-onset psychoses in adolescents does not present major problems in late-onset psychotics with good premorbid functioning, or for most autistic adolescents, but it may do so in youngsters who develop psychoses of late onset on the basis of premorbid developmental oddities, and conversely in some bright autistic adolescents who manifest hallucinatory or delusional type abnormalities and apparent incoherence of speech at adolescence.

Cantor, Evans, Pearce and Pezzot-Pearce (1982) have shown that a small percentage of bright children with early-onset psychoses express hallucinatory and unusual beliefs at adolescence, and some more show abnormalities of speech, not unlike those of adult schizophrenia. However, the phenomena in these children appear atypical in that hallucinations were visual and simple, and the unusual ideas were relatively uniform, with bodily delusions reported in every case. Petty, Ornitz, Michelman and Zimmerman (1984) have also described schizophrenic-type symptoms in bright autistic children at adolescence. Again in this study, the delusions seem particularly simple and uniform when compared with those in late-onset psychoses.

Clinically, it follows from the above studies that in any youngster presenting with psychotic symptoms, a very careful and detailed account should be obtained of the early developmental history, seeking possible indicators of early-onset psychoses. This will influence both prognosis and management, as in the presence of developmental problems the underlying deficits in social understanding and communication will need to be addressed.

THE DIFFERENT TYPES OF LATE-ONSET PSYCHOSES

Adult-type psychotic sub-divisions have been described in children and adolescents with late-onset psychoses: namely schizophrenia and manic-depressive illness, but also schizoaffective and reactive psychoses (Hudgens, 1974; Warren and Cameron, 1950). A schizophrenic diagnosis is most common, whereas manic-depressive psychoses are reported in less than one in four psychotics (Warren, 1965; Gillberg et al., 1985; Ainsworth, 1984).

However, the differentiation between the two major psychoses is not always clearcut in adolescence. Typical schizophrenic symptoms such as Schneiderian first-rank delusions and hallucinations would appear to be relatively uncommon (Garralda, 1985). On the other hand, there are indications that: (1) manic-depressive states may go unrecognized unless systematic enquiry into the main symptoms is made using standardized research schedules (Gammon et al., 1983; Carlson and Strober, 1978); (2) schizophrenic symptoms – catatonic, first rank Schneiderian symptoms – can coexist with affective symptoms in youngsters with manic-depressive pictures (Hassanyeh and Davison, 1980; Carlson and Strober, 1978; Ballenger, Reus and Post, 1982); and (3) a number of youngsters with adolescent schizophrenic diagnoses turn out to have manic-depressive illness subsequently (Carlson and Strober, 1978).

This suggests that manic-depressive psychoses may be more common in this age group than thought previously, and that symptomatologically undifferentiated psychotic pictures are likely to present at adolescence (Steinberg, 1985). This calls for careful assessment of the symptomatology, and perhaps also for a willingness to try successive trials of either anti-schizophrenic or anti-manic-depressive medication in what may often be symptomatologically mixed pictures.

THE MANAGEMENT AND TREATMENT OF PSYCHOSIS IN ADOLESCENTS

Admission to Hospital

When a teenager presents psychotic symptomatology for the first time, admission to a hospital unit is probably highly desirable, particularly at the younger end of the age range and when the symptoms are vague or confusing. This provides the opportunity for observation in a controlled environment away from sources of psychological stress or other harmful influences such as access to unprescribed drugs. It is also easier to carry out systematic physical investigations such as blood and urine screening, electroencephalography, computerized axial tomography on an inpatient basis.

The symptoms are usually distressing enough for the family to welcome admission, but this becomes essential where there is life-threatening behaviour such as suicidal threats or acts, or acting upon hallucinatory suggestions, or where there is aggression or threat to other people. A consistently disturbed sleep pattern and disruptive behaviour such as wandering in the neighbourhood partially clothed are also difficult for most families to tolerate for any length of time.

However, there are certain practical problems associated with seeking admission to an inpatient unit. The first is finding a suitable place. A specialist adolescent unit with its focus on the needs of this age group is ideal, but it is well recognized that there are not enough such places in most regions and all too many existing adolescent units have a therapeutic regime which cannot accommodate psychotic symptoms. Younger patients can be, and are often, successfully managed in children's psychiatric units, although they can seem very threatening to much younger children. Others, particularly older teenagers, can only be admitted to psychiatric wards for adults, undesirable though this can be because of exposure to a more disturbed and often very much older patient group. Another practical problem attendant upon admission is that of willingness or consent to treatment. Youngsters over the age of 16 may be determinedly opposed to admission. Although many can be persuaded by skilful handling on the part of parents or professionals, some will require compulsory admission under the terms of the Mental Health Act. Theoretically, where parents or care givers wish it, a youngster under the age of 16 may be detained and/or treated against his or her own wishes, but in practice this is not always feasible, as anyone who has tried to persuade a well-grown, suspicious, aggressive 15-year-old will testify. In such circumstances, youngsters may also be detained compulsorily. It is worth bearing in mind that there is no lower age limit for implementing the Mental Health Act. Where compulsory admission is necessary, it is likely to mean an inevitable admission to adult provision as those adolescent units which do accept psychotic patients are seldom prepared to do so on this basis, sometimes for practical reasons (e.g. lack of locked accommodation), but more usually for philosophical ones.

With the more co-operative patients, a compromise might be attendance at a Day Hospital or day unit, when such a facility is available, but only if there is minimal risk to the safety of the patient and others and the family is prepared to manage the young person at nights. Such an arrangement is less desirable if there is a possibility that the youngster is abusing drugs or alcohol or where there are known or suspected psychological stresses for him or her within the family.

Observation

After admission to resident (or day) status, it is useful wherever possible to plan a period of observation of the symptomatology and overall function of the youngster without embarking upon medication or other specific treatment. This may last for up to two weeks and should involve systematic recording of the psychotic symptomatology, any fluctuation including diurnal variation and associated mood, and the extent to which the youngster is preoccupied with or distressed by his experiences or distractable from them. Vegetative symptoms such as disturbed sleep, appetite or weight change should be noted, as should the capacity for self-care, appropriate personal hygiene and dress. Any talk of, or actions towards, self-harm or harming others should be taken very seriously and has obvious implications for staffing levels. Relationships with the patient group may be significant; many acute psychotics are withdrawn and preoccupied with their symptoms to the extent of failing even to learn the names of other youngsters, but some retain a capacity to function quite normally socially much of the time. Also the level of insight into their condition varies but most have some concept of illness and treatability, at least part of the time.

Because of the high incidence of earlier developmental or central nervous system disorder in adolescent psychosis, it is wise to carry out certain investigations, particularly in the younger patient. A thorough physical examination including specialized neurological assessment is essential in these cases. It is particularly important to carry out electroencephalography (EEGs) to exclude the existence of brain dysfunction. Routine haematology and estimation of blood electrolytes and liver function should be carried out, although only occasionally abnormal; and in the older patient, who is more likely to have had access to unprescribed drugs, a urinary screen for drug metabolites is necessary. Radiology, including plain skull x-rays, or more specifically computerized axial tomography is rather harder to justify as a routine examination, but becomes essential where there are neurological signs, an abnormal EEG recording, or any evidence of a progressive or degenerative disorder.

During the initial period of observation, it may be necessary to use tranquillizing medication symptomatically, e.g. for night sedation, agitation or the control of aggressive behaviour, but it is usually possible to withhold regular prescription until the nature, severity and persistence of the psychotic symptomatology is clear. Occasionally symptoms lessen in the new environment, and very rarely they disappear, so that one can postulate that they have arisen in response to some temporary toxin which must then be defined.

Treatment

Where symptoms persist unchanged for over a week after admission, appropriate medication with a major tranquillizer should be instituted. The principles are exactly the same as with adult psychotic patients (McKnew, 1979);

teenagers can tolerate adult doses, often with less risk of adverse side effects. Thus, the choice lies between one or other of the well-established neuroleptic drugs. For agitated, restless, acute psychotics with predominantly positive symptoms, chlorpromazine or thioridazine is likely to be effective in divided daily doses, starting with 25 mg three times a day and increasing over a week or two to a maximum of 100 mg three times a day or occasionally more, the rate of increase being determined by a balance between beneficial effects and the emergence of side effects. Trifluoperazine is the more effective drug with predominantly quiet, withdrawn youngsters, particularly those of premorbidly low intelligence, but has the disadvantage of being more likely to produce extrapyramidal side effects (e.g. muscular rigidity and tremor, restlessness, abnormal face and body movements). For this reason it is advisable to start with a low dose such as 2 mg or 3 mg twice a day and build up more gradually to 20–30 mg daily. Drowsiness as a side effect is more common with chlorpromazine and thioridazine, but this can be partly counteracted by administering at least half of the total daily dose at bedtime. Where over-sedation persists and is troublesome, haloperidol may be used instead (2.5 mg three times a day, increasing to 30 mg daily), but also has the disadvantage of more probable dystonic reactions. It has been common practice to prescribe routinely anti-parkinsonian drugs to control side effects together with major tranquillizers, but this is not always necessary, particularly as such drugs reduce the effective absorption of the neuroleptic agent. At least a third of the psychotic youngsters treated at our Regional Adolescent Unit never needed anti-parkinsonian drugs; this number is likely to be an under-estimate as many others were prescribed these drugs prophylactically. McKnew (1979) points out that there may be resistance from adolescents to the drowsiness and other side effects, evoking fears of loss of control and paranoid ideas of being poisoned, and this may lead to a youngster pretending to take, but concealing and later discarding medication. It is vital to explain beforehand the purpose of the medication and side effects and to create a co-operative relationship. However, where there remains suspicion or concern that a patient is not fully co-operating, one may change from the tablets to syrups or suspensions whose intake is easier to ensure or, if the problem persists, move on to the use of depot medication as in adults.

The use of lithium carbonate is not often indicated in adolescents, particularly in a first manic or hypomanic episode, but may be considered where either the symptoms are particularly severe or intractable or affective episodes recur. Even less commonly, it may be effective in reducing the excitability or level of aggression in some severe schizophrenics. As in adult patients, it is important to check for normal cardiac and renal function first, and to prescribe gradually increasing doses until a serum level of between 0.6 and 1.2 mmol/litre is achieved and maintained (Steinberg, 1980).

The empirical use of electro-convulsive therapy in the management of acute psychosis of the schizophrenic type has little justification, except in the extremely rare eventuality of a fully catatonic presentation.

Psychotic adolescents may benefit as much as non-psychotics from individual counselling or psychotherapy, but the approach should be supportive rather than analytic. It is sensible to capitalize on the best relationship established by the youngster with a member of staff, particularly where he or she manifests strong, even paranoid likes and dislikes, and appoint that person counsellor or individual keyworker. Counselling sessions should be frequent, daily if possible, but short, no more than half an hour each, and focus on empathic understanding of the patient's symptoms and their meaning, on explanations and reassurance about treatment methods. It is futile to attempt to persuade a psychotic out of his delusional ideas, but realistic to encourage him to be discreet about them, when talking to peers in particular.

Most adolescent psychotics are living with their families at the time of presentation and it is vital to involve the family in the management from as early a stage as possible. At the most basic level they will need, and usually seek, information and counselling about the diagnosis, treatment and prognosis, sometimes repeatedly. As well as giving such information face to face, it can be useful to refer them to or supply them with literature written for relatives, such as the various publications of the National Schizophrenia Fellowship including *Coping with Schizophrenia* by H. R. Rollin (1980). In addition, families may derive much support from each other by meeting as a group, with or without their psychotic youngsters, to air and share worries about the condition and management issues. Some family therapists (e.g. Haley, 1980) make claims for the curative value of systematic family therapy in adolescent psychosis, but this is based on an oversimplified view of the aetiology of the disorder, that is that it represents an extreme manifestation of the independence versus dependency struggle inherent in mid to late-adolescent emotional development. A more pragmatic use of family therapy concentrating on tackling specific problems as they arise (Falloon, Boyd, McGill, Razani, Moff and Gilderman, 1982) or the reduction of high "expressed emotion" (criticism and intrusiveness) and social contact in the families (Leff, Kuipers, Berkowitz, Eberlein-Frief and Sturgeon, 1982) is more realistic and less likely to raise false hopes. These approaches have been shown to reduce behaviour problems and minimize the incidence of future relapse.

Simple behavioural programmes may be employed in the management of psychotic youngsters, particularly where there is inadequate self-care or personal hygiene. The problem is in selecting useful rewards which will serve as consistent, positive reinforcements. In acute cases, relatively intact in many areas of function, preferred activities or graded contact with home and families are likely to be rewarding. It is much harder to reward appropriately more chronic psychotics whose preference may already be for inactivity and avoid-ance of interpersonal contacts. Successful management of withdrawn behaviour involves a fine balance between encouraging more social contact than the patient would naturally choose, and recognizing the need for retreat and with-drawal for the sake of greater emotional comfort part of the time. Thus, a com-promise might be that a psychotic youngster is required to be present at large group meetings such as "community" meetings, but there is no expectation, at least initially, that he or she will contribute verbally. The overall aim should be for gradually increasing the amount of time spent with others. But it must be recognized that the pace of this progress may need to be extremely slow, if the patient is not to feel too pressured and react with a sudden increase or reappear-ance of other symptoms, for example, auditory hallucinations.

On the whole, small psychotherapy groups are likely to be too stressful for psychotic youngsters, at least in the acute phase, and may enhance certain symptoms, notably persecutory or sensitive ideas.

On the other hand, the individual patient may, and often can, cope well with focused activities involving structure and a tangible task, such as artwork or craft, or even drama groups where the activity is clearly defined. Occupational therapists have valuable skills to offer the psychotic youngster in these ways.

Also, we have found it entirely feasible for many psychotics of school age to spend at least part of each day in the classroom. It is obviously essential that the teacher understands the nature of the disorder and its likely effects on cognitive function, but with this background knowledge, he or she can evaluate the present capacities of the individual youngster and provide him or her with work projects likely to be accomplished. This approach at least maintains the habit of regular school attendance, and can be a very successful way of distracting the youngster from the psychotic experiences.

In the overall management of psychotic patients in an adolescent unit, it is important to remain flexible. For example, there may be times when the young-ster needs a great deal of supervision or help with self-care such as dressing, and others when he needs to be allowed to withdraw; times when he can cope well with a group situation, and others when he is feeling too paranoid. This can pose problems when a particular unit has rigid rules and policy, as with a phil-osophy of self-responsibility and self-care at all times. Similarly, certain behav-iours, notably any form of aggression, may be taken at face value and seen as "naughtiness", with an expectation that the same sanction must be applied as in non-psychotic patients. Managing such situations requires considerable diplomacy and skill on the part of staff. However, adolescents commonly recog-nize qualitative differences in their psychotic peers, and are prepared to see them as "ill" or to make allowances, particularly when the symptoms are florid.

Outpatient management

If it is not possible or not acceptable to the family to admit a teenage psychotic, with older adolescents, or when there is no evidence of an organic basis or of self-injurious behaviour, it is quite feasible to treat them successfully on an out-patient basis, with sufficient professional input from either an independent community psychiatric nurse or adolescent unit staff. Indeed, McKnew (1979) suggests that in all cases, rapid administration of major tranquillizers in large doses as early as possible may prevent hospitalization or other care away from home. Daily visiting is desirable at first, to monitor the medication and to offer individual counselling to both the youngster and his or her family. Family work can successfully be carried out in this way, and it should also be possible for occupational therapists and/or home teachers to provide input. This form of management is not commonly practised currently, but may be expected to increase with the growing trend towards community care.

Follow-up

Even when a youngster makes a very good recovery in hospital from a first psychotic episode, follow-up after discharge is usually welcomed by the family, who often feel very vulnerable at this time and afraid of relapse. McKnew (1979) advocates the continuation of psychotropic medication for at least nine months after the symptoms have abated to prevent relapse. This requires regular psychiatric supervision which is also helpful in advising the families against overprotection or rejecting attitudes, and in assisting the gradual rein-troduction to normal life at school, college or work and socially.

However, as a number of authors (Warren, 1965; Weiner, 1970; Ainsworth, 1984) have pointed out, a substantial number of adolescent psychotics do not recover completely from the initial episode; they no longer need to be in hospital, but are likely to require careful alternative arrangements. Some may be unable to live at home and are found accommodation in hostels or even resi-dential special schools. They may also require special occupational opportuni-ties such as a sheltered workshop or access to a hospital industrial therapy or day unit. Many will need to be maintained on psychotropic medication (sometimes by depot preparations) for indefinite periods to obtain optimum function. It is clear that follow-up cannot be continued indefinitely by an adolescent psychia-tric team, and that sooner or later care must be transferred to a department of adult psychiatry. The timing of this may vary with local policy, the age of the patient and his or her educational situation. It is usually inappropriate for an adolescent team to continue follow-up in non-remitting cases and it is always better for a transfer of care to be planned well ahead so that both patient and family are properly prepared.

REFERENCES

Ainsworth, P. (1984). The first 100 admissions to a regional general purpose adolescent unit. *Journal of Adolescence* 7, 337-348.

Ainsworth, P. A case of "lethal catatonia" in a 14 year old girl. *British Journal of Psychiatry* (In Press).

American Psychiatric Association (APA) (1980). *Diagnostic and Statistical Manual of Mental Disorders* Edn 3. Washington DC: American Psychiatric Association.

Annesley, P.T. (1961). Psychiatric illness in adolescence: presentation and prognosis. *Journal of Mental Science* 107, 268-278.

Asperger, H. (1944). Die autistischen psychopathen im kindesalter. *Archiv Fur Psychiatrie Und Nervenkrankheiten* 117, 76-137.

Ballenger, J.C., Reus, V.I. and Post, R.M. (1982). The "Atypical" Clinical Picture of Adolescent Mania. *American Journal of Psychiatry* 139, 602-626.

Bender, L. (1969). The nature of childhood psychosis. In *Modern Perspectives in International Child Psychiatry*, Howells, J.G. (Ed). Edinburgh: Oliver and Boyd.

Birley, J.L.T. and Brown, G.W. (1970). Crises and life changes preceding the onset or relapse of acute schizophrenia: clinical aspects. *British Journal of Psychiatry* 116, 327-333.

Bradley, D. (1942). *Schizophrenia in childhood.* New York: Macmillan.

Cantor, S., Evans, J., Pearce, J. and Pezzot-Pearce, T. (1982). Childhood schizophrenia: present but not accounted for. *American Journal of Psychiatry* 139, 758-762.

Carlson, G.A. and Strober, M. (1978). Manic depressive illness in early adolescence. A study of clinical and diagnostic characteristics in 6 cases. *Journal of the American Academy of Child Psychiatry* 17, 139-153.

Carter, A.B. (1942). Prognostic factors of adolescent psychosis. *Journal of Mental Science* 88, 31-81.

Corbett, J., Harris, R., Taylor, E. and Trimble, M. (1977). Progressive disintegrative psychosis of childhood. *Journal of Child Psychology and Psychiatry* 18, 211-220.

Eggers, C. (1967). Wahninhalte kindlicher und prapuberaler schizophrenien. *Acta Paedopsychiatrica* 34, 326-340.

Eggers, C. (1973). *Verlaufsweisen kindlicher und praepuberaler schizophrenien.* Berlin: Springer Verlag.

Eggers, C . (1978). Course and prognosis of childhood schizophrenia. *J Autism Child Schizophr* 8, 21-36.

Falloon, I.R.H., Boyd, J.L., McGill, C.W., Razani, J., Moff, J.B. and Gilderman, A.M. (1982). Family management in the prevention of exacerbations of schizophrenia. *New England Journal of Medicine* 306, 1437-1440.

Gammon, G.D., John, K., Rothblum, E.D., Mullen, K., Tischler, G.L. and Weissman, M.M. (1983). Use of a structured diagnostic interview to identify bipolar disorder in adolescent inpatients: frequency and manifestations of the disorder. *American Journal of Psychiatry* 140, 543-547.

Garralda, M.E. (1984a). Hallucinations in children with conduct and emotional disorders: I. The clinical phenomena. *Psychological Medicine* 14, 589-596.

Garralda, M.E. (1984b). Hallucinations in children with conduct and emotional disorders: II. The follow-up study. *Psychological Medicine* 14, 597-604.

Garralda, M.E. (1984c). Psychotic children with hallucinations. *British Journal of Psychiatry* 145, 74-77.

Garralda, M.E. (1985). Characteristics of the psychoses of late onset in children and adolescents (a comparative study of hallucinating children). *Journal of Adolescence* 8, 195-207.

Gillberg, C., Wahlstrom, J., Forsman, A., Hellgren, L. and Gillberg, I.C. (1985). Teenage psychoses epidemiology, classification and reduced optimality in the pre-, peri-and neonatal periods. *Journal of Child Psychology and Psychiatry* **27**, 87-98.

Green, W.H., Campbell, M., Hardesty, A.S., Grega, D.M., Padron-Gayol, M., Shell, J. and Erlenmeyer-Kimling, L. (1984). A comparison of schizophrenic and autistic children. *Journal of the American Academy of Child Psychiatry* **23**, 399-409.

Haley, J. (1980). *Leaving home. The therapy of disturbed young people.* New York: McGraw-Hill.

Hassanyeh, F., Davison, K. (1980). Bipolar affective psychosis with onset before age 16 years: report of 10 cases. *British Journal of Psychiatry* **137**, 530-539.

Heller, T. (1969). About dementia infantilis. In *Modern Perspectives in International Child Psychiatry*. Howells, J.G. (Ed.). Edinburgh: Oliver & Boyd.

Hudgens, R.W. (1974). *Psychiatric Disorders in Adolescents*. Williams and Wilkins: Co. Baltimore.

Kallmann, F., Roth, B. (1956). Genetic aspects of preadolescent schizophrenia. *American Journal of Psychiatry* **112**, 599-606.

Kanner, L. (1943). Autistic disturbances of affective contact. *Nervous Child* **2**, 217-250.

Kolvin, I. (1971). Psychoses in childhood: a comparative study. In *Infantile Autism – Concepts, Characteristics and Treatment*, Rutter M. (Ed.). London: Churchill Livingstone.

Kolvin, I., Ounsted, C., Humphrey, M. *et al.* (1971). Studies in the childhood psychoses: II. The phenomenology of childhood psychoses. *British Journal of Psychiatry* **118**, 385-395.

Leff, J.P. and Vaughan, C.E. (1981). The role of maintenance therapy and relatives' expressed emotion in relapse of schizophrenia. A 2-year follow-up. *British Medical Journal* **139**, 102-104.

Leff, J.P., Kuipers, L., Berkowitz, R., Eberlein-Frief, R. and Sturgeon, D. (1982). A controlled trial of intervention in the families of schizophrenic patients. *British Journal of Psychiatry* **141**, 121-134.

Lloyd, H. and Ainsworth, P. (Unpublished data).

Masterson, J.F. (1967). *The Psychiatric Dilemma of Adolescence*. London: Churchill Ltd.

Maudsley, H. (1867). *The physiology and pathology of the mind*. London: Macmillan & Co.

McKnew, D. (1979). Use of psychotropic medication in adolescent psychiatry. In *The Short Course in Adolescent Psychiatry*, Novello, J.R., (Ed.). New York: Baunner/Mazel.

Nunn, K.P., Lask, B. and Cohen, M. (1985). Viruses, neurodevelopmental disorder and childhood psychosis. *Journal of Child Psychology and Psychiatry* **27**, 55-64.

Petty, L.K., Ornitz, E.M., Michelman, J.D. and Zimmerman, E.G. (1984). Autistic children who become schizophrenic. *Archives of General Psychiatry* **41**, 129-135.

Pyne, N., Morrison, R., Ainsworth, P. (1985). A follow-up study of the first 70 admissions to a general purpose adolescent unit. *Journal of Adolescence* **8**, 333-345.

Rollin, H.R. (Ed.). (1980). Coping with Schizophrenia. National Schizophrenia Fellowship.

Rutter, M., Greenfield, D., Lockyer, L. (1967). A five to fifteen year follow-up of infantile psychosis. Social and behavioural outcome. *British Journal of Psychiatry* **113**, 1183-1199.

Sanctis, S. de (1969). On some varieties of dementia praecos. In *Modern Perspectives in International Child Psychiatry*, Howells, J.G. (Ed.). Edinburgh: Oliver & Boyd.

Steinberg, D. (1980). The use of lithium carbonate in adolescence. *Journal of Child Psychology and Psychiatry* **21**, 263-271.

Steinberg, D., Galhenage, D.P.C. and Robinson, S.C. (1981). Two years' referrals to a regional adolescent unit: some implications for psychiatric services. *Social Science and Medicine* **15E**, 113–122.

Steinberg, D. (1985). Adolescent psychoses. Chapter in *Child & Adolescent Psychiatry, Modern Approaches*, Rutter, M. and Hersov, L. (Eds), 2nd Edn. London: Blackwell.

Vrono, M. (1974). Schizophrenia in childhood and adolescence. *International Journal of Mental Health* **2**, 7–116.

Warren, W. (1949). Abnormal behaviour and mental breakdown in adolescence. *Journal of Mental Science* **95**, 589–624.

Warren, W., Cameron , K. (1950). Reactive psychoses in adolescence. *Journal of Mental Science* **96**, 448–457.

Warren, W., (1965). A study of adolescent psychiatric in-patients and the outcome six or more years later: I. Clinical histories and hospital findings. *Journal of Child Psychology and Psychiatry* **6**, 1–17.

Weiner, I.B. (1970). *Psychological disturbance in adolescence*. New York: Wiley.

World Health Organization (WHO) (1978). *Mental disorders: Glossary and Guide to the Classification in accordance with the 9th Revision of the Internal Classification of Diseases*. Geneva: World Health Organization.

13. Suicidal behaviour in adolescents

MICHAEL KERFOOT

Suicidal behaviour among adolescents has in the past 20 years become a major problem to Health and Welfare services. The frequency of occurrence of such behaviour has now rendered it a relatively unremarkable phenomenon and one which has come to be regarded with some irritation as well as concern by professionals. For many adults admitted to hospital following a suicide attempt, their suicidal behaviour has been a dramatic expression of their social isolation and general poverty of existence. Their problems and life experiences, however, will often differ from those of the young adolescent. Unlike the suicidal adult, the young adolescent who attempts suicide frequently does so within the setting of the family, and in response to stresses contained there. The family unit may of course differ in some respects from the sociological ideal of the "nuclear" family, but the adolescent will generally have a number of relatives with whom, for good or ill, he has some interaction. It is clear that the family exerts a potent influence on the development of the individual, particularly the development of emotional responses, ideas, attitudes, and values. It is of value, therefore, to consider the role of the family in relation to suicidal behaviour in the young adolescent.

Within each example of adolescent suicidal behaviour there are a wide variety of variables to consider. An inventory of possibly relevant variables would include factors relating to the individual, the family and the wider society. Thus we must consider family structure and organization, family beliefs, values, assumptions, and the position of the family *vis-à-vis* the wider

Working with troubled adolescents
ISBN 0-12-179720-1

social network. Coupled with these are the individual characteristics of each of the family members, their personality attributes, pathological traits, roles, etc. Of particular importance here are the family's experiences of previous suicidal behaviour, and the degree to which the family and the wider society have accommodated to such behaviour. The consequences of suicidal behaviour will affect each of these systems – individual, family, society – though in our present state of knowledge we can only speculate about the extent to which variables within each of these systems may be individually or collectively reinforcing.

DEMOGRAPHIC CHARACTERISTICS

Both attempted suicide and completed suicide are rare in children under the age of 12 years (Otto, 1972; Shaffer, 1974), though suicidal thoughts, threats and actions occur in 10 to 30% of children aged 6 to 12 years referred to psychiatric services (Luckianowicz, 1968; Pfeffer, Conte, Plutchik and Jerrett, 1980). There is general agreement in the research that female attempters greatly outnumber males, usually in the order of 4:1, and that this is more marked in younger patients, and in those who overdose rather than use more "active" methods of self-injury. Rates for deliberate self-poisoning in girls increase rapidly from age 12 to 16 years and continue to increase into the early twenties, (Kreitman and Schreiber, 1979). Suicidal behaviour is less common among boys, especially before the age of 14 years, after which it increases gradually with age until well into the twenties (Hawton and Goldacre, 1982).

It has been suggested that there is a tendency for these patients to come from a rather higher social class group than adults who attempt suicide (Bergstrand and Otto, 1962; Jacobziner, 1965). However, this is in contrast with the finding from Australia (Kosky, 1983) that only 15% of suicidal children and adolescents come from the higher social class groups. It also contrasts with the findings from studies involving all age groups, where hospital admission following suicidal behaviour is common amongst the lower socio-economic groups.

Some studies have reported a small seasonal variation in the rates of suicidal behaviour in the young, the peak incidence being found during the earlier part of the year (Otto, 1972; Hawton and Goldacre, 1982).

FAMILY AND SOCIAL FACTORS

Disturbed family functioning and the stress that disordered interaction produces has long been associated with behavioural and emotional difficulties in children and adolescents. Commonly the problem is one of continuing conflict with a parent, usually presenting as a disciplinary crisis. Cazzullo, Balestri and Generali (1968) found that common elements in suicidal behaviour in adolescents were clearly linked to family functioning. Adolescents were seen to lack the ability to express emotional problems. In itself, this is not an uncommon feature of adolescence but for the suicidal adolescent this was often associated with a tendency in families to deny problems, or to underestimate their impact on the child.

In other families parents have been observed to be unavailable to their children in any real emotional sense and this has been particularly damaging for adolescents who are attempting to meet a variety of developmental tasks in an environment which clearly does not lend them support. A study which looked at a sample of 13 suicidal boys (Margolin and Teicher, 1968) found repeated relationship problems in the family background. The majority of mothers presented as immature and deprived in personality functioning, insensitive to the needs of their children, and unable to respond to them effectively. Role reversal between mother and child was common, a feature noted by Kreider and Motto (1974) and Kerfoot (1979b) in subsequent work in this area. The cruical factor in role reversal situations was that adolescents were again attempting to meet a number of developmental tasks but from a distorted frame of reference.

McIntyre and Angle (1973) found extremes of parental expectations and control in 60% of the 50 subjects studied. The authors proposed a rejection cycle in which the parental response to the suicidal gesture and to acting-out behaviour favoured recidivism. In later work (McIntyre, Angle and Schlicht, 1977) it was observed that hostility, indifference and parental rejection were more common in subjects than in controls, though both groups complained of not being able to communicate with their parents.

Many studies point to the pervasiveness of family breakdown in the backgrounds of young people who attempt suicide, but the criteria by which breakdown is assessed vary enormously. In his Los Angeles studies, Teicher (1970, 1975) found that nearly half of his sample had a parent, relative or close friend who had attempted suicide. Of his sample, 74% viewed family conflict as "extreme" and 16% had an alcoholic parent. Many of the sample came from broken homes and there was marked residential mobility and changes of school; 84% of those with step-parents felt in contention with an unwanted step-parent and all of the sample complained of no real communication or emotional ties with their families.

It is worthwhile examining many of these "family factors" in terms of their impact upon developing adolescents and their response to them. At a time when they are physically and emotionally in transition and when role conflict can become extreme, the adolescent may be faced with additional stresses which will serve primarily to increase their vulnerability. The position has been ably summarized by Jacobs (1971) who describes a three-stage progression to the social isolation which results in suicide attempts in adolescents. First, there is a "long-standing history of problems", often from childhood through to adolescence and this is followed by a "period of escalation" during which many new problems associated with adolescent adjustment are introduced. The third and final stage covers the weeks and days immediately preceding the attempt and is characterized by a "chain-reaction dissolution" of the adolescent's few remaining primary associations.

Emotionally detached parents make children feel unwanted and unloved. They are not available as a resource in times of stress and thus cannot satisfy the child's dependency needs. It is not unexpected, therefore, that many youngsters should respond to this continual frustration of their dependency needs by becoming angry and aggressive. Anna Freud (1958) has pointed out that where hostility and aggression are turned away from objects and employed inwardly against the self, the adolescent may display intense depression, a tendency towards self-abasement or self-injury, and may carry out suicidal wishes. A study by Green (1978) found a high incidence of self-mutilating behaviour in a group of 60 abused children when compared with controls. In the majority of cases the behaviour was precipitated by parental beatings or threatened and actual separation from the parent figure. Green concluded that a sense of worthlessness, badness and self-hatred was engendered in the child because of parental assaults, rejection and scapegoating, and that facilitated by poor ego-strength and impulse control, self-hatred was effectively transformed into self-destruction. An interesting variation on this theme (Miller, 1975) described different degrees of aggression turned inward upon the self, and also "suicidal equivalents" such as running away from home, accident-proneness, anti-social behaviour and neurotic illness (where the flight into sickness was an aggressive mechanism). Using Miller's analysis it would be possible to define many different behaviours as "suicidal equivalents" across a broad spectrum of disturbance and the usefulness of such a concept must remain doubtful.

Using a more indirect approach at assessing problems, Tuckman and Youngman (1964) considered the extent of contact with social agencies as an indicator of family disorganization and breakdown in the backgrounds of adolescent suicide attempters. They found that families with a young member who had attempted suicide had significantly greater contacts with agencies dealing with matrimonial problems and juvenile delinquency.

Parental loss is an aspect of family structure and functioning which has attracted a good deal of attention in the psychiatric literature. "Loss" is an important social and environmental correlate of suicidal behaviour and the loss can be in terms of death, desertion or separation from a significant person or the anniversary of such an event. A universal finding is that a large proportion of young suicide attempters have experienced broken homes through separation, divorce or the death of a parent (Bergstrand and Otto, 1962; Tuckman and

Connan, 1962; Jacobziner, 1965; Barter, Swaback and Todd, 1968; White, 1974; Walker, 1980). A study by Morrison (1969) found that 75% of a group of 34 adolescents referred with suicidal behaviour had experienced a recent loss (within a week) or the anniversary of a loss. In an earlier study of 84 cases, Schneer, Kay and Brozovsky (1961) concluded that in addition to the anxiety or exaggerated guilt and aggression, the loss or separation from one or both parents in varying degrees at crucial periods of development predisposed the adolescent to suicide. A similar claim has been made elsewhere for adults who attempt suicide (Greer, 1964).

It may be important to consider what specific features of "loss" situations appear to be associated with suicidal behaviour in young people. Jacobs and Teicher (1967) found that 72% of a sample of suicidal adolescents came from broken homes, but so did half of their controls. However, over half of the "attempters' " parents had remarried within five years (i.e. during the attempter's adolescence). The authors concluded that parental loss as such was only a part of the process which predisposes to later depression. This is a view shared by Crook and Raskin (1975) who stress that the important factor is parental loss due to marital discord and poor relationships. Divorce or separation may well hurt a child, regardless of age, more than the death of a parent, and a childhood characterized by this is associated with attempted suicide in later life. Although broken homes are more common among adolescents who attempt suicide than adolescents in the general population (Jacobs, 1971; Hawton, O'Grady, Osborn and Cole, 1982a), it has been suggested that they may not differ in this respect from other adolescent psychiatric patients (Mattson, Seese and Hawkins, 1969; Stanley and Barter, 1970), Recent studies by Kosky (1983) and by Kerfoot (1984) have found a significantly higher incidence of broken homes among adolescent suicide attempters, when compared with psychiatric non-suicidal controls.

PRECIPITATING FACTORS

Suicide attempts in adolescence most commonly follow quarrels with parents or with a boy or girlfriend (White, 1974; Walker, 1980; Hawton et al., 1982a), though often within the setting of more long-standing problems such as delinquency, school problems and running away from home (Otto, 1972; Kerfoot, 1984). A minority of adolescents involved in suicide attempts are found to have psychiatric illness, depression being the most common diagnosis. Taylor and Stansfield (1984) reported a high incidence of depressive symptoms, using a symptom-count, in a group of 50 school-age children who had poisoned themselves. There are difficulties, however, surrounding the diagnosis of depression in children and adolescents and the relationship between depression and suicidal behaviour is complex (Cantwell and Carlson, 1979). While many young suicide attempters and completed suicides may be depressed, the converse is not true. Moreover, it is unclear whether or not these "depressed" youngsters have a major affective disorder or are suffering from transient feelings of sadness associated with often untenable psychosocial situations (Carlson and Cantwell, 1982). Among suicide attempters boys are more likely than girls to have psychiatric disorder (Otto, 1972). More than 20% of suicide attempters will have had a previous psychiatric referral and a quarter will have made a suicide attempt in the past (Kerfoot, 1984). Physical ill-health prior to making an attempt is frequently reported (Jacobs, 1971; White, 1974; Walker, 1980) and as many as half of these adolescents will have seen their family doctor in the month preceding their attempt (Hawton et al., 1982a).

METHODS AND MOTIVATION

Between 80 and 90% of adolescents admitted to hospital following a suicide attempt will have taken an overdose of tablets. Attempts involving more violent means of self-injury are more common among boys than girls and are usually associated with a greater degree of suicidal intent (Otto, 1972). Impulsivity is a marked feature of overdosing in adolescents and the episodes usually occur when there is a strong likelihood of the event being discovered quickly. There is likely to be little evidence of premeditation. The majority of younger adolescents obtain their tablets from home and over half of the cases are likely to involve the use of prescribed medication (Kerfoot, 1984).

The motives for suicidal behaviour in adolescents are often complex to unravel. A recent study (Hawton, O'Grady, Osborn and Cole, 1982b) suggested that adolescents view their overdose as a means of gaining relief from a stressful state of mind or situation and as a way of showing other people how desperate they were feeling. The authors suggested that the appeal function of overdoses by adolescents was interpersonal rather that directed towards an outside helping agency, thus confirming earlier findings by White (1974). While acknowledging that "intent" is a very difficult concept to evaluate, it does appear likely that the majority of overdoses are taken in the secure belief that death will not occur (Kessel, 1965).

In his study of completed suicides in the young, Shaffer (1974) concludes that what finally determines a child's death by suicide is a degree of conceptual maturity; disturbed family background; depressed mental state; a precipitating incident, often of a humiliating kind; access to the means of suicide and the opportunity to use these in isolation and in addition, close experience of suicidal behaviour either through its occurrence in the family, within the peer group, or at a fantasy level.

A SYSTEMS MODEL

Researchers are generally in agreement about the importance of family disorganization and breakdown to an understanding of adolescent suicidal behaviour but little attempt is made to relate ideas to a broader conceptual framework. I believe it is possible to construct a framework which encompasses and links together the many features of suicidal behaviour in the young, so that individual incidents would have their natural history traced within the framework. This is beneficial in identifying the predicament facing the adolescent and in understanding how this relates to other problem areas, and the wider implications in terms of creating an overdosing lifestyle or "career". I have, therefore, constructed a flow chart (Figure 1) to incorporate those features of the behaviour referred to in previous research studies. These will include individual, family and wider social factors. The flow chart logically moves from vulnerability factors to precipitating factors and then considers those reinforcing and stabilizing factors which may or may not, enable the behaviour to be accepted within the family or the wider social system.

The literature has shown us that adolescents who harm themselves may be especially vulnerable to such behaviours because of a long-standing history of problems of varying degrees of seriousness. The behaviour and attitudes of parents and other family members are also given some importance as well as the more overt signs of marital failure and family breakdown. These individual and family factors may well increase the vulnerability of the adolescent to subsequent stress, especially in combination rather than individually. In addition, there may be wider social factors at work which would increase the stresses experienced by young people. These are not easy to identify, however, and would probably be described as elements of breakdown within the social fabric of society, the inappropriateness or obsolescence of some of our social institutions and the alienation which may stem from these. All these factors can, depending upon the individual concerned, shake the confidence and personal well-being of a young person and thereby increase vulnerability. In the flow chart these are referred to as "vulnerability factors".

Within the setting of such vulnerability, a precipitating event might easily spark off an impulsive response in the individual. The explanation of this may be that the event is perceived by the youngster concerned as an insurmountable obstacle, help is either unavailable or unrecognized by them and they may entertain the belief that a solution cannot be found. Frustration and stress may then create an environment where impulsive behaviour is used. Occasional reports in the literature indicate that the families of young people who make suicide attempts have often experienced similar behaviour in the past from other family members. It has been suggested that such behaviour may offer a precedent to adolescents who then model their behaviour on those around them.

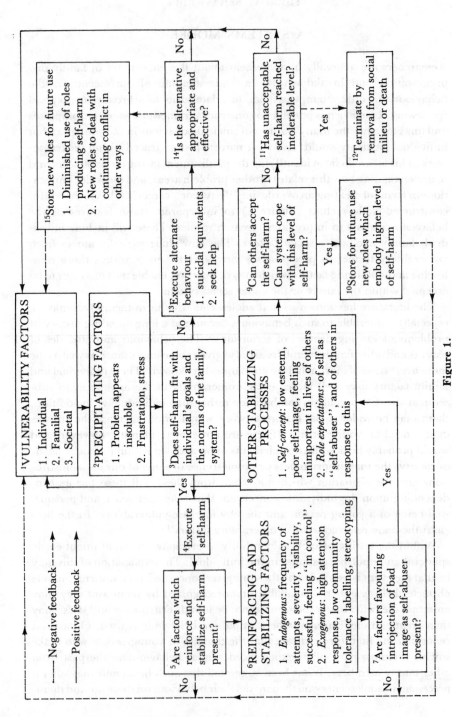

Figure 1.

Flow Chart illustrating stabilization of self-harm in family system

There is no evidence to support speculation of this kind and the best we can say is that where there is evidence of previous suicidal behaviour among family members or the peer group, then this simply makes the possibility of indulging in similar behaviour more available to the adolescent.

Following an incident of suicidal behaviour, we may then speculate about factors which further reinforce and stabilize the behaviour so that it is positively, rather than negatively, connoted. Factors which contribute to this may stem from the individual or from the social milieu in which the behaviour occurs and is responded to. Individual factors would consider those adolescents who were ''repeaters'', also the severity (impressiveness) of the episode and the apparent success in terms of the individual feeling ''in control'' of events. The literature has shown that although adolescents' responses suggest that they harm themselves in order to gain relief or to escape from intolerable stress, there is also a strong suggestion that the behaviour is aimed at seeking retribution from parents or changing the behaviour of significant others towards the adolescent. Low repetition rates amongst adolescents, which are in the order of 10% during the 12 months following the original episode, may indicate that the attempt was successful in re-establishing some sort of equilibrium or control for the adolescent.

The social milieu may provide reinforcers which stabilize behaviours. Admission to hospital guarantees high attention and the vast majority of young suicide attempters are admitted to hospital. It is also likely that the less behaviourally disturbed adolescents would be more able to have emotionally satisfying experiences as inpatients because they would be less demanding and more conforming than an unruly or aggressive person. We might also speculate that the former would be more likely to repeat their suicidal behaviour if the effects of hospitalization had proved to be particularly gratifying for them. They might also be more susceptible to the labelling and stereotyping of their behaviour once placed in a strong dependency position by hospital staff and incline towards absorbing these influences rather than resisting them.

Other stabilizing processes are concerned with the introjection by the individual of a negative self-image. Low self-esteem and a lack of investment and involvement in the family would be important here because many adolescents who present with suicidal behaviour complain of feeling alienated or isolated in relation to their family. In these situations communication appears to have broken down, there is less flexibility and openness and the adolescent may resort to actions rather than words in order to communicate distress. In addition, a poor standard of parental supervision and guidance may result in the child being more likely to act out disturbance in an impulsive manner. Communication may improve in some families following an episode of suicidal behaviour but in others it will remain unchanged or may deteriorate further. Other experiences such as delinquency, poor school/employment record, periods in

"Care" and running away from home may enhance the adolescent's negative self-concept. He or she then more easily takes on a negative role others begin to respond to. Social adversity as measured by delinquency, "Care", unemployment, low income and contact with welfare agencies is reported with consistency in the literature. If the family accepts and can cope with suicidal behaviour, then this may be therapeutic for the individual and lead towards a resolution of the difficulties. On the other hand, should such behaviour be resorted to in the future, it may embody escalating levels of gravity for the individual.

An important but complex factor here would be treatment. This is usually short-term, intensive and hospital-based, but because of the variability of treatment and the responses to it, its effectiveness is difficult to evaluate. Treatment ought to help in these situations but we are not certain that it does so. Where children are concerned there is the additional problem of having to overcome parental reluctance and resistance to follow-up. There have been no controlled evaluative studies of the effects of treatment with this age group and the few follow-up studies which have been undertaken have been fraught with methodological difficulties.

The flow chart relies heavily upon information being available with regard to follow-up, particularly concerning further episodes of suicidal behaviour. Herein lies a problem, for in order to speculate about the course of suicidal behaviour we would need to have a reasonably sized population of repeaters, and well-documented evidence of the continuing stress for individuals during the follow-up period. The flow chart may, therefore, have greater applicability when used in conjunction with older adolescents or young adults, where repeat episodes of self-harm are more common.

Clearly there are many factors which need to be kept in mind when observing and assessing suicidal behaviour in the young, and the flow chart is an attempt to draw together the main features of the problem, and to make explicit the nature of branching and feedback. It is a systems analysis of the behaviour but also illustrates the deficiencies and discrepancies which are inevitable in a diagramatic representation. The flow chart specifies alternative causal flows and the paths by which information is relayed back either to reinforce the existing system or to create alternative sequences. Embodied within the analysis are a number of propositions with regard to factors which positively or negatively reinforce suicidal behaviour, but these are entirely speculative. In addition, they are based on data from a wide variety of sources and on populations often reflecting a wide variation in age. It does, however, provide a useful framework within which to summarize many of the ideas and opinions expressed in the growing literature on this subject.

MANAGEMENT AND TREATMENT

Management of these adolescents is influenced by the degree of suicidal risk present and by the availability of supports within the immediate social situation. Where there is evidence of mental disorder then the patient may be transferred to a Child and Adolescent Psychiatry facility for further observation, assessment or treatment. Where there is no evidence of such disorder but there remains a serious risk of a further attempt, then placement may have to be made through the Social Services Department if there are substantial reasons for not returning the child home. In some families, parents may be largely unavailable to their children in any emotional sense and would be unlikely to provide the support and supervision which might greatly reduce the risk of a further attempt. In other situations the child may be beyond parental control and a danger to herself. Experience would suggest, however, that the need to transfer a child to a psychiatric facility or to a residential "Care" facility, is unlikely to arise very often. In the majority of cases the child will return home after treatment for the immediate physical effects of her suicidal behaviour.

For many youngsters, psychotherapeutic help will begin while the child is still an inpatient and will continue after the child has been discharged from hospital. The form this treatment will take is based on a careful analysis of the problems presented by the child at the time of admission. A major decision in therapy relates to the individual or group upon which the therapeutic endeavour will focus and the form the intervention will take. The family context of suicidal behaviour in the young would seem to call for a family approach in treatment, and experience would suggest that direct work which aims to explore family dynamics and to facilitate more productive interaction is an extremely profitable way in which to utilize the time available.

Family therapy is indicated where situations present as "transactional" in terms of a relationship rather than in terms of an individual's symptomatology (Walrond-Skinner, 1976). Similarly, in situations where the adolescent is responding to stress between other family members rather than being directly involved in the friction, it would be advisable to treat on a family basis. Experience would suggest that parents and children rarely discuss a suicide attempt once the adolescent returns home from hospital. There may be an inability or unwillingness on both sides to broach the subject and fears may become repressed or rationalized, rather than expressed. In such families, a family therapy approach would address itself to the difficulty, ensuring that the suicidal behaviour was acknowledged and understood by all those concerned (Richman, 1979).

There are circumstances, however, where a conjoint family approach may be contraindicated. The situation may be such that the family group is either physically or psychologically unavailable for therapy. Some individuals within families may be so emotionally deprived that they are unable to tolerate sharing a therapist with other family members. If this were so then it would be a clear indication for individual therapy rather than family therapy. In addition, agreement to a course of family therapy will mean for some family members that they are taking a risk and exposing themselves at a time when they feel vulnerable. Therapy may imply a level of trust and confidence between participants and this may be more apparent than real. In particular, youngsters who are trying to differentiate themselves and gain independence within the family group may be unwilling to join with their family in therapy. They may see a commitment to treatment as co-operating in yet another, but perhaps more subtle form of parental control, the therapist being identified with parental authoritarian figures. Indeed, the parents may well wish to promote such an identification. On the other hand, it can often be the parents who are lacking in motivation and their apathy or ambivalence may communicate itself to the child. Children are quick to comprehend their parents' attitudes and opinions, particularly if a little time has elapsed before they are seen in therapy. The therapist may, therefore, find the child declining treatment, if this is the unspoken parental message picked up by her. This is particularly true for younger children or for the more emotionally immature and dependent adolescent, who in a very real sense may have no voice of their own. In these circumstances there would be valid reasons for seeing the child individually or combining individual sessions with occasional family sessions. Whatever the decision made about therapy, the therapist's judgement must be informed judgement, based on a careful analysis of all the issues present in the case.

It will be necessary to see some adolescents alone in order to effect therapeutic change in their lives. Even the prospect of being seen individually, however, will raise for some young people fears and conflicts about their capacity to initiate and sustain interaction successfully. Some may respond to this by withdrawal, by presenting as sullen and unco-operative or by adopting a hostile and belligerent manner with the therapist. Coping with this requires immense tolerance and patience on the part of the therapist, as well as the ability to recognize the potential for change within the individual even when the problem appears intractable. Clearly some adolescents require help to overcome their reluctance or resentment in therapy to the point where they can begin to develop trust and confidence both in themselves and in others. Psychotherapy may begin, therefore, as nurturance and support, later moving on to exploration, challenge and confrontation.

Where individual psychotherapy is indicated, then this should be brief and task-oriented, rather than addressing the patient's entire experience. Experience would suggest that whatever our therapeutic aims may be, therapists stand the best chance of achieving these if they can begin to work quickly and intensively. The success of short-term therapy is largely due to the therapist and patient reaching agreement on goals early in treatment. Time-limited intervention gives an impetus to the participants in the therapeutic contract at a time when motivation is likely to be high, and when the elements of the crisis can be used to advantage. If this opportunity is missed, then the individual or family are likely to lose interest and to draw a veil over the whole incident and the importance of this significant event in their lives would be lost.

PREVENTION

Suicidal behaviour in children and adolescents is a serious problem. Until fairly recently it was not uncommon for suicidal behaviour in the young to be greeted with a certain amount of disbelief, as though young people were incapable of entertaining suicidal thoughts, let alone prepared to precipitate their own demise. Sadly, this kind of attitude may still lead to under-reporting of suicide attempts, with a consequent failure to assess carefully and follow-up the subjects concerned. Primary prevention needs to apply itself across a broad spectrum which will encompass the individual, the family and the wider community. A preliminary task in developing a preventative framework is the establishment of valid and reliable suicide rates for adolescents in different countries. Population studies have emphasized the wide disparity in the reporting of suicide statistics and under-reporting will clearly influence the development of services to meet the problem.

Continued work is necessary to develop techniques of primary prevention, particularly within schools and in community education programmes. Primary prevention should address the basic structure of social and family life, in addition to addressing the individual needs of the adolescent. Prevention would appropriately aim at education of the parents in mental health principles of child-rearing, with special emphasis on the development of self-concept, self-esteem, basic trust and feelings of self-worth and on the need for responsibility and obligations to others as well as self. Direct work of a similar nature may be undertaken within schools to help adolescents towards a realistic appraisal of the stresses they may encounter as they move into adulthood and the resources available to them in times of crisis. An educational endeavour of this kind would serve the dual purpose of general information giving and of enabling those individuals who were particularly vulnerable to use their newly acquired knowledge to gain help and support for themselves.

Techniques of secondary and tertiary prevention need to be improved in relation to those patients at high risk for further suicidal behaviour. In general, secondary prevention is concerned with individuals who have identified themselves by a suicidal act and from whom we may glean information which would help to prevent further episodes of suicidal behaviour. A component of secondary prevention is the effective assessment and treatment of all children presenting with suicidal behaviour and their families. The child psychiatric team should be available in every hospital to see children and adolescents within 48 hours of admission, in order to use the crisis of admission therapeutically.

Tertiary prevention aims to prevent suicidal acts from having a fatal outcome and is therefore a matter primarily for toxicologists and physicians. It has been suggested that overdoses may be prevented by greater care on the part of doctors in prescribing psychotropic drugs for young people (White, 1974; British Medical Journal, 1981). The impact of this may, however, be dubious since younger adolescents visit their general practitioners prior to overdose less often than their adult counterparts (Hawton *et al.*, 1982*a*) and often attempt suicide with non-prescribed analgesics or with drugs prescribed for another family member (Kerfoot, 1979*a*). Morgan and Hayward (1976) suggest that lectures and discussion groups with schoolchildren may be beneficial in modifying attitudes to self-poisoning and drug abuse and this could easily become an integral part of health education programmes. Since parental distress constitutes a major factor in child psychiatric disorder, it has been suggested (British Medical Journal, 1981) that greater collaboration between adult and child psychiatrists would make a positive contribution towards the identification and treatment of suicidal children and their parents.

For the future, research should be aimed at those services which focus upon adolescents, rather than community-wide coverage, so that specific features of adolescent disturbance, therapeutic intervention and prevention can be identified and evaluated. There can be no substitute for evaluative research in this field since failure to pursue this may well obscure true morbidity in adolescents and real suffering within their families.

REFERENCES

Barter, J., Swaback, D. and Todd, D. (1968). Adolescent suicide attempts: follow-up. *Archives of General Psychiatry* **19**, 523–527.

Bergstrand, C.G. and Otto, U. (1962) Suicide attempts in childhood and adolescence. *Acta Paediatrica Scandinavia* **51**, 17–26.

British Medical Journal (1981). Annotation: children and parasuicide. **283**, 337–338.

Cantwell, D. and Carlson, G. (1979). Problems and prospects in the study of childhood depression. *Journal of Nervous and Mental Diseases* **167**, 523–529.

Carlson, G. and Cantwell, D. (1982). Suicidal behaviour and depression in children and adolescents. *Journal of the American Academy of Child Psychiatry* **21**, 4, 361–368.

Cazzullo, C.L., Balestri, L. and Generali, L. (1968). Some remarks on attempted suicide in the period of adolescence. *Acta Paedopsychiatrica Scandinavia* **35**, 325–344.

Crook, T. and Raskin, A. (1975). Association of childhood parental loss with attempted suicide and depression. *Journal of Consultative Clinical Psychology* **43**, 2.

Freud, A. (1958). Adolescence. *The Psychoanalytic Study of the Child* **13**, 255–278.

Green, A.H. (1978). Self-destructive behaviour in battered children. *American Journal of Psychiatry* **135, 5**, 579-582.

Greer, S. (1964). Relationship between parental loss and attempted suicide. *British Journal of Psychiatry* **110**, 698-705.

Hawton, K. and Goldacre, M. (1982). Hospital admissions for adverse effects of medicinal agents (mainly self-poisoning) among adolescents in the Oxford region. *British Journal of Psychiatry* **141**, 166-170.

Hawton, K., O'Grady, J., Osborn, M. and Cole, D. (1982a). Adolescents who take overdoses: their characteristics, problems, and contacts with helping agencies. *British Journal of Psychiatry* **140**, 118-123.

Hawton, K., O'Grady, J., Osborn, M. and Cole, D. (1982b). Motivational aspects of deliberate self-poisoning in adolescents. *British Journal of Psychiatry* **141**, 286-291.

Jacobs, J. (1971). *Adolescent Suicide*. Wiley Interscience London.

Jacobs, J. and Teicher, J.D. (1967). Broken homes and social isolation in attempted suicide of adolescents. *International Journal of Social Psychiatry* **13**, 139-149.

Jacobziner, H. (1965). Attempted suicide in adolescents by poisoning. *Americal Journal of Psychotherapy* **19**, 247-252.

Kerfoot, M.J. (1979a). Self-poisoning by children and adolescents. *Social Work Today.* **10, 45**, 9-11

Kerfoot, M.J. (1979b). Parent-child role reversal and adolescent suicidal behaviour. *Journal of Adolescence.* **2**, 337-343.

Kerfoot, M.J. (1984). *Deliberate Self-poisoning in Childhood and Early Adolescence* Unpublished Ph. D Thesis, University of Manchester.

Kessel, N. (1965). Self-poisoning (Part 1). *British Medical Journal.* (27/11/65), 1265-1270.

Kosky, R. (1983). Childhood suicidal behaviour. *Journal of Child Psychology and Psychiatry* **24, 3**, 457-468.

Kreider, D.G. and Motto, J.A. (1974). Parent child role reversal and suicidal states in adolescence. *Adolescence* **9, 35**, 365-370.

Kreitman, N. and Schreiber, M. (1979). Parasuicide in young Edinburgh women: 1968-1975. *Psychological Medicine* **9**, 469-479.

Luckianowicz, N. (1968) Attempted suicide in children. *Acta Psychiatrica Scandinavia* **44**, 415-435.

Margolin, N.L. and Teicher, J.D. (1968). Thirteen adolescent male suicide attempters. *Journal of the American Academy of Child Psychiatry* **7**, 396-415.

Mattsson, A., Seese, L.R. and Hawkins, J.W. (1969) Suicidal behaviour as a child Psychiatric emergency. *Archives of General Psychiatry* **20, 1**, 100-109.

McIntyre, M.S. and Angle, C. (1973) Psychological biopsy in self-poisoning of children and adolescents. *American Journal of Diseases in Childhood* **126, 1**, 42-46.

McIntyre, Angle, C. and Schlicht, W. (1977). Suicide and self-poisoning in paediatrics. *Advances in Paediatrics.* **24**, 291-309.

Miller. J.P. (1975). Suicide in adolescence. *Adolescence* **10, 37**, 11-24.

Morgan, H.G. and Hayward, A. (1976). The effects of drug talks to schoolchildren. *British Journal of Addiction* **71**, 101-104.

Morrison, C.G. (1969). Family treatment approach to suicidal children and adolescents. *Journal of the American Academy of Child Psychiatry* **8**, 140-153.

Otto, U. (1972) Suicidal acts by children and adolescents: A follow-up. *Acta Psychiatrica Scandinavia* (Supplementum) **233**, 7-123.

Pfeffer, C., Conte, H., Plutchik, R. and Jerrett, I. (1980). Suicidal behaviour in latency age children: an out-patient population. *Journal of the American Academy of Child Psychiatry* **19**, 707-710.

Richman, J. (1979). The family therapy of attempted suicide. *Family Process* **18**, 131–142.

Schneer, H.I., Kay, P. and Brozovsky, M. (1961). Events and conscious ideation leading to suicidal behaviour in adolescents. *Psychiatric Quarterly* **35**, 507–515.

Shaffer, D. (1974). Suicide in childhood and early adolescence. *Journal of Child Psychology and Psychiatry* **15**, 275–291.

Stanley, E.J. and Barter, J.T. (1970). Adolescent suicidal behaviour. *American Journal of Orthoychiatry*. **40**, **1**, 87–96.

Taylor, E.A. and Stansfield, S.A. (1984). Children who poison themselves: a clinical comparison with psychiatric controls. *British Journal of Psychiatry* **145**, 127–132.

Teicher, J.D. (1970). Children and adolescents who attempt suicide. *Paediatric Clinics of North America* **17**, 687–696.

Teicher, J.D. (1975). Children who choose death. *Emergency Medicine* **7**, 136–142.

Tuckman, J. and Connan, H.E. (1962). Attempted suicide in adolescents. *American Journal of Psychiatry* **119**, 228–232.

Tuckman, J. and Youngman, W. (1964). Attempted suicide and family disorganization. *Journal of General Psychology* **105**, 187–193.

Walker, W.L. (1980). Intentional self-injury in school-age children. *Journal of Adolescence* **3**, 217–228.

Walrond-Skinner, S. (1976). *Family Therapy: The Treatment of Natural Systems*. London: Routledge and Keagan Paul.

White, H.C. (1974). Self-poisoning in adolescents. *British Journal of Psychiatry* **124**, 24–35.

14. Eating disorders

RACHEL BRYANT-WAUGH AND BRIAN BATES

INTRODUCTION

This chapter is concerned with eating disorders in adolescence – primarily anorexia nervosa as this is the most commonly occurring eating disorder in this age group. Bulimia, or bulimia nervosa, will also be mentioned, although in less detail as this is typically a disorder of young adults rather than of adolescents – eating-disordered adolescents are much more likely to be suffering from anorexia nervosa.

The focus of this chapter is on management issues rather than on aetiological theories, epidemiology or clinical features. This literature on anorexia nervosa is wide and a number of recent reviews of the current understanding of the disorder and results of research in this area serve as useful background reading (Garfinkel and Garner, 1982; Bryant and Bates, 1985).

Following a brief introductory summary of the defining characteristics and demographic details of both anorexia nervosa and bulimia, a number of treatment alternatives will be presented. The emphasis is primarily on techniques used in the treatment of anorexia nervosa rather than bulimia, for the reason outlined above and because bulimia is a relatively recently identified disorder, with few clearly described treatment techniques in the literature.

Working with troubled adolescents
ISBN 0-12-179720-1

ANOREXIA NERVOSA

Anorexia nervosa is often considered to be a disorder typical of adolescent females. Indeed, the majority of anorexics* are female, with onset of symptoms characteristically during the teenage years, i.e. from early to late adolescence. Yet the disorder is not restricted to female adolescents. A significant number of adolescent males with a diagnosis of anorexia nervosa have been identified (Burns and Crisp, 1984; Crisp and Toms, 1972). Estimates of the sex ratio are in the order of one male patient to every 10 to 20 females (Hay and Leonard, 1979; Welbourne and Purgold, 1984). Furthermore, the disorder has been found to occur in children of both sexes (Hawley, 1985; Fosson, Bryant-Waugh, Knibbs and Lask, 1986) and in older women, up until well past meno-pause (Kellet, Trimble and Thorley, 1976; Launer, 1978; Dally, 1984).

The precise definition of anorexia nervosa remains a matter for discussion. There are many existing diagnostic models, of which the ones provided by the DSM III (Am. Psych. Assoc., 1980) and Russell (1970) appear to have gained the widest acceptance.

The DSM III criteria are as follows:

    1. Intense fear of becoming obese, which does not diminish as weight loss progresses.

    2. Disturbance of body image, e.g. claiming to"feel fat" even when emaciated.

    3. Weight loss of at least 25% of original body weight, or, if under 18 years of age, weight loss from original body weight plus projected weight gain expected from growth charts may be combined to make the 25%.

    4. Refusal to maintain body weight over a minimum normal weight for age and height.

    5. No known physical illness that could account for the weight loss.

Russell's (1970) criteria are threefold:

    1. The patient resorts to a variety of devices aimed at achieving a loss of weight (e.g. food avoidance, self-induced vomiting, purgation, excessive exercise).

    2. The presence of an endocrine disorder (amenorrhoea in females and loss of sexual interest in the male).

    3. The presence of a characteristic psychopathology consisting of a morbid fear of becoming fat, accompanied by a distorted judgement of body size.

*This chapter uses the term "anorexic" in preference to the more correctly derived form "anorectic" in accordance with Welbourne and Purgold's (1984) plea for consistency of use of terms in the literature. They propose that "anorectic" should be used for people who have truly lost their appetite and "anorexic" for people diagnosed as suffering from anorexia nervosa.

Neither of these models are without criticism, and both are currently used in clinical settings to arrive at a diagnosis of anorexia nervosa.

Anorexia nervosa is a serious and potentially fatal disorder. Mortality rates suggested by follow-up studies have been as high as 22% (Lucas, Duncan and Piens, 1976), although most estimates are around 10 to 15% (Minuchin, Rosman and Baker, 1978). Prevalence rates are extremely difficult to determine. One study estimated that one in every 200 to 250 adolescent females would present as a "severe" case of anorexia nervosa (Crisp, Palmer and Kalucy, 1976). It is highly probable that a large number of individuals who fulfil diagnostic criteria but who can be described as "mild" cases do not come to the notice of health care professionals. Such individuals will consequently not be included in epidemiological statistics. It is certainly true that the number of individuals referred for treatment with a diagnosis of anorexia nervosa is now steadily increasing. Prevalence rates are possibly much higher than the literature would suggest.

BULIMIA

Bulimia or bulimia nervosa (the preferred American and British terms respectively), is a relatively recently identified disorder. Its literal meaning is "ox hunger" and the term has previously been used to describe the presence of insatiable hunger, particularly as the result of a brain lesion. It is currently used to describe a more specific eating disorder characterized by episodes of binge eating which may be accompanied by self-induced vomiting, laxative abuse and/or periods of excessive diet restriction. Bulimia (DSM III), bulimia nervosa (Russell, 1979), bulimarexia (Boskind-Lodahl, 1976) and "dietary chaos syndrome" (Palmer, 1980) are all terms first used in the 1970s when the severity of the problem began to be recognized. Bulimia is now generally considered to be a relatively serious disorder and one that appears to be increasing in incidence (Fairburn and Cooper, 1982, 1984; Casper et al., 1980a).

The nature of the relationship between anorexia nervosa and bulimia is far from clear. There remains considerable disagreement whether the two should be regarded as separate disorders, whether bulimia is a sub-category within a range of eating disorders grouped under the heading "anorexia nervosa" or whether anorexia nervosa and bulimia represent different points on a continuum of eating disorders (Andersen, 1983; Golden and Sacker, 1984). This confusion is partly reflected in differences in the diagnostic criteria offered in the DSM III (American Psychiatric Association, 1980) and by Russell (1979), which are listed here to parallel those for anorexia nervosa.

The DSM III criteria for bulimia are as follows:

1. Recurrent episodes of binge eating (rapid consumption of a large amount of food in a discrete period of time, usually less than two hours).

2. At least three of the following:
   (a) consumption of high caloric, easily ingested food during a binge
   (b) inconspicuous eating during a binge
   (c) termination of such eating episodes by abdominal pain, sleep, social interruption, or self-induced vomiting
   (d) repeated attempts to lose weight by severely restrictive diets, self-induced vomiting, or use of cathartics or diuretics
   (e) frequent weight fluctuations greater than 10 pounds due to alternating binges and fasts.

3. Awareness that the eating pattern is abnormal and fear of not being able to stop eating voluntarily.

4. Depressed mood and self-deprecating thoughts following eating binges.

5. The bulimic episodes are not due to A.N. or any known physical disorder.

Russell's (1979) criteria are more concise:

1. Patients suffer from powerful and intractable urges to overeat.

2. Patients seek to avoid the fattening effects of food by self-induced vomiting, purgative abuse, or both.

3. The presence of a similar morbid fear of becoming fat to that identified in anorexia nervosa.

As with the diagnostic models for anorexia nervosa, the above are only two examples of many and again not without criticism. In particular, Russell's criteria, if strictly applied, exclude individuals who use diet restriction rather than vomiting or laxative abuse as a means of controlling weight after bingeing. Fairburn (1983) suggests that such individuals should be included as suffering from bulimia nervosa.

Typical age at onset of bulimia is on average somewhat later than for anorexia nervosa. Bulimics are predominantly young adult women in their twenties, whereas anorexics are typically adolescents. As with anorexia nervosa, bulimia does occur outside its characteristic age range. It appears to be almost exclusively a disorder of females – a review of the literature mentioning male bulimics suggests that a maximum of around 1 % of the bulimic population are men (Cooper, 1985). Epidemiological data on bulimia are scanty and there have been few attempts to estimate its prevalence. Fairburn and Cooper (1984) suggest a prevalence rate among young adult women of around 1 to 2 %. It certainly does not appear to be an uncommon disorder.

Mortality rates are equally problematic. In bulimia, the incidence of deaths related directly to the eating disorder is potentially obscured by the finding that there is a relatively high suicide risk in chronic bulimics (Welbourne and Purgold, 1984). In general, bulimia is thought to have a lower mortality rate than anorexia nervosa, with deaths occurring from severe electrolyte imbalance, dehydration, etc, resulting from vomiting and laxative abuse.

TREATMENT APPROACHES

What can be done to help those with eating disorders? The current range of treatment alternatives is wide, as is the variation in settings in which these techniques are applied. There is no one treatment method of proven maximum effectiveness (for retrospective assessments of different treatment methods see Dally, 1967; Browning and Miller, 1968; Campbell, 1971; Hsu, Crisp and Harding, 1979).

The existing variety in treatment approaches is partly due to this lack of consistently good results with any one method and partly due to the fact that those offering help hold different views about the determinants of eating disorders. Underlying conceptual notions and theoretical beliefs are inevitably influential in the choice of treatment alternatives. Often a combination of treatment methods is offered, different establishments or individuals developing their own particular programme. In such cases it is impossible to identify which specific elements of the treatment programme are most effective.

Anorexia nervosa and bulimia are multi-facetted disorders which have a complex and as yet poorly understood aetiology. Particularly in the case of anorexia nervosa it would seem that a comprehensive treatment approach, involving a combination of different therapeutic methods, is advisable.

TREATMENT METHODS IN ANOREXIA NERVOSA

Currently the management of anorexia nervosa may include one or more of the following treatment alternatives:

1. Hospitalization

Admitting an anorexic to hospital has a number of advantages. First, it allows a provisional diagnosis to be confirmed, by means of observation, interview and where necessary, physical examination to exclude the possibility of other illnesses causing weight loss. Secondly, the anorexic can receive life-saving medical care in those cases where weight loss is extreme and life is endangered. Thirdly, treatment programmes can be implemented and monitored directly, thereby reducing the problems of poor adherence to recommended regimes and inadequate feedback of progress, common to outpatient treatment programmes. Finally, admission to hospital impresses upon all concerned that anorexia nervosa is a serious disorder that is not easily overcome, requiring considerable personal effort and professional help.

Of course, many inpatient programmes have disadvantages, in particular the further loss of control that so many anorexics are struggling to achieve. Furthermore, there are reports of successful outpatient treatment programmes with anorexics (Scrigner 1971, Reinhart, Kenna and Succop, 1972; Sargant and Liebman, 1984; Welbourne and Purgold, 1984), implying that hospitalization is by no means always indicated. In practice, inpatient or outpatient treatment tends to be offered in accordance with local resources and/or preferences of the treatment team.

2. Weight restoration

The most usual method used to restore lost weight is to encourage the patient to accept a high calorie diet. In many cases this not surprisingly meets with a considerable degree of resistance.

High calorie diets vary greatly in their composition and calorific value. In many treatment centres, the patient is started on high-calorie drinks (such as Complan – a powdered preparation high in calories, minerals and vitamins which is added to milk), which are gradually accompanied and eventually replaced by larger amounts of solid food. Many anorexics find it easier, particularly in the early stages of treatment, to tolerate smaller amounts of food with liquid supplements, than to be faced with a very full plate of high calorie food.

In some cases, however, virtually unlimited feeding seems to be encouraged (Dexter, 1980). This can be detrimental as it may add to fears of loss of control over food intake and in some individuals can lead to the development of bulimia (Slade, 1982). Where emaciation is extreme, overenthusiastic refeeding can be extremely dangerous and care must be taken to achieve a slow and steady pattern of increased food intake. Acute stomach dilatia and heart failure have been reported as complications of rapid refeeding in anorexic patients (Powers, 1982).

In critical situations, dietary methods of restoring weight may prove inadequate. When life is endangered, intravenous feeding may be necessary. This procedure should be viewed as a life-saving measure only and is not a satisfactory way to treat anorexia nervosa on its own. It restores physical health to a level at which further therapeutic work can be done. The use of nasogastric tubes, a painful and unpleasant process, has now largely been abandoned. Nevertheless the "tube" remains a treatment option and is sometimes used as a powerful threat to encourage a patient to eat.

3. Behaviour therapy

Behavioural techniques are often used in the treatment of anorexics, largely due to their impressive short-term effects. Treatment programmes involving behavioural methods are designed to modify the anorexic's presenting behaviour and are usually based on operant conditioning (e.g. Agras and Werne, 1978; Ollendick, 1979) and/or systematic desensitization (Schnurer, Rubin and Roy, 1973).

The use of a token award scheme is frequently encountered in the treatment of anorexics. Some programmes grant rewards (such as receiving visitors, phone calls and letters, being allowed out of bed or out of the hospital, etc.) contingent on improved eating behaviour, whilst others make rewards contingent on weight gain. Many anorexics are extremely skilled at surreptitiously disposing of food believed to have been eaten, so that measurable weight gain is often felt to be a better measure of progress.

The results of behavioural programmes are highly controversial. In the short term these may be good in that the patient puts on weight during a relatively short period of hospitalization. In the longer term however, results may prove negligible. The patient may revert to original disturbed patterns of eating behaviour or may adopt other abnormal behaviours. Bruch (1974), Bhanji and Thompson (1974) and Bemus (1978) all provide criticisms of behavioural approaches in the treatment of anorexia and highlight their potentially harmful effects in this context, the undue emphasis on weight gain without addressing other issues and their general coerciveness.

A controlled study testing the efficacy of behaviour modification in the treatment of anorexia concluded, contrary to the expectations of the authors, that there was no significant advantage to be gained from employing this treatment method in the group under study (Eckert, Goldberg, Halmi, Casper and Davis, 1979).

4. Individual psychotherapy

Psychotherapy may be used in treatment programmes to help the patient cope with the psychological adjustment required in the process of weight gain and in some cases to explore the antecedents of the anorectic illness. In the literature on anorexia nervosa, the term "psychotherapy" is used very loosely and in practice can range from supportive counselling to more formal intensive psychotherapy.

For psychotherapeutic techniques to be successful, body weight must be non-critical as malnutrition is known to disturb thought processes to a sufficient degree to hamper therapy. When the anorexic's physical state has begun to be restored, he or she becomes more accessible to the therapist and attention can be focused on more personal inner issues. The underlying influences to the development and maintenance of the anorectic illness can then be approached (Bruch, 1977; Szyrynski, 1973).

Many clinicians dealing with anorexics believe that psychotherapeutic methods are of no great value. Bassøe and Eskeland (1982) for example, stress that they make no attempt to ''penetrate the sensitive minds of our patients''. Others do believe that psychotherapy can play a useful role, although often not during the initial phase of treatment and not as sole treatment method used.

5. Group work

Many hospitalized anorexics find themselves engaging in group work. Such groups take a variety of forms, with group members being other anorexics or other psychiatric inpatients, depending on the setting. The style and emphasis of these groups depends very much on the individual group therapist and the treatment team's orientation. Amongst the more useful groups for anorexics are those that focus on social skills and interpersonal issues. The aim of such groups is to help recovering anorexics regain confidence and self-esteem. Individuals whose weight has been newly restored have been shown to have very low self-regard and to be highly sensitive in social interaction (Pillay and Crisp, 1977). Enabling such individuals to cope in the social situation of the group hopefully provides them with sufficient positive experience to be able to extend this into their everyday lives outside the hospital.

A further recent development in the group treatment of anorexics is the use of sessions aimed at influencing body image and bodily experiences (Vandereycken, 1984). Patients are encouraged to use mime and dance to develop a more appropriate sense of body awareness.

6. Family therapy

The involvement of the family in the treatment of anorexia nervosa requires that the problem be regarded as belonging to the family rather than to one individual member. The shift in emphasis must be made from ''the intra-psychic to the transpersonal approach'' (Palazzoli, 1974). Anorexia nervosa is then viewed as a symptom of dysfunctional family interaction. The task of the family therapist is to show the family what is happening and how their patterns of interaction maintain the problem, and then to help them find alternative ways of relating.

Much of the published material on the application of family therapy techniques in the treatment of eating disorders has so far come from the United States, in particular from Minuchin and his co-workers, who employ structural family therapy techniques (Barcai, 1971; Liebman, Minuchin and Baker, 1974; Minuchin, Baker, Liebman, Milman, Rosman and Todd, 1974; Rosman, Minuchin and Liebman, 1975; and Minuchin, Rosman and Baker, 1978).

Minuchin's techniques involve encouraging existing conflicts and inappropriate interaction patterns to be brought into the session so that they can be dealt with directly. Family therapy techniques are particularly appropriate in the treatment of adolescent anorectics, as they are usually still living with their parents. The efficacy of family therapy techniques is difficult to judge. Minuchin's follow-up results show a high recovery rate (Minuchin et al., 1978), but these figures have been criticized on the grounds that the patients treated were relatively young and were seen soon after the onset of their illness. Nevertheless, family therapy techniques are considered by many to represent a major contribution to the treatment of anorexia nervosa, particularly in younger patients (Bruggen, Lask, Black and Schlicht, 1981; Lask and Bryant-Waugh, 1986).

7. Medication

The use of the neuroleptic chlorpromazine (a tranquillizer from the group of phenothiazines) was first advocated in the treatment of anorexia nervosa by Dally and Sargant in 1960. Since then it has often been included in treatment regimes, to relax and calm the patient, and to reduce hyperactivity and resistance to food. In addition, this and other of the neuroleptic drugs possess mildly appetite stimulating properties alongside their tranquillizing effects.

Modified insulin treatment has been used on the basis that its hypoglycaemic effect will enhance the appetite – often it is administered in combination with chlorpromazine (Dally and Sargant, 1966; Bhanji, 1980). Insulin is, however, now relatively rarely prescribed and usually only to those over 16 years of age (Frommer, 1972).

The practice of prescribing drugs specifically to stimulate the appetite is largely inappropriate. Anorexia nervosa is invariably not, as its name suggests, a nervous *lack* of appetite but rather a denial and refusal to give in to hunger. Many recovering or recovered anorexics are able to admit in retrospect that they experienced extreme hunger. Drugs to further increase appetite are therefore considered undesirable. Furthermore, tests of the gastric constrictions of severely emaciated patients have shown that there is no significant difference to those of normal subjects (Silverstone and Russell, 1967). This finding confirms the belief that appetite in physiological terms is relatively unimpaired in patients with anorexia nervosa.

Anti-depressants may be prescribed in patients who show evidence of depression, such as sleep disturbance, excessive guilt and/or self-deprecation, consistently lowered affect, etc. Depression associated with anorexia nervosa is a common finding both in adult patients (Katz, Kuperberg, Pollack, Walsh, Zurioff and Weiner, 1984; Eckert et al., 1982) and in younger patients (Fosson et al., 1986). For this reason, anti-depressants such as Amitryptilline and Imipramine often form part of an anorexic's treatment programme.

More recently, other drugs have been administered in the treatment of anorexia nervosa; examples include cyproheptadine (an anti-histamine which has appetite stimulating properties – Halmi and Falk, 1982) and metoclopramide (an anti-spasmodic usually given for gastrointestinal disorders or nausea and vertigo – Saleh and Lebwohl, 1980). The efficacy of these drugs in treating anorexia nervosa remains extremely speculative. Goldberg *et al*. (1979) conclude from pharmaceutical research that cyproheptadine "has no side effects and *could* be useful in the general treatment of anorexia nervosa".

Other drugs such as L-Dopa (an antiparkinsonian) and phenytoin (an anti-epileptic) have also been reported in the treatment of anorexia nervosa (by Johanson and Knorr, 1977 and Green and Rau, 1977 respectively) but are not in common use in this context. In severe cases of electrolyte or metabolite imbalance, for example through laxative abuse and vomiting, or where other serious medical complications develop, more specific drug therapy may be required.

The hope still exists in some minds that it will be possible to find a "drug to cure anorexia" (Tucker, 1982). This was the title of a newspaper article about recent developments in research on an appetite controlling drug and its potential usefulness in treating anorexia nervosa (implying that anorexia nervosa involves a malfunction in appetite). Whilst the hope of a wondercure is unrealistic, it is true that drugs can play a useful role in the management of anorexia nervosa. In particular, anti-depressants can be administered where indicated and can make life a little more bearable for some depressed anorectics. The attitude that drugs have a useful place in the treatment of anorexia nervosa in conjunction with other methods is of more value that the fruitless search for a wondercure.

8. Restriction of symptomatic behaviours

In some cases, hospitalized anorectics fail to gain weight or even continue to lose, even though they appear to be consuming sufficient calories to result in weight gain. Such individuals will almost invariably be engaging in self-induced vomiting and/or laxative abuse. One of the best approaches the treatment team can take to prevent this is to assume at the outset that such behaviour will probably occur (Lask and Bryant-Waugh, 1986). Anorexics are very adept at secretly engaging in self-destructive behaviour and require supervision and constructive help to attempt to overcome this.

Another characteristic feature of many anorexics is the tendency to engage in excessive exercising as a means of burning up calories. Many treatment centres attempt to curb this activity, either by means of tranquillizers with sedating effects (Poll, 1980), or through enforced bed rest. However, even when restricted to their beds, many anorexics will spend hours flexing muscles and doing push-ups in an attempt to lose weight. The aim of medication and bed rest is both to conserve calories and to restrict the behaviour. In terms of actual weight loss, excessive exercising does not, in most cases, represent a very significant problem as relatively small reductions in weight are usually effected in this way, particularly whilst under supervision in hospital. Where weight continues to fall, vomiting and purging should be suspected.

9. Zinc

Recently, the role of zine deficiency in the aetiology and maintenance of anorexia nervosa and the use of zinc supplements in its treatment have been explored (Casper *et al.*, 1980b, Bryce-Smith, 1985). The "zinc deficiency theory" is far from being widely accepted and some carefully designed studies are needed to elucidate the role of zinc (if any) in the disorder. The association between zinc deficiency and anorexia nervosa remains at present an extremely tentative one. For many patients and parents, as well as for many professionals attempting to treat anorectics, such a theory is very appealing. It implies that the cause of anorexia nervosa or at least the trigger for it, could be a relatively simple mineral deficiency. It then follows that treatment should be directed at readjusting the individual's zinc levels through the oral administration of zinc. This treatment technique for anorexia nervosa requires further validation before it can become acceptable.

TREATMENT TECHNIQUES IN BULIMIA

Russell (1979) described bulimia as an "intractable" disorder and considered its prognosis and outcome to be more gloomy than that for anorexia nervosa. There are very few follow-up studies of bulimic patients and very little is known about long-term outcome. Bulimics tend to differ from anorexics in that they are much more likely to request professional help for treatment of their eating disorder (Yellowlees, 1985; Welbourne and Purgold, 1984). Their illness is believed on average to have existed for a longer period before professional intervention than is the case with anorexic patients (Yellowlees, 1985). This might partly be a reflection of the fact that most bulimics retain a normal weight, and are less likely to present as medical emergencies than anorexics. In addition the characteristic behaviours of bingeing, vomiting and laxative abuse tend to be secretive and may therefore pass by unnoticed for longer than obvious food refusal.

Seeing that many bulimics request treatment and have an expressed desire to attempt to recover from their disorder, what treatment methods are currently offered to them?

1. Outpatient treatment

The majority of bulimics, in contrast to the majority of anorexics, are treated as outpatients. There are, however, cases where inpatient admission is indicated, in particular when the bulimia is associated with severe depression, to the extent that the patient may be at risk of suicide, when physical health is significantly impaired, or when prolonged outpatient therapy has proved unsuccessful (Fairburn, 1982). As with anorexics a wide range of treatment alternatives may

be included in a therapeutic package, depending on the establishment and treatment team involved.

2. Behaviour therapy

By far the most common approach to the treatment of bulimia is the use of
various behavioural techniques. Freeman, Henderson and Anglim (1984) have
presented details of a schedule of response prevention where the aim is to train
patients to terminate episodes of bingeing, whilst preventing them from
engaging in self-induced vomiting or laxative abuse, eventually to the extent
that they no longer engage in such behaviours. Relaxation training may also
play a useful role in helping the bulimic to cope with the overwhelming feelings
of anxiety and guilt associated with bingeing. Self-monitoring techniques may
be used to help the individual recognize which particular situations and mood
states appear to precede a binge, so that an alternative response can be learned.

Cognitive behaviour therapy has recently developed into a widely used
therapeutic approach. In the context of bulimia, cognitive behavioural techniques may involve standard behavioural methods, such as self-monitoring and
response prevention, coupled with cognitive interactions which are designed to
reduce dietary restraint and encourage a problem solving approach, thereby
modifying both disturbed behaviour and attitudes (see Fairburn 1981, 1984 for
a detailed description of such techniques). Body image dissatisfaction appears to
be common in bulimics, thus a certain amount of cognitive restructuring
around this issue may prove of considerable therapeutic value.

3. Individual and group therapy

Group treatment of bulimics is common. This may in some instances be accompanied by individual psychotherapy. Group therapy can take a number of
forms. Some groups employ behavioural techniques designed to achieve change
in the group members' presenting behaviours. Berman, Tannenbaum and
Saynisch (1984) have reported that an adaptation of techniques used in groups
to stop smoking has proved successful with bulimics. The aim of such therapy is
to enable the group members to manage their own behaviour and to regain a
sense of control over their eating habits.

Other important aspects of group work are the exploration of cultural
influences on desired body shape and eating behaviour and the opportunity for
members to benefit from group pressure and social reinforcement. Furthermore, group instruction in nutrition and general physical needs can take place,
allowing individual members to learn how to adjust their own disturbed
patterns of eating so that they are consuming a sufficient amount of suitable
foods. In general it appears that group work is more effective with bulimics than
with anorexics.

As previously stated, individual psychotherapy is often recommended as a treatment technique for bulimia to be used concurrently or in sequence with a course of group therapy. The "psychotherapy" can range from intensive analytically oriented therapy to supportive therapy. Lacey (1983) describes a combination of individual and group therapy limited to a 10 week period, which he suggests results in a reduction in bingeing and self-induced vomiting. The emphasis of both the individual and the group work in this case is insight-oriented, the individual sessions also employing some behavioural techniques.

4. Medication

The treatment of bulimia using drugs is, like other therapeutic approaches to this disorder, in its infancy. There are as yet insufficient controlled studies to warrant the general administration of any type of medication. Bulimia has often been associated with affective disorder (Yellowlees, 1985) characterized by the frequently observed depressive symptoms exhibited by bulimics. For this reason, anti-depressants are sometimes prescribed (Pope, Hudson, Jonas and Yurgelunn-Todd, 1983). It has furthermore been noted that bulimics tend to binge and purge when they experience negative mood states, but that when their mood is normal they are able to consume and retain a meal (Davis, Solyam and Freeman, 1984). This again can be interpreted as indicating the use of anti-depressant medication. Imipramine, an anti-depressant, has been found to be effective in the short-term treatment of bulimia (Pope et al., 1983). Manserin on the other hand, another anti-depressant, has not been found to have any specific effects on bulimics' behaviour or attitudes (Sabine et al., 1983).

Of the anti-depressants, isocarboxazid and phenlzine (both monoamine-oxidase inhibitors) have been claimed to have advantageous effects in the treatment of bulimia, resulting in a reduction in bingeing and a maintenance of weight at normal levels (Kennedy et al., 1984; Walsh et al., 1982, 1984). The potential value of fenfluramine (a centrally acting appetite suppresant) in controlling bulimic symptoms is currently being investigated (Robinson et al., 1984). Anti-convulsants are also sometimes prescribed though with doubtful results.

CONCLUDING REMARKS

From the above it becomes clear that the current treatment of eating disorders can involve a variety of techniques. The mechanisms by which these disorders develop and are maintained are still relatively poorly understood – a fact reflected in the wide range of treatment approaches now in practice. Research into the details of the natural course of eating disorders and treatment outcome continues to take place, and until any one technique achieves clearly better results than any other, it would seem likely that the variety in treatment approaches will continue to exist.

One further approach, not yet mentioned, is that of self-help groups. Such groups operate outside the parameters of the work of health care professionals and consequently have not been monitored or assessed in the same way as those previously mentioned. In Britain, Anorexic Aid exists as a national network of self-help groups for individuals with eating disorders. This network was set up in 1980 by a research psychologist (Pat Hartley – see References); it operates through a national headquarters, but has a policy of groups being run locally. There are also many other local groups besides those functioning under the umbrella of Anorexic Aid.

In Canada there are some experimental self-help groups for individuals with eating disorders, which have adopted a modified version of the 12 steps successfully used by alcoholics anonymous groups (Leichner, 1984).

The value of self-help groups in the treatment of eating disorders is extremely difficult to assess. Professionals are excluded from leading the groups, thus the use of standard approaches to measurement of outcome is not possible. Whilst self-help groups have potentially positive effects in the form of support, encouragement and acceptance in a non-threatening environment, potential negative effects should not be underestimated. The competitive element in many anorexics' behaviour may result in a further restriction in food intake, sometimes resulting in a battle to see who can survive on the least. Furthermore, the emphasis on amounts of food ingested and weight fluctuations may serve to heighten the already existing destructive preoccupation in these areas.

For many professionals working with troubled adolescents, those with eating disorders are particularly difficult and frustrating. Many, especially those with anorexia nervosa, are resistant to treatment attempts, and those offering help may often feel discouraged and uncertain when faced with consistently poor results. Continued attempts to clarify the origins of eating disorders are fundamental to the search for effective treatment methods. The hope of prevention in the context of eating disorders must for the present remain an unattainable goal.

REFERENCES

Agras, S. and Werne, J. (1978). Behaviour therapy in anorexia nervosa: A data-based approach to the question. In *Controversy in Psychiatry*, Brady, J.P. and Brodie, H.K. (Eds). London: Saunders.

American Psychiatric Association (1980). *Diagnostic and Statistical Manual of Mental Disorders*, 3rd Edn. Washington D.C.

Andersen, A.E. (1983). Anorexia nervosa and bulimia: a spectrum of eating disorders. *Journal of Adolescent Health Care* 4, 15–21.

Barcai, A. (1971). Family therapy in the treatment of anorexia nervosa. *American Journal of Psychiatry* 128, 286–290.

Bassøe, H.H. and Eskeland, I. (1982). A prospective study of 133 patients with anorexia nervosa. *Acta Psychiatrica Scandinavia* **65**, 127–133.

Bemus, K. (1978). Current approaches to the aetiology and treatment of anorexia nervosa. *Psychological Bulletin* **85**, 593–617.

Berman, M., Tannenbaum, R. and Saynisch, D. (1984). "Oral habits": can bulimics switch? Paper presented at *International Conference on Anorexia Nervosa and Related Disorders* – University College Swansea September 1984.

Bhanji, S. (1980). Anorexia Nervosa: Two schools of thought. *Nursing Times* February 21, 323–324.

Bhanji, S. and Thompson, J. (1984). Operant conditioning in the treatment of anorexia nervosa: a review and retrospective study of 11 cases. *British Journal of Psychiatry* **124**, 166–172.

Boskind-Lodahl, M. (1976). Cinderella's step-sisters: a feminist perspective on anorexia nervosa and bulimia. *Signs: Journal of Women in Culture and Society* **2**, 342–356.

Browning, C.H. and Miller, S.I. (1968). Anorexia nervosa: a study in prognosis and management. *American Journal of Psychiatry* **124**, 1128–1132.

Bruch, H. (1974). Perils of behaviour modification in treatment of anorexia nervosa. *Journal of the American Medical Association* **230**, 1419–1422.

Bruch, H. (1977). Psychotherapy in eating disorders. *Canadian Psychiatric Association Journal* **22**, 102–108.

Bruggen, P., Lask, B., Black, D. and Schlicht, J. (1981). Treatment of anorexia nervosa. *British Journal of Hospital Medicine* August, 186.

Bryant, R. and Bates, B. (1985). Anorexia nervosa: aetiological theories and treatment methods. *Journal of Adolescence* **8**, 93–103.

Bryce-Smith, D. and Simpson, R.I.D. (1984). Case of anorexia nervosa responding to zinc sulphate. *The Lancet* August 11.

Burns, T. and Crisp, A.H. (1984). Outcome of anorexia nervosa. *British Journal of Psychiatry* **145**, 319–325.

Campbell, A. (1971). Critical evaluation of treatments for anorexia nervosa. *University of London Dissertation* October.

Casper, R.C., Eckert, E.D., Halmi, K.A., Goldberg, S.C. and Davis, J.M. (1980a). Bulimia. Its incidence and clinical importance in patients with anorexia nervosa. *Archives of General Psychiatry* **37**, 1030–1035.

Casper, R.C., Kirschner, B., Stanstead, H.H., Jacob, R.A. and Davis, J.M. (1980b). An evaluation of trace metals, vitamins and taste function in anorexia nervosa. *American Journal of Clinical Nutrition* **33**, 1801–1808.

Cooper, P.J. (1985). Eating Disorders. In *New Developments in Clinical Psychology*, Watts, F.N. (Ed.). British Psychological Society and Wiley.

Crisp, A.H. and Toms, D.A. (1972). Primary anorexia nervosa or weight phobia in the male: report on 13 cases. *British Medical Journal* **1**, 334–338.

Crisp, A.H., Palmer, R.L. and Kalucy, R.S. (1976). How common is anorexia nervosa? A prevalence study. *British Journal of Psychiatry* **128**, 549–554.

Dally, P. (1967). Long term follow-up and effects of treatment. *Journal of Psychosomatic Research* **11**, 151.

Dally, P. (1984). Anorexia tardive – late onset marital anorexia nervosa. *Journal of Psychosomatic Research* **28**, 423–428.

Dally, P. and Sargant, W. (1960). A new treatment of anorexia nervosa. *British Medical Journal* **1**, 1770–1773.

Dally, P. and Sargant, W. (1966). Treatment and outcome of anorexia nervosa. *British Medical Journal* **II**, 793–795.

Davis, R., Solyam, L. and Freeman, R. (1984). Mood and food: a microanalysis of bulimic episodes. Paper presented at *International Conference on Anorexia Nervosa* (op. cit.).

Dexter, J. (1980). Anorexia nervosa. *Nursing Times* February 21, 325.

Eckert, E.D., Goldberg, S.C., Halmi, K.A., Casper, D.C. and Davis, J.M. (1979). Behaviour therapy in anorexia nervosa. *British Journal of Psychiatry* **134**, 55–59.

Eckert, E.D., Goldberg, S.C., Halmi, K.A., Casper, D.C. and Davis, J.M. (1982). Depression in anorexia nervosa. *Psychological Medicine* **12**, 115–122.

Fairburn, C.G. (1981). A cognitive behavioural approach to the management of bulimia. *Psychological Medicine* **11**, 707–711.

Fairburn, C.G. (1982). Binge-eating and its management. *British Journal of Psychiatry* **141**, 631–633.

Fairburn, C.G. (1983). Bulimia nervosa. *Hospital Medicine* **29**, 537–542.

Fairburn, C.G. (1984). A cognitive behavioural treatment for bulimia. In *Eating and Its Disorders*, Stunhard, A.J. and Stellar, E. (Eds). New York: Raven Press.

Fairburn, C.G. and Cooper, P.J. (1982). Self-induced vomiting and bulimia nervosa: an undetected problem. *British Medical Journal* **284**, 1153–1155.

Fairburn, C.G. and Cooper, P.J. (1984). Binge-eating, self-induced vomiting and laxative abuse: a community study. *Psychological Medicine* **14**, 401–410.

Fosson, A., Bryant-Waugh, R., Knibbs, J. and Lask, B. (1986, In Press). Early onset anorexia nervosa – a description of 48 children.

Freeman, C.P.L., Henderson, M. and Anglim, M. (1984). Response prevention as a treatment technique in severe treatment-resistant bulimia. Paper presented at *International Conference on Anorexia Nervosa* (op. cit.).

Frommer, E.A. (1972). *Diagnosis and Treatment in Clinical Child Psychiatry*. London: William Heinemann Medical Books.

Garfinkel, P.E. and Garner, D.M. (1982). *Anorexia Nervosa: A Multi-Dimensional Perspective*. New York: Brunner/Mazel.

Goldberg, S.C., Halmi, K.A., Eckert, E.D., Casper, R.C. and Davis J.M. (1979). Cyproheptadine in anorexia nervosa. *British Journal of Psychiatry* **134**, 67–70.

Golden, N. and Sacker, I.M. (1984). An overview of the etiology, diagnosis and management of anorexia nervosa. *Clinical Pediatrics* 209–214.

Green, R.S. and Rau, J.H. (1977). The use of diphenylhydantoin in compulsive eating disorders: further studies. In *Anorexia Nervosa*, Vigersky, R.A. (Ed.). New York: Raven Press.

Halmi, K.A. and Falk, J.P. (1982). Anorexia nervosa: a study of outcome discriminators in exclusive dieters and bulimics. *Journal of the American Academy of Child Psychiatry* **21**, 369–375.

Hartley, Pat, Anorexic Aid, National Headquarters, The Priory Centre, 11 Priory Road, High Wycombe, Bucks.

Hawley, R.M. (1985). The outcome of anorexia nervosa in younger subjects. *British Journal of Psychiatry* **146**, 657–660.

Hay, G.G. and Leonard, J.C. (1979). Anorexia nervosa in males. *Lancet* **II**, 574–576.

Hsu, L.K.G., Crisp, A.H. and Harding, B. (1979). Outcome of anorexia nervosa. *Lancet* **I**, 61–65.

Johanson, A.J. and Knorr, N.J. (1977). L-Dopa as treatment for anorexia nervosa. In *Anorexia Nervosa*. Vigersky, R. (Ed.). New York: Raven Press.

Katz, J.L., Kuperberg, A., Pollack, C., Walsh, B.T., Zurioff, B. and Weiner, H. (1984). Is there a relationship between eating disorder and affective disorder? New evidence from sleep recordings. *American Journal of Psychiatry* **141**, 753–759.

Kellet, J., Trimble, M. and Thorley, A. (1976). Anorexia nervosa after the menopause. *British Journal of Psychiatry* **128**, 555-558.

Kennedy, S., Piran, N., Wilkes, B., Garfinkel, P. and Warsh, J.J. (1984). Anorexia nervosa and bulimia – response to isocarboxazid. Paper presented at *International Conference on Anorexia Nervosa* (op. cit.).

Lacey, J.H. (1983). Bulimia nervosa, binge-eating and psychogenic vomiting: a controlled treatment study and long term outcome. *British Medical Journal* **286**, 1609-1613.

Lask, B. and Bryant-Waugh, R. (1986). Childhood onset anorexia nervosa. In *Recent Advances in Paediatrics* Vol. 9, Meadows, R. (Ed.).

Launer, M.A. (1978). Anorexia nervosa in late life. *British Journal of Medical Psychology* **51**, 375-377.

Leichner, P. (1984). The anorexia nervosa and bulimia foundation of Canada. Paper presented at *International Conference on Anorexia Nervosa* (op. cit.).

Liebman, R., Minuchin, S. and Baker, L. (1974). An integrated treatment program for anorexia nervosa. *American Journal of Psychiatry* **131**, 432-436.

Lucas, A., Duncan, J.W. and Piens, V. (1976). The treatment of anorexia nervosa. *American Journal of Psychiatry* **133**, 1034-1038.

Minuchin, S., Baker, L., Liebman, R., Milman, L., Rosman, B. and Todd, T. (1974). Anorexia nervosa: successful application of a family therapy approach. *Pediatric Research* **7**, 294.

Minuchin, S., Rosman, B. and Baker, L. (1978). *Psychosomatic Families: Anorexia Nervosa in Context*. Harvard University Press.

Ollendick, T.H. (1979). Behavioural treatment of anorexia nervosa. A five year study. *Behaviour Modification* **3**, 124-135.

Palazzoli, M.S. (1974). *Self Starvation*. Chaucer: Human Context Books.

Palmer, R.L. (1980). *Anorexia Nervosa – A Guide for Sufferers and their Families*. Penguin Books.

Pillay, M. and Crisp, A.H. (1977). Some psychological characteristics of patients with anorexia nervosa, whose weight has been newly restored. *British Journal of Medical Psychology* 381-395.

Poll, G.C. (1980). A psychophysiologic disorder in adolescents: anorexia nervosa. In *A Psychodynamic Approach to Adolescent Psychiatry*, Heacock, D.R. (Ed.). New York: Marcel Dekker.

Pope, H.G., Hudson, J.I., Jonas, J.M. and Yurgelunn-Todd, M.S. (1983). Bulimia treated with imipramine: a placebo controlled double-blind study. *American Journal of Psychiatry* **140**, 554-558.

Powers, P.S. (1982). Heart failure during treatment of anorexia nervosa. *American Journal of Psychiatry* **139**, 1167-1170.

Reinhart, J.B., Kenna, M.D. and Succop, R.A. (1972). Anorexia nervosa in children: outpatient management. *Journal of Child Psychiatry* **11**, 114-131.

Robinson, P.H., Checkley, S.A., Russell, G.F.M. (1984). The action of fenfluramine in controlling bulimic symptoms. Paper presented at *International Conference on Anorexia Nervosa* (op. cit.).

Rosman, B., Minuchin, S. and Liebman, R. (1975). Family lunch session. An introduction to family therapy in anorexia nervosa. *American Journal of Orthopsychiatry* **45**, 846-853.

Russell, G.F.M. (1970). Anorexia nervosa: its identity as an illness and its treatment. In *Modern Trends in Psychological Medicine*, Price, J.M. (Ed.). London: Butterworths.

220   R. BRYANT-WAUGH AND B. BATES

Russell, G.F.M. (1979). Bulimia nervosa: an ominous varient of anorexia nervosa. *Psychological Medicine* **9**, 429-448.

Sabine, E.J., Yonace, A., Farrington, A.J., Barratt, K.H. and Wakeling, A. (1983). Bulimia nervosa: a placebo controlled double blind therapeutic trial of mianserin. *British Journal of Clinical Pharmacology* **15**, 1955-2025.

Saleh, J.W. and Lebwohl, P. (1980). Metochlopramide induced gastric emptying in patients with anorexia nervosa. *American Journal of Gastroenterology* **74**, 127-130.

Sargant, J. and Liebman, R. (1984). Outpatient treatment of anorexia nervosa. *Psychiatric Clinics of North America* **2**, 235-245.

Schnurer, A.T., Rubin, R.R. and Roy, A. (1973). Systematic desensitization of anorexia nervosa seen as a weight phobia. *Journal of Behaviour Therapy and Experimental Psychiatry* **4**, 149-154.

Scrigner, C.B. (1971). Food as the reinforcer in the outpatient treatment of anorexia nervosa. *Journal of Behaviour Therapy and Experimental Psychiatry* **2**, 31-36.

Silverstone, T. and Russell, G.F.M. (1967). Gastric "hunger" contractions in anorexia nervosa. *British Journal of Psychiatry* **113**, 257-263.

Slade, P. (1982). Towards a functional analysis of anorexia nervosa and bulimia nervosa. *British Journal of Clinical Psychology* **21**, 167-179.

Szyrynski, V. (1973). Anorexia nervosa and psychotherapy. *American Journal of Psychotherapy* **27**, 492-505.

Tucker, A. (1982). Hope of drug to cure anorexia. *Guardian* November 29.

Vandereycken, W. (1984). Body-oriented therapy in anorexia nervosa and bulimia patients. Videotape presented at *International Conference on Anorexia Nervosa* (op. cit.).

Walsh, B.T., Stewart, J.W., Wright, L., Harrison, W., Roose, S.P. and Glassman, A.H. (1982). Treatment of bulimia with monamine oxidase inhibiters. *American Journal of Psychiatry* **139**, 1629-1630.

Walsh, B.T., Stewart, J.W., Roose, S.P., Gladis, M. and Glassman, A.H. (1984). A double-blind trial of phenelzine in bulimia. Paper presented at *International Conference on Anorexia Nervosa* (op. cit.).

Welbourne, J. and Purgold, J. (1984). *The Eating Sickness*. Harvester Press.

Yellowlees, A.J. (1985). Anorexia and bulimia in anorexia nervosa: a study of psychosocial functioning and associated psychiatric symptomatology. *British Journal of Psychiatry* **146**, 648-652.

15. Approaching the incestuous and sexually abusive family

DAVID WILL

INTRODUCTION

Incest and the sexual abuse of children and young people is an area which no one working with adolescents can afford to ignore. In their survey of the recognition of child sexual abuse in the United Kingdom, Beezley Mrazek, Lynch and Bentovim (1981) found that the majority of victims were in the adolescent age range when they presented to the professionals. The purpose of this paper is to first provide an introduction to family transactional theories of incest and sexual abuse and then to describe some basic principles of clinical work with victims and their families.

A burgeoning of awareness of, and interest in, the topic of sexual abuse of children and adolescents has been reflected in an ever-growing number of books on the subject, e.g. Finkelhor (1979), Beezley Mrazek and Kempe (1981), Herman (1981), Goodwin (1982), Nelson (1982) and Renvoize (1982). However, until recently there has been very little literature which applies contemporary understanding of family systems to the incestuous and sexually abusive family. (Papers by Beezley Mrazek and Bentovim, 1981 Furniss, 1983, and Lutz and Medway, 1984, mark the beginnings of such work.)

Yet incest is a family affair and most child sexual abuse occurs within the nuclear or extended family. Incest is a symptom that may persist for years in the same family, apparently escaping detection even when more than one child has

been recruited as a sexual partner for the father. Its often persistent and enduring nature both suggests that incest may serve a function for the family system as
a whole and that powerful homeostatic mechanisms contribute to its maintenance. The power of such homeostatic mechanisms can be revealed in the way a
family may close ranks and deny the existence of problems very soon after the
disclosure of incest.

For example, the A family were seen together one week after father had been
caught in the act of incestuous activity with his 14-year-old daughter. Father
was full of remorse, mother full of recriminations and both were vocal about
their unsatisfactory marital relationship. Only a week later both parents
adamantly resisted attempts to help them explore their difficulties: they claimed
their troubles were now over and they minimized the significance of the incest.
The victim, their 14-year-old daughter, remained silent and refused to talk
further about the incest in either individual or family sessions.

Another clue to the importance of family transactional patterns in the genesis
of incest is the tendency for such patterns to be replicated from one generation to
the next. One of the long-term consequences of incest appears to be the possibility that the victim will grow up to form a family in which further incest occurs
(Steele and Alexander, 1981). A dysfunctional family transactional pattern may
be replicated from one generation to the next.

Most attempts to explain the phenomena of incest and sexual abuse tend to
stress either sociological factors (Lukianowicz, 1972; Finkelhor, 1982; Nelson
1982), or individual psychological factors in fathers (Cormier, Kennedy and
Sangewicz, 1962; Cavallin, 1966) or in both parents (Browning and Boatman,
1977). As a result, the family transactional viewpoint has been somewhat
neglected. Furthermore, there is a tendency in the literature to stress the importance of one particular type of explanation of the aetiology of incest and sexual
abuse. Thus, Lukianowicz (1972) attributes great importance to subcultural
factors while Nelson (1982) attributes most importance to the process of sexual
socialization and the effects it has on males. In this paper I hope to demonstrate
that phenomena as complex as these can only be understood by taking into
account different levels of aetiologically potent phenomena; sociological, family
transactional and individual psychological factors must *all* be considered if we
are to develop an adequate understanding of incest and sexual abuse that will
inform adequate treatment approaches.

The structure of this paper is as follows: first, two main types of family transactional pattern which have been found in incestuous and sexually abusive
families are described – the chaotic family and the "endogamous" incestuous
family. Then the genesis and dynamics of the "endogamous" incestuous family
are discussed in some detail, after which some of the more general features of
incestuous and sexually abusive families are surveyed. The final part of the
paper is a consideration of some basic principles of clinical intervention.

TWO TYPES OF INCESTUOUS FAMILY STRUCTURE

The descriptions of family structure which follow are based both on families described in the literature and on a series of some 30 families seen by myself and colleagues at McMaster University in Canada and in the Children and Young People's Psychiatric Department in Tayside. It is important to stress from the onset that the two main types of family structure described should neither be regarded as universal in incestuous families nor should they be regarded as exhaustive descriptions of the transactional patterns that underpin incest. Instead, they are descriptions of what appear to be recurring patterns in many of the incestuous families in child and adolescent psychiatric clinics.

The chaotic family

This type of family conforms to some of the conventional stereo-types of the incestuous family. In such families incest, which is often multiple, appears to be but one feature of family chaos, blurring of intergenerational boundaries and confusion of roles.

For example, the B family were referred from a social service agency after Jackie, their 16-year-old daughter, reported to the police that she had had a long-standing incestuous relationship with her father. Further assessment revealed a complex web of multiple incestuous relationships including father-daughter, grandfather-daughter, grandfather-mother, uncle-niece and brother-sister. There was a general disorganization of the family structure and a correspondingly chaotic family life-style. Basic instrumental functions were deficient: family members had difficulty getting up in the morning, the provision of meals was chaotic and there was little differentiation between parental and sibling subsystems with consequently chaotic behavioural controls.

While such chaotic families exist, incest is by no means *confined* to such families. Epidemiological work such as Finkelhor's (1980) indicates that incest, like the physical abuse of children, occurs throughout the social scale, and not solely in disorganized disadvantaged families.

The "endogamous" incestuous family

This second family constellation has attracted most of the (albeit scanty) family transactional interest in incest. From the family systems perspective the basic question that must be asked is "What function does incest serve for the family?" Like other symptoms of family dysfunction, incest may develop when the coping mechanisms of a disturbed family can no longer deal with particular conflicts, and the family considers that these conflicts are a threat to its survival. From this perspective incestuous behaviour is seen as a means of reducing tension by helping the family avoid facing conflicts that are seen as having catastrophic consequences.

One of the most influential papers on family transactional aspects of incest has been that of Lustig, Dresser, Spellman and Murray, "Incest: a family group survival pattern" (1966). This paper suggested that a feature common to "endogamous" incestuous families was an intense fear of family breakdown. Five characteristic features of such families were described.

1. An assumption by the daughter of the mother's role that is so general that the daughter becomes the central of the household.

2. An impaired sexual relationship between the parents generating unrelieved sexual tension in the father.

3. An unwillingness by the father to act out sexually outside the family that is related to the father's need to maintain the public façade of a stable and competent patriarch.

4. A fear of family disintegration and abandonment shared by all protagonists, to such an extent that any relationship is preferable to family disintegration.

5. The conscious or unconscious sanction of the non-participant mother who contributes to the assignment of the daughter in her place to care for the sexual, affectional and nurturant deprivation of the father.

Although these observations were based on a small number of families, they have provided a heuristically useful template for other workers. Thus Machotka, Pittman and Flamenhaft (1967) expand on the role of the mother, seeing her apparent denial or non-recognition of the incest as being essential to its maintenance. Gutheil and Avery (1977) further develop the notion of the defensive function of incest as a means of staving off family disintegration.

Beezley Mrazek and Bentovim (1981) further develop this sort of model by describing some of the family myths that may underpin such a dysfunctional family system and apply Minuchin's (1974) ideas about homeostasis to account for the stability of the incest.

The origin and maintenance of the endogamous incestuous family system
In my own work I have been interested in the historical roots of the fear of family disintegration that has been repeatedly described as being of special relevance in "endogamous" incestuous families. Some of the psychodynamic studies of individual members of incestuous families suggested some possibilities. Cavallin's (1966) study of incestuous fathers suggested that these men often had remote, absent mothers, while Weiner (1961) characterized the mothers of incest victims as being dependent and infantile. Sholevar (1975) describes the fathers as being highly sensitive to abandonment by their wives, relating this to their childhood experiences at the hands of neglectful mothers.

These descriptions of the individual psychopathologies of husbands and wives can be articulated in object-relations terms using some of the principles developed by Dicks (1967) in his description of the unconscious dynamics underpinning object choice and marital tensions. One dynamic that emerged in a number of the pairs of spouses was *a shared relationship with a frustrating or abandoning parent* of the opposite sex. Thus, the wife may come from a family in which her mother was abandoned by her father (either literally or emotionally), and the husband may come from a family in which he had a frustrating relationship with a critical, ungiving or abandoning mother.

Once married, the couple characteristically express their shared fear of abandonment by establishing extremely tight and closed boundaries between first themselves and then with the birth of children, their family and the outside world. Hence the relatively common phenomenon of the *isolation* of the "endogamous" incestuous family from the community, an isolation which often appears to have preceded the incest.

In their marriage the couple fail to establish and maintain the idealized relationship that each had hoped for. Each spouse starts to perceive the other as the bad, rejecting and frustrating parent. The wife's distrust and hostility often becomes expressed as sexual withdrawal and the husband's potency with his wife may become impaired by his anxieties about *her* withdrawal. The more the wife withdraws, the more intense the husband's fear of abandonment (their shared unconscious bond). The more this shared fear is aroused, the greater becomes the couple's need to maintain the integrity of the family. The breakdown of the couple's sexual relationship is perceived by both as being potentially catastrophic and as potentially implying the unthinkable – the disintegration of the family.

The husband then turns sexually to his daughter since he is unwilling to break the close family boundaries by seeking a sexual partner outside the family; to do that would be to raise the spectre of the disintegration of the family. The wife for her part *colludes* with this arrangement by "not seeing" the incest, a major factor in this collusion being *her* fear that family disintegration is a catastrophe that must not happen at any cost. To use terms developed by Kinston and Bentovim (1981), a common depth-structure in the incestuous family is one of *reversal*: the feared traumatic event from the parents' families of origin, namely disintegration, must not happen under any circumstances. This depth-structure is a generative mechanism for an all-pervasive family myth (Byng-Hall, 1973), viz. "Anything is better than family breakdown". For example, in the D family, mother had been illegitimate, her father having abandoned her mother before she was born. Father had been abandoned by his mother who had left his family for another man when he was six years old. The couple met in their late teens, each being the other's first sexual partner. From the early days of their marriage, which was soon followed by the birth of their oldest daughter, Anne, the couple lived an isolated life with little contact with family and no social life. This process of isolation was accentuated when, after some three years of marriage, mother developed agoraphobia. The marital and sexual relationship began to deteriorate and father started an incestuous relationship with Anne, which also grew to involve Sean, Anne's younger brother. These incestuous relationships continued for some two years before mother finally discovered her husband in bed with Anne.

The victim's recruitment is initially underpinned by the power of the shared family myth that family disintegration will be catastrophic. Once the incest is established it becomes a family *secret* that must not be discussed openly within the family or *a fortiori* outside it. As a result the family dynamics that activate the incest are reinforced in three main ways.

1. The incest continually strengthens the inappropriate intergenerational alliance between father and daughter and hence the inappropriate intergenerational boundaries in the family.

2. The necessity of maintaining the *secret* of incest within the family further reinforces these inappropriate boundaries.

3. The necessity of maintaining the secret from the outside world leads to the need to maintain ever more rigid boundaries between the family and the outside world.

The consequent reinforcement which results in part explains the extraordinary durability that incest may have as a family pattern and, for example, is one reason why serial recruitment of successive children as victims may occur over the years.

I wish to stress that I am not putting this model forward as a *sine qua non* for the endogamous incestuous family. It does, however, describe some of the dynamics that have been present in a number of the incestuous families I have seen.

Other family risk factors

The family transactional account of the "endogamous" incestuous family given above is a fairly general one, and does not provide a full explanation of why incest occurs in some families and not in others. It can be argued that some of the family dynamics I have described are not specific to incestuous families and similarly that many marital sexual relationships fail but incest only occurs in a minority of such cases. To explain a phenomenon as complex as incest it is necessary to develop a multi-dimensional model that incorporates the various levels of causal mechanism whose interplay results in incest. Having described the family transactional level, I will now briefly summarize some of the other factors that seem to be of importance.

(a) Traditional sex roles

Many writers on incest have been struck by the way incestuous families often seem to present a caricature of traditional sex roles (see Renvoize, 1982, for a summary of this area). Fathers are often described as being desperate to maintain a competent facade, running their families in a heavily patriarchal style, often functioning like martinets. Such behaviour, of course, requires a reciprocal submissiveness from the mother. This pattern of sex roles lends support to the feminist view that incest is related to sociological forces that define power relations between the sexes; incestuous families are often ghettoes of extreme patriarchy.

(b) Reconstituted families

Finklehor (1980) in his survey of college students found that all kinds of sexual abuse, including incest, were five times more common in families in which there was a stepfather, than in natural families. This observation, which is borne out by clinical experience, presumably reflects the weakening of the incest taboo in families in which the father is not biologically related to the children.

(c) Parental history of sexual abuse

Just as with physical abuse, there is now evidence that parents who have themselves been sexually abused as children are more likely to have families in which sexual abuse occurs (Steele and Alexander, 1981). The mechanisms whereby history repeats itself in this way are ill-understood, but it seems to me that the insights afforded by object-relations theories of marital dynamics have much to offer in furthering our understanding.

(d) Emphasis on genital sexuality

Very rigid views about sexuality appear to be common in incestuous families. Finklehor (1980) found that college students whose mothers were described as having "punitive and repressed" attitudes towards sexuality were more likely to have been victims of sexual abuse than those whose mothers' attitudes were not so rigid. Work at the sex therapy clinic at McMaster University has also suggested that spouses in incestuous families often show a coital fixation in their attitudes to sexuality. That is, sexuality becomes exclusively focused on coitus with no emphasis on other aspects. At times this can lead to very bizarre moral beliefs such as those shown by an incestuous father who believed that masturbation was a cardinal sin while incest was not (Watters, personal communication).

Summary: theories of the incestuous family
Family transactional theories have described two basic types of incestuous
family, the "chaotic" and the "endogamous". Most work has been concerned
with understanding the latter type of family in which incest seems to serve a
function for the family as a whole, particularly by being a solution to the feared
catastrophe of family breakdown. Once started, incest reinforces the dysfunctional transactional patterns that engendered it and hence can be a very enduring symptom.

Family transactional theories are not sufficient in themselves to explain the
aetiology of incest and sexual abuse. Sociological, cultural and psychological
mechanisms are also involved. The effects of patriarchy, of particularly rigid
attitudes towards sexuality, of living in a reconstituted family and of a parental
history of sexual abuse are some of the other factors that seem to be relevant.

WORKING WITH INCESTUOUS AND SEXUALLY ABUSIVE FAMILIES

In this section I will consider some of the issues that arise when working with
incestuous and sexually abusive families. Like many others in this field I have
been greatly influenced by the pioneering work of Henry Giaretto (1976, 1981).
I will consider, in turn, types of presentation, the timing of referral, the legal
context and the need for therapeutic flexibility.

(1) Types of presentation
Incest and child sexual abuse may present in an open way, when a parent,
relative, friend or victim directly reports it, or in a veiled way, through any one
of a number of psychological or physical symptoms.

(a) Open presentation
Open presentations initiated by the victim are commoner with adolescents than
with younger children. The victim may have been sexually abused within the
family for several years, but only disclose this when the relationship with the
perpetrator begins to clash with the maturational needs of adolescence. For
example, in the B family, mentioned above, the 16-year-old daughter Jackie
had been involved in an incestuous relationship with her father since she was
eight years old. Her disclosure of the incest to a school teacher was precipitated
by her father's jealous attempts to stop her going out with boys.

Many victims may report sexual abuse openly to a family member or relative
only to be disbelieved. Furthermore, open reporting to professionals may have
occurred only to be discounted. Both the influence of overly literal readings of
Freud's theory of the Oedipus Complex and of the anxiety that professionals

experience when exposed to such accusations may contribute to this discounting process. It is vital to remember that accusations of sexual abuse made by children and adolescents are far more likely to be based on reality than on fantasy (Mrazek, 1981).

(b) Veiled presentations

The plethora of symptoms that may veil underlying incest or sexual abuse have been well documented elsewhere (BASPCAN, 1981; Beezley Mrazek and Mrazek, 1981; Steele and Alexander 1981). Health visitors, general practitioners and paediatricians can expect presentations veiled by physical symptoms such as recurrent urinary infections, vaginal discharges or gonorrhoea. Those working in child psychiatry may see cases which present as secondary enuresis or enopresis or more general symptoms such as failing school performance. Seductive or sexually provocative behaviour in a pre-school or latency aged child are symptoms that should always be approached with the possibility of sexual abuse in mind.

Of special relevance to those working with adolescents are presentations such as promiscuity, running away, anorexia and, above all, suicide attempts. The possibility of sexual abuse should always be considered when assessing adolescents who make suicidal gestures. It is therefore worrying that a recent review of the characteristics and problems of such adolescents (Hawton, O'Grady Osborn and Cole, 1982) makes no mention whatsoever of the possible aetiological relevance of sexual abuse.

(2) Timing of referral

Referral may precede, follow soon after, or lag far behind, the time of the actual identification of sexual abuse, and different sorts of issues and problems may arise in each of these situations.

(a) Referral preceding identification of sexual abuse

This is probably the most difficult type of referral since the worker will have to act in some ways as an investigator or detective. This may give rise to intense anxieties about "stirring up" much ill-feeling. The worker may be reluctant to pursue the question of incest or or sexual abuse for fear of alienating and disturbing innocent parties.

Krugman (1982) has eloquently argued that this fear is seldom justified. He encourages paediatricians to confront the possibility of sexual abuse when it appears relevant. As part of the routine examination of, say, a child with recurrent urinary tract infections, the parents should be told by the physician that sexual abuse is a possible cause of the symptoms. Krugman claims that the response of the parents is virtually diagnostic. Innocent parents will show concern, puzzlement and perhaps some shock as they wonder who, if anyone, might be a possible perpetrator of abuse. On the other hand, parents who are actually sexually abusing their children will immediately become defensive, angrily asking if they are being accused.

Mrazek (1981) has described well some of the general principles of the diagnostic process in suspected cases of child abuse. He stresses the importance of establishing a trusting relationship with the victim and of evaluating the possibilities of obtaining confirmatory evidence. The worker should also be alert both to characteristic symptoms in the child and to family constellations and dynamics suggestive of sexual abuse.

The investigation of, and confrontation with, the family in which incest or sexual abuse has occurred cannot but be a stressful process. The worker requires support from colleagues and an opportunity to share his or her anxieties. The basic principle of convening a case conference with all relevant professionals, along the lines already developed in physical child abuse, is of great importance here.

In my view, it is always preferable to act on one's suspicions and attempt to investigate for incest or sexual abuse than to duck the issue and thereby run the risk of allowing sexual abuse to continue unchecked. I also think that the legal system must be involved if a worker has reasonable suspicions that incest or sexual abuse is occurring. It is rarely, if ever, possible to justify *not* involving the law on the grounds of fear of prejudicing one's professional relationship with the family. Indeed, in some parts of the world the legal system insists on legal involvement. Thus, in the Canadian province of Ontario any professional who has reasonable grounds for suspecting that physical or sexual abuse of a child is occurring is legally obliged to report his suspicions to the legal authorities and failure to do so can result in prosecution. Often the actual confrontation can be made more easy with the support of colleagues, or failing that, support from other agencies.

For example, Dinah E., aged 12 years, was referred to the psychiatric clinic by her GP at the request of a community social worker who had been involved with her family for some months and was concerned about her disturbed behaviour and secondary enuresis. In an interview just before the clinic appointment Mrs E. told the social worker that Dinah had, on a couple of occasions, accused her maternal uncle, who lived next door, of sexually interfering with her. Mother had initially discounted these accusations, but then revealed to the social worker that she herself had had an incestuous relationship with the same man, who was her older brother.

The social worker took no further action until the appointment with myself and a clinic social worker. With our support he was able to raise the issue of sexual abuse with the family in a session during which Dinah repeated her accusations and father looked nonplussed. Together with the social worker we insisted that the police be informed and although the parents felt unable to do this themselves, they gave the social worker permission to do so. Following a physical examination by a police surgeon, which also revealed signs of physical abuse, Dinah was taken into care.

It seemed to us that our main function had been to provide the social worker with the support he required to take the appropriate action. Thereafter the structure provided by the area's Child Abuse case conference system maintained that support.

(b) Referral immediately following the revelation of incest or sexual abuse
Central issues in these referrals include the need to anticipate rapid denial, the need to establish open communication and the need to ensure the safety of the victim(s).

I have described above how family members who one day have been enraged at the perpetrator may completely retract their views and deny that there are any family problems the next. Two further points should be made about this phenomenon. First, a common dynamic is the projection of blame from perpetrator to victim. For example, in the C family, the 11-year-old daughter, Marie, had been sexually abused for a period of some two years by her 17-year-old brother Donald. Donald had taken flight after his parents had discovered him in bed with Marie, whom he had blackmailed into silence by threats of violence. At our first interview with the family both parents were furious with Donald. However, before long, mother, who was closely attached to her son, began to question his guilt, suggesting instead that Marie was the guilty party because she must have led him on.

Secondly, in view of the possibility of rapid denial, it is always essential to have legal backing for any treatment programme. This is in keeping with the observations of experienced workers like Giaretto (1981) who argue that a degree of compulsion is required if treatment is to be effective, and that this compulsion comprises part of the inevitable confrontation of the perpetrator with reality, which is a vital part of treatment.

The importance of establishing open communication about the sexual abuse within the family lies in the incapacitating effect that secrets can have on the family and on therapy. There may be a tendency for secrets to persist after exposure of sexual abuse; the victim's siblings may not be informed and this in turn leads to the generation of fantasies and to the possibility of therapeutic paralysis. I will often use the first family session to ensure that all family members know what has happened. For example, in the C family mentioned above, Marie's five other older brothers had not been informed why Donald had suddenly left home. They had been puzzled by this and shared the belief that somehow Marie was responsible. They had tended to shun Marie who had become more and more isolated and upset. My first task in the family session was to help the parents explain to the whole family why Donald had left. Although apparently surprised by what they had learnt, the boys expressed their concern for Marie who was much less isolated and cut off from her brothers by the next session.

It is vital to ensure the safety of the victim immediately following exposure. In some cases the legal system may have intervened by removing the perpetrator from the home, but in other cases the evidence may be too insubstantial for legal proceedings to be initiated. It may then be necessary to remove the victim to a place of safety or to take other steps to ensure that the perpetrator ceases to have access to the child. Thus, in the case of the E family mentioned above, Dinah was taken into care and not allowed to spend time at home until her parents moved house away from their close proximity to the uncle, who had abused Dinah. In the case of the C family, Donald, Marie's brother, denied sexually abusing his sister but agreed to move out of the home to a hostel.

(c) Referral long after the event

A common problem in these referrals is that the family may deny the relevance or pertinence of past incest or sexual abuse to their current problems. I have described elsewhere (Will, 1983) the D family who were referred because their 10-year-old son was showing a marked deterioration in his school performance. Father had been imprisoned some 18 months previously for incestuous activity with his 13-year-old daughter and 12-year-old-son. At the first family session there was evidence of the continuing relevance of some of the dynamics that had underpinned the incest: intense rivalry between mother and daughter for the parental role, and a marked split in the siblings with a victim sub-system and an isolated 10-year-old. When the issue of incest was raised by the therapists, mother refused to discuss it on the grounds that it had been exhaustively discussed in the past and could have no relevance to the present problems.

In this situation the therapist is often made to feel that she/he is intrusive and destructive, and opening old wounds. However, the impulse under these circumstances to duck the issue should be resisted if, as in this case, it is obviously relevant to the family's current problems. A direct confrontation, exploiting one's expert status, may be the necessary and sufficient intervention, e.g. "As experts we can tell you that we must talk about the incest and its consequences if we are to help your family function more happily." (Further developments in therapy with this family will be considered below.)

(3) The importance of the legal context

I have already stressed the importance of involving the legal system in cases of incest and sexual abuse. However, the legal context in which one works may itself have significant effects on practice: the timing of referrals, the degree of flexibility possible in treatment and even attitudes towards investigating sexual abuse, may all be affected. Consider, for example, the quite significant differences in working in Scotland and Ontario.

In Scotland until now the practice has been that those found guilty of incest are imprisoned. Should the perpetrator of incest or sexual abuse return home on release from prison, the customary practice is for the victim(s) to be removed from the house and placed in care. Hence a successful legal investigation of incest will lead to the family's equilibrium being considerably disrupted. It is often argued (Renvoize, 1982, for an account) that the legal consequences may be just as harmful as the effects of the incest itself (e.g. the victim's feelings of guilt may be greatly accentuated if, say, father is removed from the home). This can lead to the view that it is better *not* to report sexual abuse to the legal authorities.

In Ontario, Canada, the situation is very different. Incest and other forms of familial sexual abuse are dealt with by a Family Court and there is far more flexibility in sentencing practices: probation orders with conditions of residence outside the home and conditions of attendance for therapy may be used rather than automatic prison sentences for the perpetrators. There is often much closer co-operation between the legal system and the caring professions which results, for example, in pretrial referral of perpetrator and family. The results of such pre-trial assessments will often influence the type of sentence made by the Court. Thus, if family members and, in particular the spouses, show signs of wishing to co-operate with a treatment programme, a deferred sentence may be made whose final consequence will depend on response to treatment. On the other hand, the perpetrator who continues to deny his responsibility for the sexual abuse will be more likely to receive a custodial sentence, if only to guarantee a degree of safety for the victim(s).

I found it much easier working in Ontario than in Scotland. Inflexible legal practice does not sit easily with flexible treatment programmes. However, in my view, it is indefensible *not* to report sexual abuse for fear of the legal consequences. There is already evidence of discontent within the Scottish legal system about the current laws of incest (Scottish Law Commission, 1980). As expertise in the therapeutic management of incest and sexual abuse develops, and a viable alternative to purely custodial management becomes available, the legal system may well respond by taking a less rigid and more flexible approach to sentencing. There is evidence that this is already happening in parts of England (Bentovim, personal communication). Such changes can only come about if there is co-operation between the caring professions and the legal system.

(4) The need for therapeutic flexibility

The treatment of incest and sexual abuse is not a field for therapeutic purists (Beels and Ferber, 1969). Experienced workers such as Giaretto (1976, 1981) and Beezley Mrazek and Bentovim (1981) all stress the need for an approach that utilizes a number of different treatment modalities. Thus, Giaretto's treatment programme will usually involve, in sequential order, individual counselling, marital counselling, family counselling and group counselling for both parents and child. To provide such a variety and intensity of different therapeutic approaches requires considerable resources, which are unlikely to be available except in a specially funded programme.

Usually a compromise will have to be made between the ideal and the possible. Bentovim and Furniss (1983), in their treatment programme at Great Ormond Street, provide weekly group therapy for victims while acting as consultants to community social workers who are working with the families, by having occasional joint sessions with them, with various sub-systems and the whole family, including fathers. At present I have no special treatment programme for these families, treating each case as it comes, often using a variety of different approaches. A summary of my involvement with the D family will illustrate this.

As mentioned above, the identified patient, John, the 10-year-old son, had been referred by the GP for failing performance at school. Other family members were mother in her late thirties – a housewife, Anne aged 13, Sean aged 12 and Alison aged 5. Father had been imprisoned some 18 months earlier for incestuous involvement with the two older children and still had a year of his sentence to serve.

After an initial assessment, members of the family were confronted with the fact that the incest and its consequences were still affecting the way they were functioning and that it was important to discuss this. In the next two sessions mother was encouraged to open communication about what had happened and, for the first time, all the children were given the same information. A start was made at discussing the implications of the incest and at helping family members talk about the absent father.

These initial family sessions were very "sticky" with many silences. In particular, it seemed impossible for there to be any meaningful discussion about the conflicting feelings raised by father's imprisonment. Moreover, the relationship between mother and Anne appeared to be very fraught. Individual sessions were held with Anne and mother. While mother, with some difficulty, talked about her guilt, Anne was almost totally non-communicative.

A family sculpt was performed in the next family session, in the hope that it might help free communication. The sculpt was revealing: when sculpting the family's relationship with the imprisoned father, John positioned himself with Alison close to and facing father, while the other family members were positioned far from father with their backs turned towards the two youngest children. Following this, John was able to talk about how he felt guilty about missing his father, whom mother had divorced. In the following session John appeared to be closer to his two older siblings and from that point on his presenting symptoms rapidly disappeared.

The momentum started by the sculpt was maintained for the next few sessions, during which family members were able to show some of their feelings about the changes that had occurred since father left. This led on to the exposure of the rivalry between mother and Anne for the parental role. For example, Anne would often attempt to discipline or order her younger siblings around, and if mother objected to this, she would turn sullen and glower. I then had three dyadic sessions with mother and Anne during which Anne was able, haltingly, to express some of her anger towards her mother. She had told her mother about the incest on two occasions (before mother had caught father in bed with her) and had not been believed. Mother was able to express her remorse and self-recrimination about this.

Mother began to complain about the disobedience and fighting that had come to dominate the three older children's relationships with her. She also revealed that she had been quite severely agoraphobic for the previous 10 years. Family sessions were resumed with a view to helping mother establish herself in a parental role with the children by establishing clearer intergenerational boundaries. Concurrently, she was referred to a clinical psychologist for systematic desensitization which provided rapid symptomatic relief of her agoraphobia. Her increased self-confidence reinforced the structural family work with its emphasis on increasing her authority and effectiveness as a parent.

Things went well over the next three months and I began to think of discharging the family. However, more friction developed, in the form of persistent and rather vitriolic fighting amongst the three older children. At family sessions these three became more and more sullen, saying little despite mother's and my attempts to explore the reasons for the fighting. After three virtually identical sessions about these issues I felt stuck and asked for a consultation from the team with which I work. We decided to use a Milan group-type consultation with one of my colleagues interviewing the family, while I and the rest of the team watched behind the one-way screen.

The team felt that the children were being difficult at home and went "on strike" in the family sessions because they remained worried about their mother and, in particular, about what would happen to her and themselves once father was released from prison. They continued to be "difficult" and resistant to therapy since they wanted to ensure that the family, and particularly mother, remained in contact with the clinic. As an intervention we positively connoted the children's attempts to ensure that contact continued and assured them that we would continue to meet until after father was released from prison. This consultation freed things up and my recent work with the family has been concerned with the anxieties they feel about father's imminent release from prison.

This example of work which is still in progress illustrates some of the challenges involved in working with incestuous and sexually abusive families. Several therapeutic approaches – psychodynamic, behavioural, structural, action-orientated and strategic – have been used in individual, dyadic and family sessions. This indicates the importance both of therapeutic flexibility and of adopting a therapeutic stance which will be responsive to the needs of different family members. Providing help for such families may at times be taxing but can also be highly rewarding.

CONCLUSIONS

Both the theoretical understanding and the clinical management of incestuous or sexually abusive families require an integrated approach. Understanding derived from sociology, theories of family dynamics and individual psychology is necessary to provide adequate theoretical models. Clinically, a multi-modal approach integrating different types of therapy is required to provide adequate help for these families.

I should like to acknowledge the stimulation provided by my former colleagues in the Family Consultation Group at McMaster University, in particular Coco Johnson. I have also found discussions with Arnon Bentovim very helpful. Above all, I should like to thank Joyce Morrison whose collaboration in clinical work with these families has been invaluable.

An earlier and shorter version of this paper was delivered at a Conference on the Sexual Abuse of Children organized by the Dundee Coordinating Committee for the Care of the Abused Child in September 1982.

REFERENCES

BASPCAN (1981). *Child & Sexual Abuse.*
Beels, C.C. and Ferber, A. (1969). Family therapy: a view. *Family Process* **8** 280–332.
Beezley Mrazek, P. and Bentovim, A. (1981). Incest and the dysfunctional family system. In *Sexually Abused Children and Their Families*, Beezley Mrazek, P. and Kempe, C.H. (Eds). Oxford: Pergamon.
Beezley Mrazek, P. and Kempe, C. H. (Eds) 1981). *Sexually Abused Children and Their Families*. Oxford: Pergamon.
Beezley Mrazek, P. and Mrazek, D. (1981). The effects of child sexual abuse: methodological considerations. In *Sexually Abused Children and their Families*, Beezley Mrazek, P. and Kempe, C.H. (Eds). Oxford: Pergamon.
Beezley Mrazek, P., Lynch, M. and Bentovim, A. (1981). Recognition of child sexual abuse in the United Kingdom. In *Sexually Abused Children and Their Families*, Beezley Mrazek, P. and Kempe, C. H. (Eds). Oxford: Pergamon.
Bentovim, A. and Furniss, T. (1983). *Workshop on Sexual Abuse and the Family*. Institute of Family Therapy, London. February 1983.

Browning, D. and Boatman, B. (1977). Incest: children at risk. *American Journal of Psychiatry* **134** 69–72.

Byng-Hall, J. (1973). Family myths used as a defence in conjoint family therapy. *British Journal of Medical Psychology* **46**, 239–250.

Cavallin, H. (1966). Incestuous fathers: a clinical report. *American Journal of Psychiatry* **122**, 1132–1138.

Cormier, B., Kennedy, M. and Sangewicz, J. (1962). Psychodynamics of father-daughter incest. *Canadian Psychiatric Association Journal* **18**, 203–217.

Dicks, H. V. (1967). *Marital Tensions*. New York: Basic Books.

Finklehor, D. (1979). *Sexually Victimised Children*. New York and London: Free Press.

Finklehor, D. (1980) Risk factors in the sexual victimisation of children. *Child Abuse and Neglect* **4**, 265–273.

Finklehor, D. (1982). Sexual abuse: a sociological perspective. *Child Abuse and Neglect* **6**, 95–102.

Forward, S. and Buck, C. (1981). *Betrayal of Innocence: Incest and its Devastation*. Harmondsworth: Penguin.

Furniss, T. (1983). Family process in the treatment of intrafamilial child sexual abuse. *Journal of Family Therapy* **4**, 263–278.

Giaretto, H. (1976). Humanistic treatment of father-daughter incest. In *Child Abuse and Neglect: The Family and the Community*. Helfer, R.E. and Kempe, C.H. (Eds). Cambridge, Mass: Ballinger.

Giaretto, H. (1981). A comprehensive child sexual abuse treatment program. In *Sexually Abused Children and Their Families*, Beezley Mrazek, P. and Kempe, C.H. (Eds). Oxford: Pergamon.

Goodwin, J. (1982). *Sexual Abuse, Incest Victims and Their Families*. Bristol: John Wright.

Gutheil, T. G. and Avery, N.C. (1977). Multiple overt incest as a defence against loss. *Family Process* **16**, 105–116.

Hawton, K. O'Grady, J. Osborn, M. and Cole, D. (1982). Adolescents who take overdoses: their characteristics, problems and contacts with helping agencies. *British Journal of Psychiatry* **140**, 118–123.

Herman, J. L. (1981). *Father-daughter Incest*. Cambridge, Mass: Harvard University Press.

Kinston, W. and Bentovim, A, (1981). Creating a focus for brief marital and family therapy. In *Forms of Brief Therapy*, Budman, S.H. (Ed.). New York: Guilford.

Krugman, R. (1982). *Presentation at a Conference on Child Sexual Abuse*, Dundee. Co-ordinating Committee for the Care of the Abused Child.

Lukianowicz, N. (1972). Incest: I. Paternal Incest. II. Other types of incest. *British Journal of Psychiatry* **120**, 301–313.

Lustig, N., Dresser, J.W., Spellman, S.W. and Murray, T.B. (1966). Incest: a family group survival pattern. *Archives of General Psychiatry* **14**, 31–40.

Lutz, S.E and Medway, J.P., (1984). Contextual family therapy with the victims of incest. *Journal of Adolescence* **7**, 319–327.

Machotka, P., Pittman, F. and Flamenhaft, K. (1967). Incest as a family affair. *Family Process* **6** 98–116.

Minuchin, S. (1974). *Families and Family Therapy*. London: Tavistock.

Mrazek, D. (1981). The child psychiatric examination of the sexually abused child. In *Sexually Abused Children and Their Families*, Beezley Mrazek, P. and Kempe, C.H. (Eds). Oxford: Pergamon.

Nelson, S. (1982). *Incest: Fact and Myth*. Edinburgh: Strathmullion.

Renvoize, J. (1982). *Incest: A Family Pattern*. London: Routledge and Kegan Paul.

Scottish Law Commission. (1980). Memorandum No: 44. *The Law of Incest in Scotland.*

Sholevar, G. (1975). A family therapist looks at the problem of incest. *Bulletin of the American Academy of Psychiatric Law* **3**, 25–31.

Steele, B.F. and Alexander, H. (1981). Long-term effects of sexual abuse in childhood. In *Sexually Abused Children and Their Families*, Beezley Mrazek, P. and Kempe, C.H. (Eds). Oxford: Pergamon.

Weiner, I.B. (1961). On incest: a survey. *Excerpta Criminologica* **4**, 137–155.

Will, D. (1983). Some techniques for working with resistant families of adolescents. *Journal of Adolescence* **6**, 13–26.

16. Teenage mothers

EARLADEEN BADGER

INTRODUCTION

The first of 10 national health goals selected by the American Academy of Pediatrics for the Eighties is that "all children should be wanted and born to healthy mothers" Graham, 1980). These rights of birth are in jeopardy if a child is born to an unmarried teenager.

Some facts: half of all unmarried female teenagers in the U.S.A. are sexually active (Pittman, 1985). While only one fifth of those who become pregnant say they want a baby (Zelnik and Kanter, 1979), nearly all of them keep their babies (McGee 1982). One out of eight children are born under these circumstances (National Centre for Health Statistics, 1983)

The increase in both the percentage of women who are unmarried and their rate of childbearing coupled with the decrease in the fertility rate of married women has sharply increased the percentage of all American births occurring out of wedlock in the past two decades. Between 1940 and 1960, the proportion of babies born to unmarried mothers fluctuated at 4 to 5%. In 1980, out-of-wedlock births made up nearly half (48%) of total births to non-white women (of whom more than 90% are black), while the comparable figures for Caucasians was 11%. Among teenage women in 1980, the proportion of out-of-wedlock births was 85% for blacks and 33% for Caucasians (Thornton and Freidman, 1983; Pittman, 1985).

The trend in non-marital fertility among teenagers is especially unfortunate because many of the significant health risks and social and economic

Working with troubled adolescents
ISBN 0-12-179720-1

disadvantages associated with teenage childbearing are particularly serious for
unmarried teenagers. Mortality risks are higher for both baby and mother when
the mother is a teenager than they are when the mother is in her twenties.
Though government-mandated programmes now keep more pregnant teenagers in school, adolescent mothers still receive less education than other adolescents. This, along with child care problems in often fatherless homes, can
impede their search for, and commitment to, a job, which in turn increases the
chances that they will find themselves on welfare (Baldwin, 1980).

Nationally, we have only begun to recognize the magnitude of the problem
and to acknowledge that it is not going to go away without agency help (Alan
Guttmacher Institute, 1981). With federal assistance, some junior and senior
high schools are establishing creative programmes in parenthood education,
and some hospitals and health clinics are initiating specialized pre- and postnatal services for the adolescent mother and her at risk infant. Health education
and social service agencies have also begun to modify traditional services as they
discover new ways to further the physical, psychological and economic well-
being of the young mother and her child.

Recognizing the mutually reinforcing nature of health and educational intervention in maximizing the potential of high risk infants as well as the importance of early maternal-infant attachment, the Newborn Division, Department
of Pediatrics, at Cincinnati University Hospital (CUH) undertook a pilot study
in 1972 to determine whether an intensive but broadly defined educational
programme for adolescent mothers and their first-born infants might prove
successful within the paediatric setting of a large medical centre. We expected
that such a comprehensive programme would reduce the gaps in existing health
care services, but we also hoped to focus the energies and resources of the non-
medical sectors of the community to meet more effectively the multiple needs of
the adolescent mother and her child.

THE INFANT STIMULATION/MOTHER TRAINING (IS/MT)
MODEL

The Infant Stimulation/Mother Training (IS/MT) Project was conceived as an
attempt to intervene in the lives of CUH's welfare population of teenage
mothers and their first-born infants. It was hypothesized that this population of
infants was developmentally at risk due to the immaturity of their mothers
coupled with the social circumstances that interfered with the mothers' role as
primary caretakers of their infants. While the critical period of intervention in
the lives of poverty infants who routinely experience developmental delays has
not been clearly demonstrated, maternal deprivation studies with lower animals
(Dennenberg, 1964; Harlow, 1963) and humans (Goldfarb, 1955; Provence
and Lipton, 1962) suggest that the qualitative aspects of the early mother-infant

relationship shape the infant's personality (Caldwell, 1964; Thomas, 1970) and influence his/her social development. The mothers we proposed to serve were exposed to external pressures which interfered with their ability to respond unselfishly to their infants. The social stigma of being unmarried and "on welfare" was compounded by their inability to find employment without a high school diploma. When teenage mothers return to school, their infants are likely to be cared for by a succession of substitute mothers. Any one or all of the substitute mothers may give sufficient care, but multiple mothering typically results in a discontinuity of mother-child relations.

The IS/MT model (weekly postnatal mother-infant classes) was intended to reinforce the mother's role as primary caretaker of her infant and to provide satisfaction in that role at regular intervals. More important than the possibility of accelerating development during the first year of life was the goal of preventing developmental delays in infants whose mothers were only minimally involved in their care. Because mother love in infancy and childhood is basic to sound mental health, intervention with at risk mothers beginning at the birth of their children was an attempt to establish that the cumulative deficits observed in maternally and environmentally deprived youngsters at three years of age are not inevitable.

The IS/MT Project was also designed to test whether an intensive educational programme for at risk mothers and their infants might prove successful within the setting of a paediatric medical centre. From the outset, the project was considered to be service- as well as research-oriented. An infant curriculum (Badger, 1971a) and a mother training model (Badger, 1971b; Badger, 1972), developed and tested at the University of Illinois and at parent-child centres in Illinois and Georgia, were chosen as the primary means for achieving the educational goals of the programme. In addition, extensive medical and nutritional services were provided as part of the preventive thrust of the project. Finally, special attention was given to the tactical problems of transferring a proven intervention model to the multiple problems of the socially disadvantaged, teenage mother.

PILOT PROJECT

Subjects

Forty-eight mother-infant pairs were recruited on the postpartum unit of CUH during January and February 1973 and randomly assigned to one of the two treatment groups: one-and-a-half-hour weekly classes or monthly home visits (Figure 1). In order to assess the developmental risk of infants of high risk mothers (aged 16 and younger) and the impact of a group instructional approach in modifying and shaping maternal behaviours, lower risk mother

TREATMENT GROUPS

	CLASSES	VISITS
	Mother training programme weekly classes	Monthly supportive home visits
SUBJECT GROUPS		
Old mothers: 18 years or older, mature infants	12 mothers and infants	12
Young mother: 16 years or younger, mature infants	12	12

Fig. 1. Experimental design includes a total of 48 socially disadvantaged mother-infant pairs, recruited during the lying-in period, and randomly assigned to either class or home visiting groups.

(aged 18–19) and their first-born were included in the treatment design.

The 24 mother-infant pairs assigned to class groups were recruited first to ensure their commitment to attend classes. Since every mother who met the criteria for selection (on welfare, living within a three-mile radius of the hospital) agreed to participate, we were assured of a random sample in both treatment groups. Infants were firstborn, gestationally mature and had five-minute Apgar scores over seven. Further, groups were matched for race and sex with nine blacks and three Appalachian whites in each of the four groups.

Attrition was not as high as might have been predicted among a socially at risk population. During the first six months, one white mother-infant pair was lost in each of the high risk (aged 16 and younger) treatment groups. During the second six months, the young white mother-infant pair rejoined the home visit group, but four additional white mother-infant pairs were lost – two in the high risk class treatment group and two in the lower risk home visit group. The remaining six white mother-infant pairs continued in the project, but the loss of matching pairs limited the final analysis of testing data to the black population or a sample of 36 infants at 12 months.

Treatment I (weekly classes)

Weekly classes for the 24 mother-infant pairs assigned to the mother training group began in February 1973 and continued until infants were 12-months-old.

High risk mothers and lower risk mothers met separately because of their different lifestyles and circumstances. All classes, however, coincided with evening paediatric clinics at CUH and doctors, nurses and social workers were available for consultation. Mothers brought their infants to class and the following training goals (Badger, 1976) were emphasized:

1. Mothers were led to understand that how they interact with their babies now will make an important difference in their later development.

2. Mothers were encouraged to respond to their infants' vocal behaviour and to their behavioural indicators of stress.

3. Mothers were taught to observe their infants carefully as they interacted with play materials so that they could select those activities that evoked interest rather than boredom or stress.

4. Mothers were taught a sequence of infant development skills which enabled them to choose appropriate materials that stimulated their child's growth.

The instructor demonstrated appropriate maternal behaviours as she used manipulative toys and materials to play with the infants. Since the teenage mother typically has difficulty responding to her infant's demands, the weekly classes provided many opportunities for her to experience success and satisfaction in mothering. A variety of standard educational techniques (i.e. repetition, reinforcement, group pressure and confrontation) were used by the instructor. When, for example, a baby vocalized, the instructor repeated the baby's vocal pattern. She then encouraged the mother to respond in a similar way to the infant: "See – see what he's doing? Now, you do it." As the mother tried to repeat the instructor's demonstration, the instructor praised or reinforced her behaviour. On occasion, the group might exert pressure to censure a mother's behaviour or the instructor might confront an individual mother: for example, "This is your baby and he needs and wants you now." Personal growth and opportunities for attitudinal change were facilitated through this method of group instruction. Information about infant nutrition, family planning and health care were included. Finally, many incentives were offered to encourage regular attendance and to ensure programme commitment. Cab pools provided transportation to and from classes; programme toys were given free; younger mothers earned eight units of high school credit; and babies were regularly photographed. Films, slides and pamphlets were offered as educational supplements; and individual attention from the clinic doctor or health service team was available on request during class time.

Treatment II (monthly home visits)

Mothers in the home visit group received the services of an interested resource person – a nurse or social worker – and toys like those given to mothers in class group. No group instruction, however, was provided, nor was high school credit earned. Instead, mother-infant pairs were visited at home once a month, infant sensorimotor development was assessed, and problems related to health and nutrition were discussed. Favourable response from the participating mothers, especially lower risk 18 to 19-year-olds, was observed regularly, and project staff suggested that the service aspect of this intervention had a positive influence on infant performance.

Assessment

In order to measure possible differences between child performance in the two treatment groups, three of the Uzgiris-Hunt Infant Ordinal Scales of Psychological Development (Uzgiris and Hunt, 1975), Object Permanence, Development of Means, and Vocal Imitation were administered monthly to each infant (Figure 2). Although previous studies (Lewis and McGurk, 1972) reported no significant differences in infant performance as measured by standardized tests in socially disadvantaged populations before the age of 18 months, the Bayley Scales of Infant Development (Bayley, 1969) were nonetheless included when

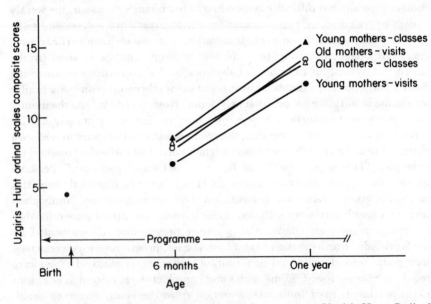

Fig. 2. Six and 12 month mean composite testing scores on Uzgiris-Hunt Ordinal Scales of Psychological Development for four groups of matched infants. Analysis of variance indicated a significant difference between infants (young and old mothers) in home groups and infants (both young and old mothers) in home visiting groups at the $p < .01$ level. The treatment effect was primarily apparent in the young mothers' groups.

infants reached their first birthday (Figure 3). All testing was completed by one certified Bayley tester who did not know the treatment assignment of the infants.

In addition to assessing infant development with the Bayley and Uzgiris-Hunt Scales, maternal data were collected from an entry questionnaire, in a social history interview, and from observations on class participation and attendance.

Infant Data

In an analysis of infant testing data at 12 months – Uzgiris-Hunt and Bayley Infant Scales – infants of high risk class mothers performed significantly better than infants of high risk mothers in the home visit group (Figure 4). For example, infants of high risk mothers in the home visit group had a mean Bayley Mental score of 79, which was significantly less than the mean score of 99 obtained by infants of high risk mothers who attended classes (t(16) = 2.40, p < .05). This treatment effect was not apparent in infants of lower risk mothers, whose infants performed equally well in class and home visit groups (Tables 2, 3, 4).

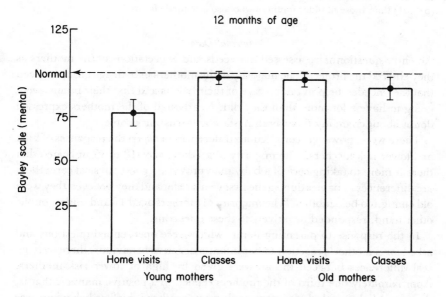

Fig. 3. Mean 12 month score on Bayley Mental Scales for each of four treatment groups. Infants of young mothers in home visited group had mean mental score of 79, which is significantly less (p < .05) than mean score of 99 obtained by infants of young mothers in class group. Other intergroup differences are not significant.

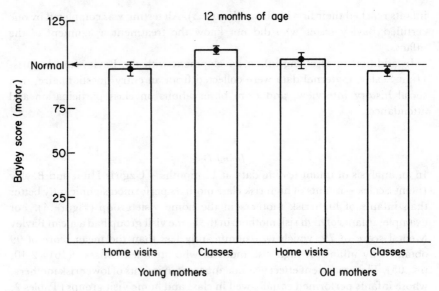

Fig. 4. Mean 12 month score on Bayley Motor Scales for each of four treatment groups. Infants of young mothers in class group performed significantly better (p < .05) than those in home visiting group. Motor scores of these infants were significantly better (p < .01) than those of older mothers who also attended classes.

Maternal Data

An entry questionnaire assessed the needs and expectations of the mothers as they entered the project. The majority of the mothers in both age groups agreed that they needed help in taking care of their babies and that their infants were going to have a lot more than they did. Nearly half of the mothers expressed doubt about changing the way things are and trusting people.

There were, however, conspicuous differences between the responses of high and lower risk mothers. The majority of mothers aged 18 to 19 indicated that there is more to taking care of a baby than providing good physical care; there are differences in babies during the first year of life; and they believed they were old enough to be a mother. The majority of mothers aged 16 and under, on the other hand, responded negatively to these questions.

In the response to parenting items, which were open-ended questions and asked for a mother's reaction to her infant's negative behaviour, there were no real differences between the answers given by high or lower risk mothers. Approximately one third of the mothers replied in a positive manner, that is, they would play with their infant or distract him/her if his/her behaviour was negative. The other mothers, however, either did not know what they would do or would alternate between slapping, scolding, holding, or offering a bottle or pacifier.

Social history data revealed that 88% of the high and 68% cent of the lower risk mothers were unmarried; 65% of all mothers continued to live at home. Returning to high school for the young and employment for the older mothers were facilitated by help from the extended family. Among the white Appalachian population who did not receive such help, there were problems that in turn explain their high attrition rate: one of the mothers was a chronic runaway; one was committed to a psychiatric facility; and one moved to another city to live with distant relatives.

Class participation was not strikingly different between high and lower risk mothers. Although the high risk mothers did not have a significantly greater atttendance rate (81%) than the lower risk mothers (75%), the level of involvement of the high risk mothers was judged to be more intense. For example, group indentity as evidenced by spontaneity in sharing, volunteering comments and providing feedback was more quickly established with the high risk mothers. In contrast, six classes were required before the lower risk mothers began to share information openly about their infants and themselves. The lower risk mothers tended to see themselves as private individuals; they were more introspective, suspicious, and defensive toward group instruction. Their participation was generally less enthusiastic than that of the high risk mothers.

Formative Evaluation

At the conclusion of the IS/MT Pilot Project, we were able to provide partial answers to the following questions:

1. Are infants of socially disadvantaged teenage mothers (aged 16 and under) in jeopardy? Testing data at 12 months suggest that infants of adolescent mothers begin to fall behind very early in life and are indeed in jeopardy, but this was not apparent in infants of high risk mothers who attended weekly classes. The performance of these infants matched or surpassed that of the infants of the lower risk, more mature mothers.

2. Can a mother training programme be used effectively with the teenage mother and her infant, considering the special problems of school continuation, peer pressure and surrogate mothering of the infant? The feasibility of training classes as a viable means of serving at risk mothers and their infants seemed to be confirmed by the high rate of attendance and participation in the weekly classes. Young inner-city black mothers apparently are interested in learning good mothering techniques and are responsive to the idea at the time their babies are born. Some of the white Appalachian mothers included in the study, however, were less able to attend classes regularly or to return to high school. Perhaps they were lacking in the kind of family support and stability that would allow them to make plans for themselves. The white mothers who remained in the study, on the other hand, were responsive to the services offered and, although the test results of their infants were not included because of attrition, they benefited from the programme.

3. How did 15 to 16-year-old mothers differ from 18 to 19-year-old mothers as participants in mother training classes? At the time of recruitment, younger mothers more readily felt they could manage one evening a week than did older mothers. This was somewhat surprising, since the younger mother would be returning to school during the day. The older mother, on the other hand, had completed high school and, for the most part, indicated no immediate plans to seek employment outside the home. Generally speaking, the younger mothers appeared to be more interested in the classes and willing to invest the time to learn parenting skills than did the older mothers, who felt they already knew these things by reason of their age. The autonomy of the older mothers was further reinforced by their financial independence, since they qualified for a monthly welfare check or had the potential ability to get a job. Conversely, the younger mothers were obliged to remain at home under the supervision of their own mothers, and their only option toward independence was to complete their secondary education. Most of the younger mothers planned to return to school, and this decision meant surrendering their baby to the maternal grandmother for primary care.

It appeared that the significantly accelerated motor development of the infants of high risk mothers who attended classes over that of the infants of lower risk mothers who also attended classes may be a result of observed differences in their phsyical and emotional responsiveness; high risk mothers participated more readily in physical play with their infants and were generally spontaneous in these interactions; lower risk mother, though just as attentive to their infants, were more often self-conscious and inhibited in demonstrative play with their infants.

4. Is birth or the perinatal period an optimal time for intervention in a poverty population whose children routinely experience developmental delays? Project staff suspected that most of the high-risk mothers viewed their participation in the mothers' training classes as a means of more clearly establishing their role as mothers, perhaps in competition with their own mothers, who were assuming primary care of their infants as they returned to school. If this observation was true, it builds a strong case for reaching the teenage mother during the perinatal stage of her infant's development. Ultimately she must assume primary responsibility for the child. To postpone the parenting role until she reaches the age of majority can be damaging not only to the child's development, i.e. feelings of rejection, but also to the mother's own feelings of self-worth and to her later success as a mother.

5. Is group instruction more effective than an individualized approach? The initial resistance and suspicions of some of the mothers in the lower risk group toward a
class instructional approach, the child-related interest and involvement
observed by the home visitors of the older mothers who were in the home visit
treatment group, and the comparable performance at 12 months of both groups
of infants of 18 to 19-year-old mothers suggested that group or individual
instruction may be equally viable interventions with older, more mature
mothers. As noted previously, the treatment effect as measured by infant performance at 12 months of age occurred primarily in the comparisons of infants
of mothers aged 16 and younger; and since high risk mothers in the home visit
group were observed by project staff to be minimally involved with their infants,
the group instructional approach seemed to be especially effective in helping the
younger mothers attach to and respond appropriately to the developmental
needs of their infants. The satisfactions a new mother experiences in her associations with a peer group of young mothers, the therapy provided through the
sharing of common problems, the availability of positive adult teaching models,
and the interest and concern extended toward her and her infant by attendant
staff, all serve to influence her growth as a person and as a mother in positive
ways.

6. What kind of mothers cannot be served with a mother training programme model? Our
experience indicated that only a few mothers had personal problems that were
so long-standing and of such magnitude, and whose resources were so limited,
that they were unable to profit from a programme of this kind. This was
especially true among the white Appalachian mothers. Three of these mothers
eventually lost custody of their infants.

*7. What are the advantages of carrying out a mother training programme under the umbrella
of a medical centre?* During the first year of life, an intervention programme
which includes comprehensive medical services and provides useful information in the areas of health, nutrition and child development facilitates the
maximum development of infants. Our observations and developmental testing
of the 42 infants who we were able to follow during the first year of
life seemed to affirm that infants develop and thrive when (1) they are well
nourished; (2) they develop a strong primary attachment to their mothers;
(3) mothers consistently and appropriately respond to the physical and emotional needs of their infants; (4) mothers provide them with varied mouthing,
visual and manipulative experiences; and (5) preventive health services and
crisis treatment are easily accessible. Overall, mothers who attended weekly
classes seemed to have greater awareness of their babies' physical welfare, and
to rely more on a health facility when they sensed a problem. It may be of
greater significance that no hospitalizations occurred among the infants in the

class groups compared to the hospitalization of three infants in the home visit groups.

The ease of recruitment of high risk mothers during the lying-in period following delivery suggests that educational intervention during infancy may be an important new dimension of both behavioural paediatrics and early childhood education. Further, services are readily available from persons in several professional disciplines – doctors, nurses, social workers, nutritionists, psychologists – and these can be integrated into a single, co-ordinated effort. Changes in attitudes were noted in the medical and nursing staff as regards the outcomes for the teenage mother and her infant. We began to hear about the "smart" babies in the mother training classes. Attitudinal changes of this kind argue for the expansion of health service-related programmes that are distinguished by a human response to their delivery of care.

IS/MT SERVICE PROGRAMME

Based on the salutory effects of the mother training classes on high risk mothers and their first-born infants, there was a commitment to extend and adapt the pilot project to include subsequent young mothers delivered at CUH. Beginning in September 1974, 15 high risk mothers and their first-born infants were recruited each month on the postnatal unit. They were offered a series of 20 weekly classes, beginning when infants were three to five weeks old, and continuing until they were approximately six months of age. Classes included a curriculum (Badger, 1977) that was both infant- and mother-specific. Programme goals and teaching strategies were the same as those in the pilot project. Incentives to ensure participation (e.g. high school credit, cab pools, free programme toys, photos of babies, consultation with clinic health care staff) were likewise included. This service programme was offered to over 1,000 mothers and their infants through 1982, and is currently being replicated successfully in other hospitals and service agencies. As in the pilot project, virtually all mothers approached in University Hospital's postpartum unit the second or third day following delivery expressed interest in joining the mother training class programme. Their actual participation, however, did not match that of the mothers in the pilot project (Table 1), nor did we think it would. There are several explanations we are prepared to offer:

1. Mothers in the pilot programme knew they were part of an experimental study and there was status in "belonging".

2. The person who designed the pilot project was also responsible for recruitment and delivery of the classes.

3. Supportive home visits were made (by this same person) when special

problems were apparent or when attendance in classes began to lag in the pilot project.

4. There was a real "push" not to lose a single mother-infant pair in the pilot project for fear of jeopardizing the quasiexperimental treatment design.

As we moved into a service programme, there was a larger population of mother-infant pairs to recruit and involve. Division of labour occurred as one staff member became responsible for recruitment and another was the class leader. There was less time to make home visits as a follow-up to a missed class. Clearly, the variations in class participation and attendance could be a measure of a mother's interest and motivation in extracurricular learning experiences. But, there were two other factors that helped to explain the class attendance and attrition figures:

1. Secondary schools were increasingly responsive to the teenage mother's desire to return to school. Late afternoon and early evening classes became available. Some mothers elected to attend them, especially if their own mother was not available during the day to care for their infant. In doing so, they were unable to attend our class programme because of the conflict in time.

2. Poor family support also negatively affected class participation and attendance. As was the case with our white Appalachian mothers in the pilot project, and which was evidenced further in our service programme, young mothers needed encouragement and help from adult family members if they were going to complete their education and get off welfare.

Table 1. Attendance figure of 771 mothers recruited shortly after delivery for IS/MT Service Programme from September 1974 – September 1978 (class groups 1-49)

	Completed programme High school credit > 15 classes	High attenders 11–15 classes	Medium attenders 6–10 classes	Low attenders 1–5 classes	Never attended classes
Total mothers recruited (16 years and younger)	771	315	50	68	114	224
White mothers	98	15	2	7	13	61
Black mothers	673	300	48	61	101	163

Referring to Table 1, a total of 771 mothers were recruited for the 49 class groups who completed the service programme/from 1974–78. Ninety-eight or 13% were white mothers; 673 or 87% were inner-city black mothers.

Only 17 white mothers (17% of those white mothers recruited) came to more than half the classes offered them; 15 received high school credit for their participation. The remaining 81 white mothers recruited came to less than half the classes; and of them, 61 (or 62% of all white recruited) never came at all.

Of the total number of black mothers recruited for participation, 52% completed more than half the classes; 45% received high school credit for their level of participation. The remaining 325 black mothers recruited came to less than half the classes; and of them 163 (or 24% of all blacks recruited) never came at all.

In searching for the answers to why the white mothers were such low attenders, we reviewed all of their recruitment face sheets. We found that 31 (or 32% of the white mothers recruited) were lost between the time they left the hospital with their infants and the time their class group was scheduled to begin (a three-to-four week period). The address in the hospital record was either incorrect or they had moved out of the area. Another 29 (or 30% of the white mothers recruited) changed their mind about participating in the class programme after they returned home. Some cited family problems as the reason; others just said they were no longer interested. Since approximately half were already married and did not plan to return to school, earning high school credit was not an incentive for participation. Although most did not actually volunteer that their husbands disapproved of their attending classes, we believe this was a determining factor when they refused to attend the first class.

Programme adaptations

Two adaptations were made as we began to replicate the pilot project as a service programme. We shortened the length of the programme and we initiated a training programme for the new class leaders and those who chose to replicate our programme.

The rationale for limiting the number of classes weas related to the number of mothers in the target population we wished to serve. With an annual delivery population at University Hospital of approximately 500 mothers (aged 16 and younger), we projected recruitment of half of them who lived within a three-mile radius of University Hospital and for whom cab pools to and from classes could easily be arranged. A series of 20 weekly postnatal classes was roughly half the number of classes attended by mother-infant pairs in the pilot project.

Capitalizing on the interest evinced in the pilot project by professional staff within the medical centre and the community at large, we also trained a new class leader as part of the delivery of each series of 20 classes. This person was called a co-leader. In the 97 groups of mother-infant pairs who completed the service programme from 1972–84, co-leaders have included professional social workers, educators and nurses from the medical centre and allied community agencies, as well as university students in special education, medicine, child development, nursing, community health, psychology and social work, who elected to take a field placement in our programme. The net impact of this professional training programme has been a proliferation of infant stimulation/parenting programmes within the greater Cincinnati area. In addition, concentrated training in early educational intervention has been provided to medical, educational and social service professionals within and outside Ohio through a three-day short course, entitled "Infant Enrichment Through Mother Training".

LONGITUDINAL FOLLOW-UP

Since few researchers (Furstenberg, 1976; Osofsky and Osofsky, 1970) have reported on the long term intervention effects on teenage mothers, this became a growing concern as we evaluated continued impact of a mother-infant class programme carried out during the first year of life. The personal growth of mothers observed by staff members led them to ask, "How long-lasting are the attitudinal and behavioural changes in mothers brought about in the programme?" Previous assessment of programme effects had included (1) infant performance, (2) mother-infant interaction, and (3) mastery by mothers of curriculum content (Badger, 1976, 1977). All of these effects were quantifiably positive while classes were in progress or shortly thereafter. The follow-up evaluation measures relatively long term effects of the programme related to the realization of personal aspirations in a population of high risk mothers.

The most apparent consequences of adolescent childbearing and childrearing among the University Hospital population, where 90% of the patients are medically indigent, include (1) interrupted school plans, (2) limited child care facilities or family support, and (3) repeat pregnancies.

When a young mother returns home with her first-born infant, we learned that any romanticized notion she may have had of complete contentment in caring for a baby of her own disappears. If she acts on her plans to complete high school in order "to get off welfare", get a job, and become self-supporting, she will probably do so within one to three months after delivery. In the absence of quality day care centres or licensed day care homes, and with the disappearance of the extended family, she will have a difficult time carrying out her decision to return to school. She may resort to casual child care arrangements, and her concern then becomes, "Is it fair for me to try to better myself at the expense of my child?"

If, on the other hand, the teenage mother chooses to stay home and become a full-time mother, she quickly abandons hope for personal achievement. As a single parent without a high school education, she knows she will continue to remain "on welfare". Her feeling of powerlessness increases and she begins to accept her future as "fated". One of the manifestations of this attitude towards herself and her future is a second, unplanned pregnancy within two years after the birth of her first child.

The three- and five-year follow-up of those mothers we were able to locate from the pilot project, and a telephone survey completed during 1977 and 1978 (class groups 1–38) on those mothers who participated in the adapted service programme, provide some data which suggests that a mother training programme seems to affect positively the ability of young mothers to realize educational and employment goals and to plan and limit family size.

Pilot Project

As reported previously, the attrition of white Appalachian mothers and the loss of matched pairs of infants in the class and home visit groups limited the final analysis of testing data to the black population or a sample of 36 mother-infant pairs at 12 months. We were subsequently able to locate 34 of these mothers who agreed to be interviewed in their homes when their children were three years of age. (We were unable to locate two mother-infant pairs in the home visit group.)

The follow-up evaluation of these 34 mother-infant pairs, which is reported elsewhere, (Badger, 1981), included testing of the child with the McCarthy Scales, as well as assessing the mother's social circumstances through a questionnaire that included data on 15 social variables and yielded a maternal risk score (MRS). Prenatal history, age and education of mother, family structure, socially deviant behaviour, neighbourhood area within Cincinnati and welfare status were critical variables in describing the profile of the high risk mother. As we looked more closely for possible differences in family functioning between the class and home visit groups, we made an unexpected discovery: the 18 mothers, collapsing high and lower risk mothers, who participated in the mother training classes demonstrated higher aspirational level and more upward mobility than did mothers in the comparison home visit group (N = 16). Fourteen of these 18 mothers were either attending college or working with only partial welfare assistance. Of the 16 mothers in the home visit group, only one mother was enrolled in a job training programme; nine were totally dependent on welfare. Statistical analysis indicated a significant difference between the two groups of mothers in their realization of school and/or employment goals ($X^2(1) = 17.59$, $p < .001$). Only four of the class mothers and six of the home visit mothers were married at this time ($X^2(1) = .94$, $p > .05$).

Child care arrangements also differed dramatically between the two groups. Class mothers who were employed or enrolled in continuing education programmes reported makeshift plans for the care of their children. Seven of the children from the classes were in unlicensed day care homes, as opposed to only one child of mothers in the home visit group. Further, only six of the mothers in the class group were primary caretakers of their children, as opposed to more than twice as many (13) of the home visit group. Since child performance at three years of age as determined by the McCarthy Scales was not significantly different for class versus home visit children, we speculated that: (1) children of mothers who attended classes may be somewhat jeopardized at three years of age as their mothers pursue personal goals: (2) it is possible that this trend may be reversed in the future as their mothers experience greater fulfilment and success; and (3) upward mobility on the part of the mothers should be reflected ultimately in the lives of the children.

Perhaps the most startling difference between the two groups was the data concerning subsequent pregnancies. In the class group, two of the 18 mothers (11%) had subsequent pregnancies (1 < 2 yrs. apart; 1 > 2 yrs. apart). In the comparison home-visit group, seven of the mothers (44%) had subsequent pregnancies (3 < 2 yrs. apart; 3 > 2 yrs. part; and 1 had 2 others > 5 yrs. old). Statistical analysis indicated a difference in fecundity between class and home visit mothers that was significant ($X^2(1) = 4.64$, $p < . -05$).

In the five-year follow-up, we were only able to locate 28 mother-infant pairs (15 from the class group and 13 from the home visit group). The composition of the groups was similar: eight high and seven lower risk mothers in the class group versus six high and seven lower risk mothers in the home visit group; six male and nine female children in the last group versus five male and eight female children in the home-visit group. The Kent Quick Test (Kent, 1946) was administered to the children in order to determine if there were any measureable congitive differences between the two groups of children at five years of age. The group mean scores (35.73 for the class children and 32.08 for the home visit children) were not statistically significant in a paired t-test. In the standardization of the test, however, the norm of Scale A when administered to five-and-a-half-year-old children is 35–38. As we inspected individual scores of class and home visit children, we found that nine children in the mother training group scored 35 or above in the test; only four of the children in the home visit group scored 35 or above. This group difference was in the right direction, but was not statistically significant ($X^2(1) = 2.39$, $p > .05$)

Upward mobility as determined by employment continued to favour the mothers in the training classes. Thirteen of the class mothers were employed full-time and were not receiving any welfare assistance, as opposed to four in the home visit group. This was statistically ($X^2(1) = 9.11$, $p < .01$). Two mothers in the training classes and four in the home visit group reported that they were married ($X^2(1) = 1.22$, $p > .05$).

Seven out of the 15 mothers in the class group, as compared to 10 out of the 13 mothers in the home visit group, had another child; of those 10 mothers, two had two more children, and one had three more children. The group difference was in the right direction, but was not statistically significant $(X^2(1) = 2.68, p < .05)$.

Child care arrangements for the 13 mothers in the class training group included all-day centre care for eight of the children and home care by the maternal grandmother or a babysitter for the remaining five children. The nine unemployed welfare mothers in the home visit group were primary caretakers of their children, though six reported that their children were attending pre-school, Head Start programmes on a part-time basis. The four employed mothers in this group had their children enrolled in day care centres. The comparable number in both groups who were enrolled in either day care centres or pre-school, Head Start programmes seemed to confound any explanation regarding the impact of these programmes on the children's Kent Quick Test scores.

There are, however, some tentative interpretations we are able to make as we compared the children's Kent Quick Test scores with their mothers' employment and their enrolment in day care centres or pre-school programmes (Table 2). First, since the Kent Quick Test assesses school readiness skills of size, shape, colour and number concepts, we expected that more of the class-trained than the home visit mothers would be providing learning experiences for their children in these areas. One of the questions asked each mother in both groups at the time of the five-year follow-up was, "What are you doing to get (child's name) ready for kindergarden?" (All of the children were five-and-a-half years of age, and were to start school the following month.) Twelve of the class-trained mothers, as opposed to six of the home visit mothers, indicated that they had bought books or were otherwise working on school-related concepts with their children. It is interesting to note that the four mothers in the home visit group who so replied also served to identify the four children in that group who had the highest Kent Quick Test scores. The typical response of mothers of children with the lowest scores was "buying him/her new clothes".

Secondly, if the success of parents as determined by employment and upward mobility is reflected in their children's school performance, motivational behaviours (i.e. attention span and persistence to task) and self-image may be more important indices of school-related achievements. The cumulative long-range effects of IS/MT may be not only a young mother who escapes poverty and welfare dependency, but a child who escapes failure in the public school system.

Thirdly, day care centres are funded at a level so as to include little more than a nutritional diet, adult supervision and a safe environment. We know that single, female parents who are marginally employed have a difficult time providing development-fostering experiences to their preschoolers. Mother training classes are a beginning of a support system. In the absence of quality day care programmes, we can expect that many of the children will be behind as they enter the public school system.

Table 2. Comparison data of child performance, maternal employment and child care arrangements in five-year follow-up of 28 mother-infant pairs included in Pilot IS/MT Project.

	Mother training group				Home visit group		
Child Subjects	(1) Kent Quick Test score	(2) Mother Employed	(3) Child care	Child Subjects	(1) Kent Quick Test score	(2) Mother Employed	(3) Child care
1.	48	Yes	Day care centre	1.	45	No	Pre-school
2.	47	Yes	Day care centre	2.	44	No	Mother
3.	44	Yes	Grandmother	3.	36	No	Pre-school
4.	43	Yes	Day care centre	4.	35	No	Pre-school
5.	42	Yes	Day care centre	5.	34	No	Pre-school
6.	37	Yes	Day care centre	6.	33	Yes	Day care centre
7.	37	Yes	Grandmother	7.	33	No	Pre-school
8.	36	No	Pre-school	8.	32	Yes	Day care centre
9.	35	Yes	Day care centre	9.	28	No	Grandmother
10.	33	Yes	Day care centre	10.	28	Yes	Day care centre
11.	32	Yes	Babysitter	11.	25	No	Pre-school
12.	30	Yes	Day care centre	12.	25	No	Mother
13.	28	No	Mother	13.	19	Yes	Day care centre
14.	23	Yes	Grandmother				
15.	21	Yes	Grandmother				

Service Programme

In order to validate further the follow-up findings in the pilot programme, we decided to look at changes that might have occurred over a period of time, albeit a shorter period of time, in mothers who had been enrolled in the series of 20 classes in the adapted service programme.

We attempted to contact the 225 mothers recruited for the service programme from September 1974 to December 1975 (class groups 1–17), and were able to complete telephone interviews with 114 or 40% of them. The survey was made during January 1977 when the youngest infants were at least one year of age. The interview questionnaire consisted of 20 items that could be answered within a 10-minute period. We tried to eliminate interviewer bias by not pairing a mother with a staff member she had previously known. Questions were asked concerning the mother's present circumstances (i.e. continued schooling or employment, child care arrangements, subsequent pregnancy) as well as her plans for the future.

In the analysis of the data collected by the telephone survey, the 114 mothers were divided into two groups: those who had attended more than half of the classes (N-64) and those who had attended fewer than half of the classes (N = 50) (Table 3).

Table 3. Results of initial telephone survey completed on 114 mothers who were recruited for IS/MT Service Programme from September 1974 to December 1975 (class groups 1–17).

	n = 64 High attenders > 10 classes	n = 50 Low attenders < 10 classes	Chi square statistic and significance level
1. Working or going to school – Yes	90.6%	58%	16.53 p < .001
2. Mother takes care of baby most of the time	20%	40%	5.42 p < .10
3. Mother is pregnant or has another baby	11%	32%	7.408 p < .01
4. Is it difficult to do what you planned, having a baby? – Yes	22%	24%	.29 NS
5. What are your plans for yourself in the next two years? – No plans	12.5%	24%	3.39 NS

Differences in the responses between the two groups (high versus low attenders) that would favour high attenders, and therefore recommend classes as a vehicle for changing the behaviours of adolescent mothers, were anticipated. But would there be, in fact, an already apparent trend in the behaviour of the high attenders that would affirm the findings of the longer range, follow-up study with the pilot group?

In order to determine whether the two groups were in fact two different populations of adolescent mothers, the mean maternal risk scores (MRS) for the two groups were compared. One might reasonably presume that the high attenders had initially been more emotionally mature, had higher aspirational levels and benefited from better family support systems. In fact, however, the initial MRS mean scores were comparable.

The comparable initial MRS made the follow-up differences all the more striking. Differences were most conspicuous in three areas:

1. Of the high attenders, 91% were working or going to school versus 58% of the low attenders.

2. Of the high attenders, 20% were primary caretakers of their child versus 40% of the low attenders.

3. Of the high attenders, 11% were pregnant or had had a subsequent pregnancy versus 32% of the low attenders.

To discover motivational differences that might have existed between high and low attenders related to continued education or employment, we compared responses to a related question, "What are your plans for yourself in the next two years?" Plans for completing school and/or finding employment were highly similar within the two groups. Eighty-four per cent of the high attenders and 72% of the low attenders provided information about a variety of training programmes and/or jobs they intended to pursue. The plans offered by both groups, like the mean initial MRS, appeared to be comparable. A minority of respondents indicated "no plans" for the future (13% of the high attenders and 24% of the low attenders). Only four of the 114 mothers mentioned marriage as a possible plan within the next two years.

A cluster of four questions was intended to evaluate the mother's adjustment to her present circumstances. To the first, "Is it difficult to do what you planned, having a baby?", a majority of mothers in both groups responded, "No." The second, "What is most different about your life now that you have a baby?", generated a variety of responses, including more responsibility, limited freedom and insufficient money. Approximately one-fourth of each group reported no differences. To the third question, "Does a baby get in the way of your good times?", a majority of mothers in both groups answered, "No." The fourth question asked, "If you had it to do over again, would you have a baby at age 15?", a majority of mothers in both groups said they would not.

In spite of the commonalities which existed in both groups – future plans, initial MRS and adjustment to present circumstances – a dramatic difference was found in the greater percentage of high attenders who were able to act on their plans, 91% versus 58% of the low attenders.

Since high attenders were acting upon their plans to complete schooling or to become employed, it is not surprising that fewer of them were primary care-takers of their infants, 20% versus 40% of the low attenders. Child care arrangements varied, including grandmother or other relatives and casual babysitters. In spite of the possible jeopardy to the infant as the adolescent mother pursues personal goals, more than 90% of the mothers in both groups said they were satisfied with their child care arrangements. Contradictory evidence, however, casts some doubt on the validity of that response in both groups, since approximately 50% of all mothers indicated that they would choose to place their babies in a day care centre if one were available.

Fewer of the high attenders had repeat pregnancies, 11% compared to 32% of the low attenders. Approximately one-third of the high attenders reported using no form of birth control, compared to almost half of the low attenders. It would again seem that high attenders are better able to put plans for limiting family size into action, just as they did regarding plans for continuing education and employment.

In January 1978 we called back the same mothers (class groups 1–17) who had been called in January 1977. Their babies were between two and three-and-a-half years of age. We were able to reach approximately two thirds of those mothers by telephone. Again we broke the sample of 77 mothers into two groups – 44 mothers who were high attenders, and 33 who were low attenders. Differences between the two groups are described in Table 4. It is apparent that the group differences were remarkably attenuated one year later; 55% of the high attenders were working or going to school, as opposed to 48% of the low attenders, which was not statistically significant. Child care arrangements were comparable, as were repeat pregnancies, though 15% of the low attenders reported having more than two babies at that time. Slightly encouraging, perhaps, is the differential response to their plans for the future. Significantly fewer of the high attenders than the lower attenders had ''no plans''.

Table 4. Results of repeat telephone survey completed on 77 mothers from the sample of 114 mothers reported on in Table 3.

	n = 44 High attenders > 10 classes	n = 33 Low attenders < 10 classes	Chi square statistic and significance level
1. Working or going to school – Yes	55%	48%	1.16 NS
2. Mother takes care of baby most of the time	48%	48%	.51 NS
3. Mother is pregnant or has another baby	32%	33%*	1.024 NS
4. Is it difficult to do what you planned, having a baby? – Yes	16%	12%	7.16 p < .05
5. What are your plans for yourself in the next two years? – No plans	9%	33%	8.95 p < .05

* Of the low attenders, 15% were mothers of more than two babies at this time, while none of the high attenders had more than two children ($x^2(2) = 8.14$, $p < .02$).

We also attempted to contact all mothers who had been invited to participate in class groups 18–28. Their babies were between one and two years of age, and this was the first time we attempted to reach them. Of the 171 mothers recruited for these classes, we were able to talk to a total of 63 in the follow-up telephone survey (37%). Results on the same five sample questions are described in Table 5. Although the differences between high and low class attenders are not as dramatic as those reported in the telephone survey of January 1977, they are nonetheless encouraging. Following through on work or school plans was

Table 5. Results of initial telephone survey completed on 63 mothers recruited for IS/MT Service Project from January 1976 to February 1977 (class groups 18–28).

	n = 38 High attenders > 10 classes	n = 25 Low attenders < 10 classes	Chi square statistic and significance level
1. Working or going to school – Yes	74%	44%	6.32 $p < .05$
2. Mother takes care of baby most of the time	34%	48%	1.23 NS
3. Mother is pregnant or has another baby	15%	28%*	1.024 NS
4. Is it difficult to do what you planned, having a baby? – Yes	26%	8%	5.99 $p < .05$
5. What are your plans for yourself in the next two years? – No plans	18%	12%	1.37 NS

* Of the low attenders 4% had more than two other babies at this time. None of the high attenders did.

reported by 74% of the high attenders versus 44% of the low attenders, which was statistically significant. Almost twice as many of the low attenders as the high attenders reported repeat pregnancies or another baby. And in a realistic view, 26% of the high attenders versus 8% of the low attenders said it was difficult to follow through on their own personal plans with a baby to care for.

CONCLUSIONS

While the initial thrust of the IS/MT pilot project was to intervene during infancy within a population who were developmentally at risk because of mother immaturity, the follow-up evaluations reported suggest that the postnatal classes also affect the teenage mother's ability to realize future educational and employment goals and to plan and limit the size of the family. Insofar as programme goals are translated, the infant outcome seems to be inextricably intertwined with the personal development of mothers. It was serendipitous to discover in a three- and five-year follow-up of the pilot project that a mother training programme carried out during the infant's first year of life might also be rated highly as a job development programme for adolescent mothers.

Through the delivery and evaluation of postnatal classes for teenage mothers and their first-born infants over a period of nine years (1973–82) we learned:

1. Shortly after delivery in the hospital postpartum units is an optimal time and place to recruit teenage mothers for educational intervention. Our experience suggests that almost all adolescent mothers respond favourably

to their infants, and seem eager to learn parenting skills at this time.

2. Within the poverty population, the birth of the first baby may be a critical time to intervene. What a young mother wants and hopes for her infant, which she may have missed, can serve to motivate and mobilize her at a turning point in her life. So it seemed to be with the young mothers in the IS/MT pilot project.

3. A home visit made after the mother and infant's discharge from the hospital and prior to the time of the first class can sensitize the class instructor to family strengths or weaknesses that may offset the young mother's participation in the programme. Lack of support from the extended family, as noted regularly in our white Appalachian population, may negatively influence a young mother's ability to utilize extra-familial resources.

4. A group instructional approach that is both child- and mother-centred, and features demonstrations and positive feedback by the instructor as mothers interact with their infants, is an especially effective teaching technique in shaping adolescent attitudes and behaviour. Extrinsic reinforcers such as high school credit, cab pools, free toys and photos of infants positively influence class participation and indirectly tell a young mother that the programme is important for her and her infant.

5. Mother-infant classes which are carried out in a paediatric clinic as part of the delivery of well-baby care can individualize and integrate services from several professional disciplines into a single co-ordinated effort. The humanistic delivery of medical, social and educational services, difficult as it is to evaluate, may be a critical variable in explaining programme effectiveness.

6. In the absence of quality day care programmes or adequate family support, infants of adolescent mothers may be in jeopardy as their mothers pursue educational and employment goals. A society that cares for its children must provide adequate child care.

7. Weekly postnatal mother-infant classes are an economically feasible means of helping an especially high risk population of mothers and infants. The IS/MT model, however, is only the beginning of a support system that communities must build upon if teenage welfare mothers and their infants are going to escape the culture of poverty.

REFERENCES

Alan Guttmacher Institute. (1981). *Teenage Pregnancy: The Problem That Hasn't Gone Away*. New York: The Alan Guttmacher Institute.

Badger, E. (1971a). *Teaching Guide: Infant Learning Program*. Paoli, Pa: The Instructo Corporation.

Badger, E. (1971b). A mothers' training program – the road to a purposeful existence. *Children* 51, 168–173.

Badger, E. (1972). Mothers' training program – a sequel article. *Children Today* **3**, 7-12.

Badger, E., Burns D. and Rhoads B. (1976). Education for adolescent mothers in a hospital setting. *AJPH* **66**, 469-472.

Badger, E. (1977). The infant stimulation/mother training project. In *Infant Education*, Caldwell, B. and Stedman, D. (Eds). New York: Walker Publishing, 45-62.

Badger, E., Burns, D. and Veitze, P. (1981). Maternal risk factors as predictors of developmental outcome in early childhood. *Journal Infant Mental Health* **2:1**, Spring, 33-43.

Baldwin, W. (1980). *Adolescent pregnancy and childbearing – growing concerns for Americans.* Population Bulletin **31**, 2.

Bayley, N. (1969). *Bayley Scales of Infant Development.* New York: The Psychological Corporation.

Caldwell, B. (1964). Mother-infant interaction during the first year of life. *Merrill-Palmer Quarterly* **10**, 119-128.

Dennenberg, V.H. (1964). Critical period, stimulus input emotional reactivity: a theory of infantile stimulation. *Psychol Rev* **71**, 335-351.

Furstenberg, F. (1976). *Unplanned Pregnancy: The Social Consequences of Teenage Childbearing.* New York: The Free Press 1976.

Goldfarb, W. (1955). Emotional and intellectual consequences of psychological deprivation in infancy: a re-evaluation. In *Psychopathology of Childhood*, Hock, P. and Zubien, J. (Eds). New York: Grune and Stratton, 105-119.

Graham, B.D. (1980). *An agenda for America's children.* Annual Report from the American Academy of Pediatrics.

Harlow, H.F. (1963). The maternal affectional system. In *The determinants of Infant Behavior*, Foss, B. (Ed). New York: John Wiley, 3-33.

Kent, G. (1946). *Kent Series of Emergency Scales (Scale A).* New York: The Psychological Corporation.

Lewis, M. and McGurk, H. (1972). Evaluation of infant intelligence. *Science* **178**, 1174-1177.

McGee, E. (1982). *Too Little, Too Late: Services for Teenaged Parents.* A report of the Ford Foundation, New York.

National Center for Health Statistics. (1983). *Monthly Vital Statistics Report.*

Osofsky, H. and Osofsky, J. (1970). Adolescents as mothers. Results of a program for low income pregnant teenagers with some emphasis upon infant development. *Am J Orthospsychol* **40**, 825-835.

Pittman, K. (1985). *Preventing Children Having Children.* Conference Report of the Children's Defense Fund, Washington, D.C.

Provence, S. and Lipton, R.C. (1962). *Infants and Institutions: A Comparison of Their Development with Family-Reared Infants During the First Year of Life.* New York: International University Press.

Thomas, A., Chess, S. and Birch, H. (1970). The origin of personality. *Scientific American* **233**, 102-109.

Thornton, A. and Freidman, D. (1983). *The changing American family.* Population Bulletin **38:4**, October.

Uzgiris, I. and Hunt, J. (1975). *Assessment in Infancy: Ordinal Scales of Psychological Development.* Urbana: University of Illinois Press.

Zelnik, M. and Kanter, J.F. (1979). Reasons for nonuse of contraception by sexually active women aged 15–19. *Family Planning Prospectives* **11:5**, September/October, 289-296.

17. Recent developments in work with young offenders

DENIS W. JONES

INTRODUCTION

Work with young offenders in the late 1970s was greatly influenced by a mood of fatalism. Studies showed the failure of correctional programmes in the U.S.A. (e.g. Lipton, Martinson and Wilks, 1975; Lerman, 1975) and the U.K. (e.g. Cornish and Clarke, 1975; Brody, 1976). The failure of legislative strategies, such as the 1969 Children and Young Persons Act in England and Wales, to achieve intended objectives (Morris and McIsaac, 1978; Thorpe, 1983a), and the ability of states in the U.S.A. to avoid Supreme Court decisions covering childrens rights to due process and fair hearings (see Kittrie, 1971), combined to reduce effective opposition to new policies based upon punishment, incarceration and deterrence. This contributed towards a rapid rise in the number of young offenders in custody. In England and Wales, for example, the number of male young offenders under 17 sentenced to custodial institutions rose from 2,408 in 1968 to 7,700 in 1981 (Jones, 1985a).

During periods of economic depression young people are an easy target for general societal discontent (Pearson, 1983). Young offenders are a particularly easy target – the undeserving segment of an unappreciated group. In Britain, Conservative Party conferences and gatherings have resounded to the rhetoric of "law and order" emotionalism (Whitelaw, 1979; Brittan, 1985), while the Labour Party has been preoccupied with the issue of police accountability. However, in recent years there has been a recognition by many practitioners of political realities, and the development of programmes targeted at specific areas

Working with troubled adolescents
ISBN 0-12-179720-1

in the juvenile justice system. In the U.K. this has been aided by the recognition by some socialists that law and order is an issue with which they must engage (e.g. Lea and Young, 1984; Birley and Bright, 1985), and by the development of supportive organizations (e.g. Association for Juvenile Justice; Justice for Children; Childrens Legal Centre).

This chapter will review some of the significant recent developments in work with young offenders and suggest future strategies.

PREVENTION

Crime prevention is an irresistible concept, but one which has dangers when applied to individuals. It can all too easily be used to justify a widening of the net of social control and an invasion of liberty (Billis, 1981), and as a residual category under which vague, unspecific, unassessable schemes can be established (Smith, 1980).

Longitudinal studies have shown that it is difficult to identify accurately future delinquency at an early age. Even the ''best'' predictors – family size, single parenthood, poor housing, deprived neighbourhood and parental criminality – identify almost half of likely offenders incorrectly (West, 1982; Osborn and West, 1978). Hill (1985) found that measurements of the personality and behaviour of those in institutions after sentencing added little to the efficiency of predictors of recidivism based on data available at the time of sentencing. However, in a reworking of the data from the Cambridge Study in Delinquency Development, Farrington (1985a) suggests that it *is* possible to achieve higher predictive success when focusing upon chronic or persistent offenders.

In a review of recent delinquency prevention programmes, Farrington (1985b) criticizes the trend to target such programmes on organizations – particularly schools – areas and the environment, and not on individuals. He claims that the work of Elliott, Ageton and Canter (1979), which has extended and developed Hirschi's (1969) influential work which related delinquency to the lack of intimate attachments, aspirations and moral beliefs that bind most people into general law-abiding behaviour, has yet to be validated, despite having become the major basis for delinquency prevention funding in the U.S.A. He also claims that the work of Rutter and Giller (1983), while being ''the best and most comprehensive review of the literature on juvenile delinquency ever published'' (Farrington, 1985b, pp. 10–11), significantly undervalues Schweinhart and Weikart's (1980) evaluation of the Perry pre-school project. This was a variety of Head Start which showed significant effects of pre-school enrichment programmes, designed to improve intellectual ability, on future delinquency.

Farrington suggests that experimental preventive programmes should be developed. These would be aimed at high risk groups, such as children born to convicted parents, with the objective of improving parental skills and behaviour and developing childrens' intellect. Programmes aimed at the wider environment, of value in themselves, should also be developed, but with little expectation of an impact upon delinquency.

One such preventive strategy, which avoids the danger inherent in focusing upon individuals, is that of "situational crime prevention" and "target hardening". This derives in some measure from the demonstration of the link between architectural design and criminal opportunity by Oscar Newman (1973), who proposed the concept of "defensible space" (see also Coleman, 1985).

Examples put forward include measures to increase the risk of apprehension by, for example, having conductors on public transport and caretakers in blocks of flats, or by siting vulnerable objects, such as telephone kiosks, in more noticeable situations. Better housing design and management can reduce unsupervised semi-public areas on housing estates. Better lighting, and more efficient repair and maintenance, can reduce the spiral of neglect which attracts vandalism. Low-cost security measures to vehicles and houses can reduce criminal opportunity (Clarke, 1980; Mayhew and Clarke, 1982). New leisure facilities can create legitimate opportunities. The overall effectiveness of such strategies will depend upon whether the crimes prevented are opportunistic or premeditated. If the latter, then criminal activity could simply be diverted to other targets. Fortunately, it is known that the former predominates, creating wide scope for such measures.

INSTITUTIONS

Evidence of high recidivism by those discharged from institutions, together with high cost, has made institutions an easy target. In England and Wales a recent investigation by the Social Services Inspectorate has disclosed the poor resources, living conditions, situation and staffing abilities in the Community Home sector, which is funded by local government (D.H.S.S., 1985). Cost factors have placed great strain on child care institutions in the private and voluntary sector, resulting in large scale closures (Berridge, 1984). Only where political conditions over-ride these factors have institutions been allowed to develop.

Custodial institutions

Despite recidivist rates of around 80% over a two-year period, Detention Centres and Borstals (renamed Youth Custody Centres) in England and Wales have expanded in the 1980s, as a result of their association with political philosophies of punishment, retribution and degradation. As Rutherford (1986) has stated, it is ironic that "the only deliberately punitive institutions within the prison system (are) exclusively for its youngest inmates".

In 1979 Home Secretary Whitelaw announced an "experimental" tougher regime in several detention centres in the U.K., the evaluation of which showed no significant impact upon recidivism (Home Office, 1984). Undeterred by the absence of deterrence, the regime has now been extended to all detention centres. As the research suggested that young people grew to enjoy certain activities, such as military drill, this has been reduced and replaced by more unproductive and unstimulating tasks (Brittan, 1985).

Ironically, it seems that magistrates are now undermining the government's intention by sending more young people to youth custody, which still retains some of the aura of "training", and less to detention centres (Sumner, Jarvis and Parker, 1986). As a response, the notion of differential treatment has been dropped, the government proposing to allocate inmates to either detention centre or youth custody on the basis of availability (Home Office, 1986).

Residential institutions

Institutional care has had little effect on recidivism. Pre-treatment delinquency, delinquency during treatment, and family environment are better predictors of recidivism than any form of treatment given to date.

At the same time, the pattern of misbehaviour *during* treatment can be strongly affected by treatment programmes. (For research reviews, see Rutter and Giller, 1983, chapter 9; Cawson, 1984; Lipton *et al.*, 1975; Wright and Dixon, 1977.)

It is too easy to dismiss residential care on the basis of these findings. They may reflect institutional factors that can be altered. For example, staff attitudes and behaviour have been shown to be reinforcers of negative client behaviour (Cawson and Perry, 1977; Ackland, 1981). The ease with which institutions can reject young people with whom they fail, resulting in placement in more restrictive settings, allows the avoidance of self-questioning by adults and a transfer of blame onto young people (Millham, 1981).

It may be significant that the most exciting institutional initiatives in Britain are occurring in settings which find it difficult to reject youngsters, and which have reasonably secure funding. Reid (1982) and Brown (1985) both give examples of the use of social skills training and the application of social learning theory (Spence, 1982) with difficult or damaged young people, and both indicate initially promising results.

The most successful application of social learning methods in institutional settings to date is the Achievement Place model originating in Kansas (Kirigin, Wolf, Braukmann, Fixsen and Phillips, 1979). This uses a system based upon contracts, points, intensive social reinforcement and self-government, in small family-style living situations. Young people progress through the scheme to placement at home, where support is provided for parents and young people to maintain achieved change. Results suggest positive effects upon social functioning, classroom behaviour and parental involvement, though it remains to be seen whether such effects transmit through to offending behaviour. (The Achievement Place model is discussed in greater detail in chapter 10 – Ed.)

COMMUNITY BASED PROGRAMMES

At first sight, community based work with young offenders has the attraction of being cheaper than residential care, though this is not necessarily the case (see Knapp, 1985). It does, however, avoid disruption to young people's family life, schooling, peer group interactions and developmental experiences, and allows work to be undertaken based upon actual life experiences, the application of learned skills and behaviour, and immediate feed-back of the effectiveness of skills training.

Police cautioning and diversion from court

The fear of appearance before a juvenile court may be a more effective deterrent than the actual experience itself. In addition, cautioning and diversion strategies are cost effective from the point of view of police, courts and families. This combination of objectives has caused the growth of cautioning to be *the* major feature of juvenile justice developments over recent years on both sides of the Atlantic. For example, the number of cautions issued to male juveniles in England and Wales had risen from 19,000 to 88,000 between 1954 and 1983 (Jones, 1985a).

Available evidence suggests that, while diversion has been effective with respect to recidivism, it has also had some serious unintended consequences. Research in both the U.S.A. and Britain indicates that one of the major effects has been the widening of the net of social control. Formal cautioning has more often replaced previous "no further action" strategies, or informal police warnings, than prosecution. (See, for the U.K., Ditchfield, 1976; Farrington and Bennett, 1981; and on the U.S.A., Rausch and Logan, 1983.) Research also suggests that, by giving greater discretion to police officers, judgements of "good parenting" which ignore cultural factors can lead to bias in cautioning practice on the basis of class (Bennett, 1979), colour, age and sex (Landau and Nathan, 1983; Fisher and Mawby, 1982).

A recent initiative has been the development of "instant" cautioning, whereby cautions are administered at the point of arrest without further police enquiries if an admission of guilt is forthcoming (Home Office, 1985). This may well be based upon police operational requirements, with the intention of reducing the workload resulting from the increase in cautioning, rather than upon any expectation of effectiveness.

A more useful development would be to concentrate cautioning developments upon young people currently prosecuted, thereby avoiding net widening effects. All cautioning schemes need careful monitoring to ensure their effectiveness.

Mediation and reparation

Developments in mediation and reparation help to focus much more attention upon the victims of crime. While there are many pilot schemes (see Marshall and Walpole, 1985), the project gaining most attention in the U.K. has been the Northamptonshire Juvenile Bureaux schemes based in Corby and Wellingborough (Centre for Youth, Crime and Community, 1984). Reparation, in fact, is a small part of a larger juvenile diversion strategy which has had a substantial impact upon the local juvenile justice system. The Bureau is staffed by five workers, one each from police, probation, youth work, social work and education, and deals with all arrested juveniles. Between November 1981 and November 1982 the Bureau received 492 referrals, of whom 77 were involved in some form of offence resolution. This took one of three forms – direct reparation to the victim, a direct apology to the victim, or indirect reparation to society. In the first published review of the scheme, Blagg (1985) argues that reparation is more meaningful to the young offender when the victim is an identifiable individual than when it is an organization, such as a department store or municipal agency.

Similar initiatives have taken place in the U.S.A. and elsewhere (Marshall and Walpole, 1985; Galaway, 1983). There is a real danger of a "bandwagon" effect, as practitioners disillusioned with current strategies seize upon the new "miracle cure". Mediation and reparation call for skilled and sensitive work, and may require re-training of current juvenile justice practitioners. It is to be hoped that public confidence in an initiative with potential for offenders and victims alike is not damaged by insensitive and untrained staff.

Intermediate treatment and the LAC 83/3 initiative

"Intermediate Treatment" (hereafter I.T.) was created in the U.K. in the late 1960s, with the objective of becoming a form of intervention situated "intermediately" between those interventions that removed the offender from home and those that supervised the offender in the community. As such, it was part of a vague and sometimes confused political strategy designed to abolish custodial sentences for young offenders, raise the age of criminal responsibility, and transfer power over disposal from magistrates to social workers. Decisions over disposal would be based upon detailed assessment of the "real" causes of behavioural problems of which delinquency was only a "symptom". It appears that the clientele of I.T. were to be those young people then in Approved Schools and Detention Centres, though this is also vague.

However, due to the lack of implementation of key sections of the 1969 Children and Young Persons Act; to a change of political climate; to a reaction by magistrates and police to their loss of power; and to the timidity, confusion and lack of self-confidence of the social work profession, this target group remained in institutions – whose numbers, contrary to the spirit of the Act, substantially increased – and I.T. found itself a service without a client. Not surprisingly, a new clientele was found, based around young children believed to be "at risk" of offending, and the service provision was modelled on traditional youth work methods, a service from which many of the first I.T. officers came. (This is, inevitably, a very brief history. For more details see Thorpe, 1983*b*; or Tutt, 1982.)

By the end of the 1970s, therefore, I.T. had acquired a confusion of aims and objectives and a mixture of client groups. The availability of funds for I.T., at a time when other youth work funding was being cut, meant that it was applied to every possible form of work with young people from the cradle to the age of maturity. Under I.T. could be found play groups, education, residential care, activities, holidays, arts and crafts, family therapy, group work, individual counselling, and traditional uniformed groups. (A few I.T. schemes had avoided this and applied themselves to specific management of offenders. These are discussed in a subsequent section.) The initiative announced under Local Authority Circular 83/3 (D.H.S.S., 1983) could almost be seen as a response to Preston's call for a "central directive" to help focus I.T. (Preston, 1982). Under this initiative £15 million was made available for the establishment of new alternative to custody projects in England and Wales by voluntary bodies, designated by local authorities. The intention was to provide space for local authorities to transfer resources from residential to community care, and to promote an inter-agency initiative. Funding criteria necessitated local authority involvement, monitoring of project's impact on local juvenile justice systems, and local authority indication of plans for long term funding.

Despite some problems related to short term funding, initial fears that projects would widen the social control net do not appear to have materialized. In general terms, the initiative appears to have been successful in promoting greater inter-agency co-operation, focusing I.T. upon serious offenders at risk of custody, increasing awareness of the interaction of different components of the juvenile justice system, and in some areas has had a significant impact upon custodial sentencing (Edwards, 1986).

One of the hallmarks of the initiative has been the flexibility allowed to each project to respond to local conditions and develop internal strengths. The following description of one project indicates one method that has been adopted.

The Well Hall Project is managed by the Rainer Foundation and provides alternatives to custody for young offenders in the London Borough of Greenwich. It has been operational from the winter of 1983/84. The Project has established tight referral systems to ensure that placements are only offered to young people seriously at risk of custody. Over 50% of referrals are, as a result, diverted towards other non-custodial sentences. Following a referral, the Project prepares a detailed "assessment" report which is presented to Court, discussing previous and current offending in the context of an individually prepared alternative to custody programme, designed to deal with offending behaviour.

Due to major concern with establishing credibility with magistrates, young people and other professionals (Jones, 1985b), and to the preparation of high quality reports, the Project has had 75% of the places that it has offered accepted at the point of sentence.

To design treatment programmes, the Project is assisted by a clinical psychologist, Dr Barrie Brown (see Brown, forthcoming). Programmes derive from social learning theory, involve group work and individual counselling, and are designed to focus directly on the criminal behaviour that is the reason for referral. There is an emphasis on increasing knowledge of the operation of the juvenile justice system, but throughout placement the key theme is the exploration of the consequences of crime for self, victim and society and the reinforcement of non-criminal behaviour. There is a commitment to avoid intrusion into other areas of young peoples' lives unless specific assistance is requested. Programmes in general involve 168 hours' attendance over the period of a four-month deferred sentence.

Initial results, after 18 months of operation, indicate that over four-fifths of young people committed to the Project maintain over 80% attendance; that custodial sentencing in Greenwich has fallen by one third; and that there has been a significant reduction in the frequency and seriousness of reoffending during and after the programme. However, most young people leaving the Project have reoffended, and 40% have received custodial sentences (Jones, 1986). Significant gaps in referral systems have been identified. More detailed recidivist data will be collected following a search of Criminal Record Office files.

Other community based initiatives

Many young offenders have skills deficits that can be related to the development and maintenance of offending behaviour (see Spence, 1982, for a review). Inappropriate behaviour during interactions with the police can contribute to the likelihood of arrest. Several projects have developed using social skills training methods as an integral part of their work.

The Shape Project in the West Midlands of the U.K. uses methods derived from the Achievement Place Project. Adjudicated offenders aged from 16 to

24, referred by probation officers and social workers, are given short term living accommodation, work experience, employment preparation and "survival" skills training (Ostapuik, 1982). Over a 26-week placement, group responsibility and self-government are encouraged, and behaviour modification programmes using financial rewards developed. Early results suggest that 70% of those completing the programme have not reoffended within 12 months.

The Shape Project indicates how the boundaries between "residential" and "community based" programmes can become blurred, in that Shape's links to the local community are such that few of the features usually associated with residential care apply. The Birmingham Action for Youth Centre (B.A.Y.) indicates how day care provision can blur the boundaries between "schooling" and I.T. This centre provides an alternative to residential care for young people via attendance for five days per week over an average eight-month period. After skills assessment, skills training programmes focused upon education, self-management and daily routine are developed. Earned points provide access to special activities. Work experience allows the application of learned skills. Initial results suggest that only five of the first 24 young people completing the programme had been placed in institutions of any form after six months (Preston, 1982).

In the United States, the Kentfield Rehabilitation Programme in Michigan was devised to keep serious juvenile offenders at home by the provision of wage based public works, part-time schooling, behavioural group sessions and points based reward systems. Results were such that local financial support was forthcoming (Davidson and Robinson, 1975). Fo and O'Donnell (1975) report on a scheme that trained sessional workers to work with young offenders in the community, using contracts as a basis for the development of relationships, and report a reduction in behaviour problems targeted and a significant reduction in delinquent behaviour despite this *not* being a specific target. A similar concept, though more focused upon offending behaviour, has been developed by the Rainer Project in Southend, Essex, England, with substantial achievements (Rainer Foundation, 1985).

In Basingstoke, Hampshire, England, the Woodlands Project, established by the Rainer Foundation at the request of local magistrates, encourages young offenders who would otherwise be likely to receive custodial sentences to script "cartoons" and video-films of their past offences, provides individual counselling, and develops individual "reparation" projects to the area of the community in which the key referral offence has taken place. In total opposition to the national trend, custodial sentences given to young people fell from 18 in 1980 to two in 1983 (Rutherford, 1986, pp. 136–147).

Many young offenders receive institutional placement due to the absence of a living situation in their home community. The development of professional fostering schemes (Hazel, 1978) as an alternative to such placement can itself reduce the dangers of institutionalization, but can also be combined with other community based provisions to provide comprehensive packages of offence-focused work.

SYSTEMS MANAGEMENT

A large proportion of juvenile criminality is unplanned, opportunistic and irrational, committed for excitement or immediate gratification. However, as young people grow through adolescence "spontaneous desistance" (Trasler, 1979) may occur, possibly due to changes in status from "schoolchild" to "young adult", alteration in peer group relationships, changing leisure patterns and assumption of responsibility. Official intervention of all types is spectacularly unsuccessful in affecting offending patterns, with possibly more negative than positive consequences due to the effects of labelling and the association of offenders with each other.

A strategy of delinquency management, aimed at reducing the negative impact of official reaction to criminal behaviour by young people, has developed in certain parts of England and Wales. This is based upon careful monitoring of the inputs and outputs of local juvenile justice systems and the identification of key decision makers and key stages in the reaction to criminal careers. One of the first findings was the discovery of the key role played by the recommendations contained in reports submitted to courts by social workers and probation officers. The more serious the sentence, the more likely were magistrates to be making the sentence recommended to them (e.g. Reynolds, 1982; Thomas, 1982; Thorpe, Green and Smith, 1983). In many areas, the majority of young offenders in residential care did not satisfy a "care and control" test designed to justify such placement (e.g. Paley and Green, 1979).

In order to slow down the climbing of the steps of the tariff ladder into custody or care, three key stages were identified at which steps could be diverted off the rungs. These were: (a) the first appearance in court; (b) the first statutory involvement of welfare agencies; (c) the first entry into residential care. By extending police cautioning, providing a range of non-statutory welfare interventions in support of low tariff sentences, extending the range of statutory interventions in the fields of supervision and I.T., and providing specific alternatives to residential care or custody, it is possible to hold young people within the community until "desistance" or "growing out of crime" (Rutherford, 1986) occurs.

Several local authorities, mainly in the North of England, have developed such programmes under the framework of I.T., with significant success in reducing placements in care and sentences to custody (Thorpe, 1983b). The most celebrated attempt to alter the operation of the institutional response to young offenders is that of Jerome Miller in Massachusetts during the early 1970s. After attempting to reform the institutions and encountering fierce opposition, Miller realized how fragile such reforms were, and how easy it would be to reverse achievements in areas such as dress and appearance. As an alternative, he closed all the large training schools, transferring young people home, to fostering or to small group homes provided by the private sector. These reforms seem to have been sustained (Rutherford, 1986, chapter 3).

CONCLUSIONS

Interesting developments *are* taking place in work with young offenders despite an unsympathetic political climate. Many are based at local level, showing that it is possible to develop practices at this level that can lead to a reversal of national trends.

Ray Jones (1983) has set out an agenda for the future. He identifies the need to react to delinquency, to avoid over-reaction, to avoid intervention that promotes delinquency, to be aware of deprivation as well as delinquency, to make sense to recipients of the service, to be acceptable to the community, and to aim at effectiveness. Overall, he calls for interventions that allow young people to grow out of criminality, a strategy similar to Rutherford's "developmental" approach that supports the home, school and young person in order to keep the offender in the community (Rutherford, 1986).

Young people have a strong sense of justice. There is a need to separate elements of justice and welfare currently intertwined in juvenile justice systems. Sanctions can then be related to criminal behaviour, providing they are also based on the sort of humanitarian approach advocated by Jones, while a range of support, advice and assistance can be provided on a voluntary basis (see Harris, 1985). It is not possible to force someone to receive help!

A humanitarian ethos must pervade institutions. There is a need to reduce internal rules and procedures designed to ensure smooth running of the institution but which stigmatize and dehumanize the young people within them. If young people have to be removed from their home and families, the experience should be as minimally detrimental as possible, involving few restrictions on basic rights. There are still far too many young people living in drab, understimulating, reactive institutional settings. Pressure is on the residential sector. The institutions that survive should be the ones that can show a high commitment to staff development and the application of specific working methods to identified problems. These should be methods which young people themselves have been involved in identifying, though financial considerations may be more influential than professional ones.

In both community based and residential settings there should be a healthy scepticism about treatment effectiveness, and a suspicion of treatment pro-grammes involving restrictive and controlling practices. Basic rights, such as food, pocket money or family contact, should not be used as treatment tools. There is a need to avoid being over-concerned with consideration of cost effec-tiveness and recidivism rates. More humane, less destructive methods have justification in themselves.

Local initiatives should be encouraged and given secure funding over a reasonable time period. Short term funding places unrealistic stress on the pro-duction of "results" from early, experimental phases of project development. It also diverts attention from service delivery to fund raising, and increases staff insecurity.

Inter-agency co-operation needs to be promoted, and professional barriers reduced, without jeopardizing confidentiality. Voluntary bodies working with delinquents should be given the power to take over family work from the social services department. As Rutter and Giller (1983) argue, such family involve-ment can be a crucial component of delinquency reduction (see Preston, 1982).

If the child care system does not respond to the needs of young people, there is a real danger of the displacement of young offenders into residential educational settings (Berridge, 1984) or private psychiatric settings (Schwartz, Jackson-Beeck and Anderson, 1984). With this can go loss of human rights and the loss of controls on abuse of professional power.

Overall, however, must be the need to recognize Brooke's dictum that "the notion that creation of new structures will remedy existing problems" is invalid (Brooke, 1979). Society needs to be helped to accept a certain level of adolescent misbehaviour without subjecting the culprits to massive doses of social control. More than anything else, there is a need to give adolescents meaningful roles in society (Morash, 1983), to create bonds to social institutions, to develop a sense of self-esteem and self-confidence, and to create the stable base from which the risks that promote developmental, psychological, educational and personal growth can be taken.

I would like to thank John Coleman, Helen Edwards, Chris Green and David Murray-Smith for comments on an earlier version of this paper.

REFERENCES

Ackland, J.W. (1981). Institutional reactions to absconding. *British Journal of Social Work* **11**, 171–187.

Bennett, T. (1979). The social distribution of criminal labels. *British Journal of Crimino-logy* **19**, 134–145.

Berridge, D. (1984). Private childrens homes. *British Journal of Social Work* **14**, 347–60.

Billis, D. (1981). At risk of prevention. *Journal of Social Policy* **10**, 367–379.

Birley, D. and Bright, J. (1985) *Crime In the Community*. London: Labour Campaign for Criminal Justice.

Blagg, H. (1985). Reparation and justice for juveniles. *British Journal of Criminology* **25**, 267-279.

Brittan, L. (1985). Short sharp shocks: a new sense of purpose. *Community Care* **2-5-85**, 16-18.

Brody, S.R. (1976). *The Effectiveness of Sentencing*. London: H.M.S.O. Home Office Research Study 35.

Brooke, R. (1979). *Law, Justice and Social Policy*. London: Croom Helm.

Brown, B. (1985). An application of social learning methods in a residential programme for young offenders. *Journal of Adolescence* **8**, 321-331.

Brown, B. (forthcoming). Services for adolescents. In *Community Psychology*, Koch (Ed.). London: Academic Press.

Cawson, P. (1984). Young Offenders and residential care. *Research, Policy and Planning* **2**, 7-12.

Cawson, P. and Perry, J. (1977). Environmental correlates of attitude among residential staff. *British Journal of Criminology* **17**, 141-156.

Centre for Youth, Crime and Community (1984). *Crime Prevention: Diversion – Corporate Action with Juveniles*. Northampton: Northamptonshire County Council.

Clarke, R.V.G. (1980). 'Situational' crime prevention: theory and practice. *British Journal of Criminology* **20**, 136-147.

Coleman, A. (1985). *Utopia on Trial*. London: Shipman.

Cornish, D.B. and Clarke, R.V.G. (1975). *Residential Treatment and its Effect on Delinquency*. London: H.M.S.O. Home Office Research Study 32.

Davidson, W.S. and Robinson, M.J. (1975). Community psychology and behavior modification: a community-based program for the prevention of delinquency. *Journal of Corrective Psychiatry and Behavior Therapy* **21**, 1-12.

Department of Health and Social Security (1983). *Further Developments of Intermediate Treatment*. London. Local Authority Circular 83/3.

Department of Health and Social Security (1985). *Inspection of Community Homes*. London: H.M.S.O. Social Services Inspectorate.

Ditchfield, J.A. (1976). *Police Cautioning in England and Wales*. London: H.M.S.O. Home Office Research Study 37.

Edwards, H. (1986). Personal Communication. Juvenile Offenders Team, National Association for the Care and Resettlement of Offenders. London.

Elliott, D.S., Ageton, S.S. and Canter, R.J. (1979). An integrated theoretical perspective on delinquent behavior. *Journal of Research in Crime and Delinquency* **16**, 3-27.

Farrington, D.P. (1985a). Delinquency prevention in the 1980s. *Journal of Adolescence* **8**, 3-16.

Farrington, D.P. (1985b). Predicting self-reported and official delinquency. In *Prediction in Criminology*, Farrington, D.P. and Tarling, R. (Eds). New York: SUNY.

Farrington, D.P. and Bennett, T. (1981). Police cautioning of Juveniles in London. *British Journal of Criminology* **21**, 123-135.

Fisher, C.J. and Mawby, R.I. (1982). Juvenile delinquency and police discretion in an inner city area. *British Journal of Criminology* **22**, 63-75.

Fo, W.S.O. and O'Donnell, C.R. (1975). The Buddy System: effects of community intervention on delinquent offences. *Journal of Behavior Therapy* **6**, 522-524.

Galaway, B. (1983). The use of restitution as a penal measure in the United States *Howard Journal* **22**, 8-18.

Harris, R.J. (1985). Towards just welfare. *British Journal of Criminology* **25**, 31-45.

Hazel, N. (1978). The use of family placements in the treatment of delinquency. In *Alternative Strategies for Coping with Crime*, Tutt, N. (Ed.). Oxford: Blackwell and Robertson.

Hill, G. (1985). Predicting recidivism using institutional measures. In *Prediction in Criminology*, Farrington, D.P. and Tarling, R. (Eds). New York: SUNY.

Hirschi, T. (1969). *Causes of Delinquency*. Berkeley and Los Angeles: University of California Press.

Home Office (1984). *Tougher Regimes in Detention Centres*. London: Prison Department Young Offender Psychology Unit.

Home Office (1985). *The Cautioning of Offenders*. London. Circular 14/1985.

Home Office (1986). *Criminal Justice: Plans for Legislation*. London: H.M.S.O. Cmnd. 9658.

Jones, D.W. (1985a). Justifying Juvenile Injustice – The Juvenile Justice System in England and Wales. Unpublished M. Sc. thesis, University of Salford.

Jones, D.W. (1985b). The need for credibility. *Initiatives* 5, 12.

Jones, D.W. (1986). The Well Hall Project: Interim Report. London: Rainer Foundation. Unpublished.

Jones, R. (1983). Justice, social work and statutory intervention. In *Providing Criminal Justice for Children*, Morris. A. and Giller, H. (Eds). London: Arnold.

Kirigin, K.A., Wolf, M.M., Braukmann, C.J., Fixsen, D.L. and Phillips, E.L. (1979). Achievement Place: a preliminary outcome evaluation. In *Progress in Behavior Therapy with delinquents*, Stumphauzer, J.S. (Ed.). Springfield, Illinois: Chas C. Thomas.

Kittrie, N. (1971). *The Right to be Different*. Baltimore: John Hopkins Press.

Knapp, M. (1985). *The Comparative Costs of Intermediate Treatment and Custodial Sentences*. Canterbury: University of Kent. Personal Social Services Research Unit.

Landau, S.F. and Nathan, G. (1983). Selecting delinquents for cautioning in the London Metropolitan Area, *British Journal of Criminology* 23, 128–149.

Lea, J. and Young, J. (1984). *What is to be done about Law and Order*. Harmondsworth: Penguin.

Lerman, P. (1975). *Community Treatment and Social Control*. Chicago: University of Chicago Press.

Lipton, D., Martinson, R. and Wilks, J. (1975). *The Effectiveness of Correctional Treatment*. New York: Praeger.

Marshall, T. and Walpole, M. (1985). *Bringing People Together: Mediation and Reparation Projects in Great Britain*. London: Home Office Research and Planning Unit Paper 33.

Mayhew, P. and Clarke, R. (1982). Vandalism and its prevention. In *Developments in the Study of Criminal Behaviour*. Volume 2, Feldman, P. (Ed.). London: Wiley.

Millham, S. (1981). The therapeutic implications of locking up children. *Journal of Adolescence* 4, 13–26.

Morash, M. (1983). Two Models of Community Correction: one for the ideal world, one for the real world. In *Evaluating Juvenile Justice*, Kluegal, J.D. (Ed.). London: Sage.

Morris, A. and McIsaac, M. (1978). *Juvenile Justice*. London: Heinemann.

Newman, O. (1973). *Defensible Space*. London: Architectural Press.

Osborn, S.G. and West, D.J. (1978). The effectiveness of various predictors of criminal career. *Journal of Adolescence* 1, 101–107.

Ostapuik, E. (1982). Strategies for community intervention in offender rehabilitation: an overview. In *Developments in the Study of Criminal Behaviour*, Volume 1, Feldman, P. (Ed.). London: Wiley.

Paley, J. and Green C. (1979). Are we sitting on the offence. *New Society* 21–6–79.

Pearson, G. (1983). *Hooligans*. London: Macmillan.

Preston, M.A. (1982). Intermediate treatment: A new approach to community care. In *Developments in the Study of Criminal behaviour* Volume 1, Feldman, P. (Ed.). London: Wiley.

Rainer Foundation. (1985). *The Rainer Project*. (Southend). London.

Rausch, S.P. and Logan, C.H. (1983). Diversion from juvenile court: panacea or Pandora's box? In *Evaluating Juvenile Justice*, Kluegal, J.R. (Ed.). London: Sage.

Reid, I. (1982). The development and maintenance of a behavioural regime in a secure youth treatment centre. In *Developments in the Study of Criminal Behaviour* Volume 1, Feldman, P. (Ed.). London: Wiley.

Reynolds, F. (1982). Social work influence in juvenile court disposal. *British Journal of Social Work* **12**, 65–76.

Rutherford, A. (1986). *Growing Out of Crime*. Harmondsworth: Penguin.

Rutter, M. and Giller, H. (1983). *Juvenile Delinquency: Trends and Perspectives*. Harmondsworth: Penguin.

Schwartz, I. Jackson-Beeck, M. and Anderson, R. (1984). The "Hidden" system of juvenile control. *Crime and Delinquency* **30**, 371–85.

Schweinhart, L.J. and Weikart, D.P. (1980). *Young Children Grow Up*. Ypsilanti, Michigan: High/Scope Press.

Smith, G. (1980). *Social Need*. London: Routledge and Kegan Paul.

Spence, S. (1982). Social skills training with young offenders. In *Developments in the Study of Criminal Behaviour* Volume 1, Feldman, P. (Ed.). London: Wiley.

Sumner, M., Jarvis, G. and Parker, H. (1986). Sentencing Trends. *British Journal of Criminology* **26**.

Thomas, H.A. (1982). The road to custody is paved with good intentions. *Probation Journal* **29**, 93–97.

Thorpe, D. (1983*a*). Deinstitutionalisation and justice. In *Providing Criminal Justice for Children*, Morris, A. and Giller, H. (Eds.). London: Arnold.

Thorpe, D. (1983*b*). National trends in intermediate treatment. *Orchard Lodge Studies of Deviancy* **3**, 75–88.

Thorpe, D., Green, C. and Smith, D. (1983). *Punishment and Welfare* (4th edition). Lancaster: Centre for Youth, Crime and Community: Occasional Papers in Social Administration 4.

Trasler, G. (1979). Delinquency, recidivism and desistance. *British Journal of Criminology* **19**, 314–322.

Tutt, N. (1982). An overview of intervention with young offenders: the political and legal contexts. In *Developments in the Study of Criminal Behaviour*. Volume 1, Feldman, P. (Ed.). London: Wiley.

West, D.J. (1982). *Delinquency: Its Roots, Careers and Prospects*. London: Heinemann.

Whitelaw, W. (1979). Speech to 1979 Conservative Party Conference, cited Home Office (1984). p. 1.

Wright, W.E. and Dixon, M.C. (1977). Community prevention and treatment of juvenile delinquency: a review of evaluation studies. *Journal of Research in Crime and Delinquency* **14**, 35–67.

18. Intervention with runaway youth and their families: theory and practice

PAUL R. ADAMS AND GERALD R. ADAMS

I. UNDERSTANDING RUNAWAY BEHAVIOUR

Introduction

Every year thousands of families are confronted with a runaway child or teenager. While everyone acknowledges running as a growing problem (Libertoff, 1980), too few professionals are equipped to deal with this often difficult and frustrating group of needy youth and their families. In this chapter we discuss the problems relating to runaway behaviour which make it such a significant concern, and offer practical suggestions for intervention with runaway youth and their families. The effort has been made to provide information useful to human service providers in a broad range of professional disciplines and agency settings. However, assuming that effective intervention requires knowledge and understanding, we begin with a discussion of theoretical issues related to runaway behaviour.

Definition

The definition of runaway behaviour has been a troublesome issue. The *National statistical survey on runaway youth* (Opinion Research Corporation, 1976) concluded, after extensive debate about alternatives, that an acceptable definition of running away should include operational specifications on (a) age of youth, (b) absence of parental or guardian permission, and (c) a criterion on time gone. The first two definitional dimensions have been universally accepted (e.g. Bock and English, 1973; Goldmeier and Dean, 1973; Leventhal, 1963, 1964), while the last criterion has not been rigorously defined and specified between studies. The most frequent age and time criterion includes youth under the age of 18 years, and absence of more than 24 hours or away overnight.

Assumptions

Underlying this chapter are certain assumptions which are neither original nor unique to the authors; they are explicated only to illustrate clearly the authors' perspectives. The assumptions are as follows: (a) runaway youth are *not* a homogenous group, despite the large body of literature and research which treats them as such. (For some potentially useful typologies of runaways, see Adams, 1980; Brennan, 1980; and Orton & Soll, 1980); (b) runaway behaviour is a problem in its own right, and is also symptomatic of other problems; (c) runaway behaviour represents a continuum of responses ranging from a pattern of chronic maladaptation on one extreme, to the opposite extreme of being a fundamentally healthy reaction to a pathological environment; (d) runaway behaviour may have multiple causal and contributory factors such as individual psychopathology, non-pathological psychological problems, inadequate or abusive parenting, dysfunctional patterns of family interaction, environmental stressors, and peer influences; (e) there are identifiable sub-groups of runaway youth, representing distinct populations of runaways, each requiring markedly different long-term intervention efforts; and, (f) effective intervention with runaways requires accurate assessment of the problems which appear etiologically linked to the runaway behaviour, and which may contribute to a re-occurence of running.

Potential negative consequences of running

Runaway behaviour has clearly definable negative life event consequences, and creates diminishing life choices which place the adolescent at risk in completing several developmental tasks of adolescence (Young, Godfrey, Matthews and Adams, 1983). One of the most paradoxical realities of adolescence is the quest for independence and autonomy while maintaining familial ties and relations. Available evidence has demonstrated that "typical" adolescents find it difficult to establish this balance (Sullivan and Sullivan, 1980). Given the strained relations between the runaway youth and his or her parents, prior to running, it should come as no surprise that returning adolescents find parental controls become more stringent and tense (Opinion Research Corporation, 1976). Other data indicate that when reconciliations are made between youth and parents, they are made in a subdued, uncommunicative environment, which may be overtly tense and highly explosive (Gottlieb and Chafetz, 1977).

Runaways, on average, receive poor treatment (Adams, 1980). Indeed, girls who encounter the legal system as a result of running away often find more problems than assistance. Libertoff (1976, 1980) and Young and Pappenfort (1977) have noted the inappropriateness of subjecting adolescent runaways to the juvenile justice system. Treatment itself is generally poor and the stigmatizing effects of juvenile justice action are likely to have unfortunate effects in the future.

The National Youth Alternatives Project study on the alcohol use and life stress of adolescent runaways and their families (Van Houten and Golembiewski, 1978) indicated that runaways tend not to differ from non-runaways in amount of liquor consumption and frequency of drinking. However, it was found that runaways tended to have begun drinking at earlier ages and drank for different reasons (i.e. drinking to escape versus social drinking). While some experimentation with substance use is expected of many contemporary adolescents, runaways appear to be at greater risk, with few parental and societal sanctions or controls which might limit such behaviour.

A growing sense of sexuality is a normal developmental outcome of adolescence; however, both male and female runaways may, of necessity, come to sell sex for favours (Baizerman, Thompson and Stafford-White, 1979; Chapman, 1976; Perlman, 1980). According to Boyer and James (1981), it is estimated that there are 600,000 prostitutes between 6 and 16 years of age, with the majority emerging from runaway and abandonment backgrounds. Elswhere, the unintentional "drift" into sexual deviance by runaways has been described (Boyer and James, 1981; Davis, 1971; James and Vitaliano, 1979).

Since most runaway youth are still in school and run during the school year (Opinion Research Corporation, 1976), academic progress is at least temporarily interrupted. Runaways tend to have more difficulty in school than non-runaway comparisons (e.g. Brennan, Huizinga and Elliott, 1978; Shellow, Schamp, Liebow and Unger, 1967; Walker, 1976), and at least one longitudinal study indicates these vocational training difficulties continue into adulthood (Olson, Liebow, Mannino and Shore, 1980).

Another risk of running away is that it can result in premature pregnancy and early parenthood (Baizerman et al., 1979; Chapman, 1976; Perlman, 1980). Perlman (1980) noted that for many female runaways, a sense of failure in parent-child relations stimulates many towards intentional pregnancy. In so doing, the runaway feels mother love makes her existence purposeful and orderly; thus the baby will solve all problems. However, the challenges of early parenthood are many. For example, motherhood may remove the youth from her peer groups and from the dating opportunities which provide for social development.

Further evidence indicates that teenage childbearing is associated with delayed growth and development of the runaway's offspring. Marecek (1979) has illustrated in a comparison of black youths having given birth prior to 18, between 18 and 19, and between 20 and 25 years of age, that over a seven-year period several undesirable consequences emerged for the offspring. Children born of adolescents are at risk of becoming socially maladjusted, likely to have extensive peer relationship problems, and often maintain a propensity toward temper tantrums and impulsivity.

In sum, although running away is not a new phenomenon in the United States, this teenage enigma has recently grown to crisis proportions and thus has become a significant social issue (Gordon, 1981). The runaway problem must be viewed as both an adolescent and family problem (Adams, Gullotta and Clancy, 1985; Wodarski and Ammons, 1981). Runaways place themselves at risk of not completing the normal process of development during adolescence and are likely to experience many negative life event consequences. The family of the runaway is also at risk as a malfunctioning structure, or at best, a structure which must adjust to an adolescent in crisis. This review indicates that the runaway and his or her family are at risk in numerous ways and require continued and extensive attention.

Theoretical perspectives on runaway behaviour

Much of the existing research focusing upon runaway youth has been either descriptive or atheoretical. However, Brennan *et al* (1978) have proposed two useful theoretical perspectives. *Strain theory* proposes that deviant behaviour, such as running away, is the product of socially induced pressure towards deviance, in contrast to a psychopathological perspective which suggests runaway behaviour is an expression of undesirable impulsive tendencies. Thus, potential sources of strain in the home, school or peer group may function as primary agents in creating a sense of personal alienation. In particular, Brennan *et al*. (1978) suggest that feelings of estrangement from family members place a youth in a state of personal "drift", creating a setting for alienation from family norms. While in a state of alienation the youth is likely to turn to the school or peer setting for allegiance and commitment. Should the youth be exposed to a non-conforming peer group or a hostile or rejecting school environment, increased alienation and/or a non-conformist peer group may set the stage for "flight" from the home.

In contrast to strain theory, *control theory* maintains that deviance, in the form of runaway behaviour, can be readily accounted for by a failure of a youth to adequately internalize the social pressures (and/or establish the necessary social linkages to conventional groups) which reinforce compliance to normative behaviour. Thus, Brennan *et al*. (1978) conclude that some runaways are youth whose early socialization produced weak personal commitments to conventional norms and low levels of integration into conventional social groups and institutions. Further, control theory assumes that an integration and personal commitment towards socially accepted normative behaviour insulates a youth from forces associated with deviant activities and runaway behaviour. Thus, weak bonds with the family, school, work or general social community, when coupled with exposure to deviant social behaviour, increase the probability of youth running away from their homes.

Individually, both strain and control theory offer important perspectives to the study of runaway behaviour. However, be it due to interpersonal stress or weak socialization, youth who experience a weakened or attenuated family bond are likely to turn to either the school environment or peer group for allegiance and commitment. Should either the school or peer environment fail to offer support for the youth's personal needs, or provide a non-conformist social environment, there is an even greater probability that neither peers nor teachers will offer a supportive social environment which could buffer the weakened ties with family members and norms. It has been argued that this very condition of weakened interpersonal relations creates deindividuation (Adams and Munro, 1979). That is, finding oneself uncommitted or unattached, an individual is likely to experience a sense of loss of oneself. Typically reported in clinical cases as an unpleasant negative experience, deindividuation is likely to motivate a person toward re-establishing a sense of commitment, self-identity and direction. Thus running away may actually be seen as an attempt toward reindividuation.

Psychological correlates of runaway behaviour

Running away has been defined, historically, as a behavioural manifestation of psychopathology (Riemer, 1940). In fact, the American Psychiatric Association once officially endorsed the "runaway reaction" as a specific mental disorder (Bock and English, 1973). Numerous investigations comparing runaway and non-runaway youth can be found which tentatively support this position. For example, Jenkins and Stahle (1972) indicate that runaways are typified as insecure, unhappy, impulsive children who as adults are likely to have emotional problems. Beyer (1974) reports that runaways are more likely than their non-runaway siblings to have lower self-esteem and show greater signs of depression. Bartollas (1975) and Bassis (1973) present evidence that many runaways see their personal life as an unmanageable and misunderstood problem. Further, runaways have been found to have lower self-regard than their non-runaway peers (Brandon, 1974; Wolk and Brandon, 1977). Edelbrock (1980) describes running away as symptomatic of psychopathology and maladaptation. Unfortunately, we cannot positively state that these factors are *antecedents* to, or *consequences* of, running away. For example, Justice and Duncan (1976) summarize evidence that several correlate behaviours (e.g. drug abuse) to runaway behaviour may be aftermaths rather than causal factors in running away (see Ambrosino , 1971a, 1971b; Pittell, 1968; Robins and O'Neal, 1959).

Although runaway youth have often been seen as pathological deviants who

have neither the stability nor courage to face a difficult situation, counter-
literature suggests that many runaways have psychological aptitudes and abilities equivalent to those of non-runaway peers (Adams and Munro, 1979;
Elenewski, 1974; Maulfair, 1974). In contrast to the "psychopathology"
explanation, it has been argued that running away may be a very rational
(psychologically sound) alternative for youth to take, given certain situational
specifics (Baler, 1939; Libertoff, 1976; Outland, 1938; Robey, Rosenwald,
Snell and Lee, 1964; Skinner and Nutt, 1944). Wilgosh and Paitick (1974)
found no differences between runaways and non-runaways in IQ, self-concept,
or family history relating to crime or separation. Goldmeier and Dean (1973)
argue that runaways are motivated by multiple factors which cannot be reduced
to simple psychopathological explanations. Their data suggest a complex interaction among family (conflict) factors, school (academic achievement) stress,
and interpersonal communication as causal agents. In particular, these
researchers suggest that runaways have a great deal of difficulty communicating
with, and relating to, adults. Therefore, many runaways are likely to be found
in conflicting and stressful situations prior to running away (Roberts, 1982).

However, it is important to note that this same investigation reports that both
runaway and non-runaway youth were found to hold positive self-concepts, to
feel they could handle most of their problems, to get along with siblings, and to
have friends who would listen to them. Earlier research by Gothberg (1947)
reported similar conclusions. Female runaways were found to have a strong
ego, to resent being "put down", to be most sensitive to their environmental
surroundings, while projecting their anxieties to people in authority to a greater
extent than non-runaway female adolescents. A strong ego might be expected
from the nature of runaway behaviour. It seems unreasonable that a weak ego
with inadequate coping strategies would lead to runaway behaviour.

Leventhal (1963) found that runaways felt they had less control over their
environment when compared to non-runaways. The runaway youth were not
found to be intellectually inferior or to hold poor self-concepts. They felt they
could not control the environment around them, so that running away might be
seen as both an alternative and a call for help. Further research (Leventhal,
1964) suggested that runaways may be more inclined to be impulsive, show
poor signs of judgement and maintain feelings of helplessness. These latter findings may be a function of loss of control, which can be reflected by internalized
tension and anxiety. However, a more recent investigation by Goldberg (1972)
found that runaways were more demanding, showed greater difficulty in
tolerating or sustaining close interpersonal relationships, were easily frustrated,
and had a generally impulsive nature.

Likewise, one can argue that a clear case for runaways evolving from a particular social class is not justified. Youth from a variety of home backgrounds
have chosen this alternative (e.g. see Hildebrand, 1968; Gottlieb and Chafetz,

1977). Some evidence also suggests that an equal and often greater number of females to males choose this action (Community Health and Welfare Council, 1972; Chapman, 1976; Raphael and Wolf, 1974; Hildebrand, 1963; *U.S. News and World Report*, 1973; Porter, 1970). Furthermore, these youth are reflecting a growing trend across many social classes and situations (Nye and Edelbrock, 1980), which indicates that the problem may not be one of simple situational causation, but a question of challenging an entire social system (see Wein, 1970; Chapman, 1976; Raphael and Wolf, 1974, for case illustrations).

How then do we reconcile reported differences in the research literature on runaways? It is relatively easy to review selective material that supports a "pathological model" of runaway behaviour. Closer scrutiny of the literature, however, leads us to refute such a perspective on the grounds that runaways show both desirable and undesirable attributes. For example, an integration of the two bodies of literature suggests that adolescent runaways are reasonably intelligent, not particularly psychopathic, perhaps inclined towards negative self-concepts, and likely to show signs of interpersonal communication problems. Yet neither perspective is indisputably correct. Walker (1976) has cautioned against overgeneralization from the existing multidisciplinary literature on runaways, indicating that inconsistent definitions for operationalizing runaway behaviour, quasi-experimental and pre-experimental designs, and failure by researchers to specify the limitations of their data, make it difficult to synthesize and draw conclusions from the existing data.

Family conflict and runaway behaviour

Recognizing the immature social development of many runaways, it should be no surprise that these youth experience conflicting parent-child relations. Parental conflict, alienation from parents and interpersonal tension have been consistently reported in the home life of runaways (e.g. Adams *et al.*, 1985; D'Angelo, 1972; Tobias, 1970; Wattenberg, 1956; Hildebrand, 1963, 1968; Blood and D'Angelo, 1974). In the *National statistical survey on runaway youth* (Opinion Research Corporation, 1976), the negative family dynamics associated with runaway behaviour included parents saying unpleasant things about their youth, paternal drinking problems and heavy use of physical punishment by the father. Further, runaways were more likely to come from single-parent or very large (eight or more family members) households. Thus, individual involvement with the runaway child may be limited due to family disorganization or size. The major differences in child-rearing practices which differentiated runaway from non-runaway youth were that parents of the latter were likely to (a) offer more supervision, (b) help with school work and related activities, (c) remain open to discussion about problems, and (d) express happiness with their youth. In summary, non-runaway families, when contrasted with runaway households, differed in degree of togetherness, communication, and respect for their children.

Evidence by Gullota (1978), however, suggests somewhat different family dynamics for runaways and throwaways. For runaways, family disturbance was predominantly associated with specific parental control issues related to friends, schooling, grooming and behaviour. Throwaways were more inclined to come from families experiencing incestual or abuse problems.

An investigation by Wolk and Brandon (1977) offers further clarification of the parental control variable. Ineffective parental supervision for boys, and overcontrolling and punitive behaviour by parents for girls, were associated with runaway behaviour. Wolk and Brandon argue that, due to ineffective parenting, girls run away to escape a punitive and overcontrolled environment. Boys, on the other hand, due to poor supervision, develop immature and non-adaptive behaviours which lead to runaway tendencies.

These studies suggest the possibility of extensive problems in the families and homelife of runaway youth. The data indicates that intervention programmes which fail to include family therapy are destined for failure. Runaway and throwaway youth come from conflicting and disturbed homes with particular problems associated with poor communication, lack of emotional warmth and ineffective supervision and control. Furthermore, evidence reported by Gottlieb and Chafetz (1977) suggests that interpersonal confrontation, which often leads to runaway behaviour, is preceded by a long history of disagreements and skirmishes. However, on the positive side, little evidence exists to suggest that it is due to a deliberate attempt to hurt the other. Indeed, there appears to be ongoing effort to minimize hurt and to attempt compromise, by both youth and parent.

But what happens when the child runs away and later returns home? Without therapeutic intervention, reconciliation is tense but slightly more subdued. Gottlieb and Chafetz (1977) report a fatalistic quality to the nature of reconciliation: "The fatalistic mode results in both parents and children abandoning any hope of altering or changing one another's attitudes, values, or perceptions. Both parents and children make the best of a difficult situation – interacting, but rarely communicating or sharing feelings and hopes." (p. 222). Hence the "natural" reconciliation process occurring when a youth returns home does not necessarily assure an improved family environment. In far too many instances an uncommunicative environment, lacking in warmth, tense and potentially explosive in nature, is likely to exist. This condition might well look and sound like a "cold war" experience.

Given the complexity of the issues involved in runaway behaviour, what can be suggested as appropriate and useful guidelines for effective intervention and therapeutic efforts? Specifically, once a runaway youth makes contact with a social agency providing services to youth and their families, what steps must be taken to assist them, and in what sequence? The remainder of this chapter will address these critical questions.

II. INTERVENTION AND TREATMENT EFFORTS

Overview

There are three general "phases" that summarize and prioritize the provision of services to runaway youth, regardless of the sub-type of runaway. The first phase includes two components: *crisis intervention* and *stabilized placement*. The second phase also consists of two components: *supportive counselling* and *assessment*. All four components are essential as a bare minimum of service. The third phase includes three components: *long-term therapy* (which may involve family and/or individual therapy); *education/training*; and *support services*. The youth and family members may require none of the third phase components, or may need any combination of them.

These three general phases and their components are listed in order of suggested priority, but flexibility is possible. Components Ia, Ib, IIa and IIb (crisis intervention, stabilized placement, supportive counselling and assessment) may be provided concurrently, if the situation allows. Component IIIa (long-term counselling) is recommended as next in priority unless placement stability is threatened by lack of support services, in which case component IIIc (support services) may become critical to the continuation of longer-term therapy. More detailed discussion of each component follows.

The agency (or individual service provider) first interacting with the youth logically should assume responsibility for crisis intervention, and the initiation of efforts for stabilized placement. Assessment and supportive counselling may be undertaken by the same agency, or may be referred to another service provider. This depends largely on the nature of the agency first contacted, (including the agency's roles, limitations, and policies).

The reader would be well advised, in the discussion which follows, to pay close and thoughtful attention to each question individually. The page constraints of this chapter forced extreme condensation of material. What should be literally pages of discussion is limited to asking a single germane question, or making one summary observation. The reader will find that each question, however, virtually bursts with implications when given careful consideration.

Ia. Crisis intervention

The *purpose* of crisis intervention is to defuse existing and impending crises. Runaway behaviour may (a) be a crisis in itself; (b) indicate crisis situations at home or in the youth's life; and, (c) bring potential crises in its wake. The *responsible party* for crisis intervention is the agency initially accepting contact with the youth. The *desired outcome* is to resolve immediate crises sufficiently that a stable placement is possible. (*Note*: if the youth has made only telephone contact with the agency, the first priority is to establish face-to-face contact, since only then do any other services become feasible.)

There are a number of *important issues* that must be addressed during a crisis intervention effort: (a) Why is the youth at your agency? Is the youth requesting help, or being "forced" to seek help? (b) Has the youth actually run away, or is a run pending? (c) What are the youth's perceptions of the cause/ motive/justification for running away? (d) Are there issues necessitating legal action? (e.g. Has the youth been physically or sexually abused? Has the youth been involved in serious criminal activities? Is the youth in any legal trouble, actual or potential?) (e) Can the parents be contacted? (i.e. Will the youth consent to it? Can the parents be reached at this time?) (f) What are the youth's immediate needs regarding food, shelter, medical attention and psychiatric help?

Ib. Stabilized placement

The *purpose* of this component is to secure a living arrangement which is appropriate to the youth's needs and maximizes the likelihood that the youth will remain settled long enough to do an adequate assessment. The *responsible parties* are the youth and the agency initially accepting contact with the youth. The *desired outcome* is a stable placement which allows for thorough assessment and eventual provision of any long-term intervention or services that may be necessary. (*Note*: this component, though critical, is not always possible; some youth will continue to run. However, it is essential to make the attempt to arrange a stable placement; no further intervention is possible if a youth is not present to participate in the intervention process.)

The *important issues* to be considered during this process include: (a) Has the youth actually run, or is a run pending? (b) If the youth has left home, was leaving voluntary, or was she/he asked to leave? ("Asking" could have been covert rather than direct.) (c) What placement options are available? (e.g. return home, live with other family members, stay with friends, foster care, etc.) (d) Of the available options, which one is most feasible? (Remember that child protective agencies may need to be involved in out-of-home placements.) (e) Will the youth give a verbal agreement to stay in the placement, once arranged? (Some people advocate formalizing such agreements in a signed "contract".)

IIa. Supportive counselling

The *purpose* of this component is to maintain the stability of the placement. The *responsible parties* are the youth and either the agency first accepting contact with the youth, or the agency charged with "case management" responsibilities for the youth. The *desired outcome* of the supportive counselling is to maintain a stable placement in order to facilitate the assessment process. (*Note*: this step does not constitute psychotherapy. It may include stress reduction, ventilation, encouragement, emotional support, and continued crisis intervention; but the intent of supportive counselling is not therapeutic change, it is maintaining the stability of the placement.) The *important issues* to consider for supportive counselling include: (a) Is the youth being accurately heard and understood by the intervention agents? Is that understanding being conveyed in a manner that is credible to the youth? (b) What are the primary emotions currently shown by the youth and/or the parents, and what can be done to alleviate excessively painful or unpleasant ones? (c) What current problems does the youth have which may affect placement stability? What can be done to resolve or alleviate those problems? (d) What are the youth's perceptions of the current placement, and commitment to staying there? (e) Can anything be done to increase the stability of the placement? If so, what?

IIb. Assessment

The assessment includes a thorough examination of several inter-related areas: the problem situation, the youth, and the parents and family. Each of these components of assessment will be considered separately. The *purpose* of assessment is first to delineate the problems as defined by the youth, by the parents and by the interviewer; and then to ascertain individual and family strengths, capabilities, and resources. The *responsible parties* include the youth, the parents and either the agency first accepting contact with the youth, or the agency accepting a referral for long-term therapy. The *desired outcome* is manifold: accurate identification of major issues; prioritization of issues; identification of family resources; tentative selection of possible intervention strategies; formulation of some initial steps toward problem resolution; and initial commitment of both the youth and the parents to active participation in therapy. In addition, there is a particular need for accurate assessment of the parent's marital relationship and its impact on the youth; assessment of family patterns of interaction and communication; and assessment of parenting styles. (*Note*: this component does not constitute therapy; the intent is only to select an intervention strategy appropriate to the identified problem issues. As such it is preliminary to actual therapy. *Note*: returning the youth to the parental home is generally desirable during the assessment period, but these are situations where clinical judgement would suggest that it is not the best option. In such cases, it should be actively opposed.)

The *important issues* to consider in *assessing the problem situation* include: (a) What is the presenting problem? (b) What are the underlying issues and problems? (c) How much agreement and disparity exist between the youth's perceptions and parental perceptions (if parents are available)? (d) How do youth/parent perceptions compare with those of an objective observer (i.e. the interviewer)? (e) Which of the issues and problems identified are resolvable, and which are not? (e.g. a parent who is alcoholic, verbally abusive, overtly hostile toward the youth, and who refuses to be involved in any treatment efforts, may present a virtually "unresolvable" problem. Such an obstacle would be far easier to circumvent than to surmount.) (f) If the problems appear resolvable, are the parties involved willing to participate in change efforts? (This includes a willingness to change their own behaviours, not just those of the other people involved.) (g) What resources, internal and external, do the participants have which might assist change efforts? (h) What are the highest priority issues? Do family members agree on prioritization? (i) For the high priority issues, what are all the potential alternatives for resolving the problem? (j) What are the pros and cons of each alternative (including the feasibility and the willingness of the family to implement it)? (k) Which is the best option for each problem, considering all relevant factors? (l) In general terms, what must be done to implement the best option? Who will be responsible for doing what? (m) What outcome is anticipated if change efforts are successful? (n) How will progress toward the desired outcome be measured? (o) If the chosen alternative does not seem effective, then what?

The *important issues* to consider in *assessing the youth* include the following: (a) Is there a history, or any current symptoms of, psychopathology? (One does not want to assume that pathology underlies all runaway behaviour, but it should at least be considered and eliminated). (b) Are there any contributory medical problems, e.g. endocrine dysfunction, neurological problems, etc.? (This, too, should be considered and eliminated.) (c) Is there a history of delinquent or antisocial behaviours? (d) Are there non-pathological psychological problems (e.g. anxiety, poor self-esteem)? (e) What are the contributions (if any) which each of the following areas make to the runaway behaviour: problems with parents; problems with siblings; peer group interaction and influences; environmental stress factors (e.g. poverty, high-crime neighbourhoods); other stress factors? (f) What are the youth's assets/deficits pertaining to: general intellectual ability; academic performance; social skills; problem solving ability; coping skills; communication skills? (g) What is the youth's history of drug/alcohol usage: substance used; frequency of use; physical addiction; psychological dependence? Is substance abuse severe enough that it may interfere with change efforts? Does the youth perceive the substance abuse as a problem? Is the youth willing to seek treatment for substance abuse if judged necessary? (h) What is the youth's willingness to be involved in long-term change efforts? Will the youth make a commitment for personal change?

The *important issues* to be considered in *assessment of parents/family* include: (a) Is there any history, or any current symptoms, of parental psychopathology? (Consider and eliminate.) (b) Are there medical problems that might underlie any aberrant parental behaviour? (c) Is there a history, or any current indication of, child neglect or abuse (physical, sexual or verbal)? (d) Is either parent alcoholic, or an abuser of other substances (including prescription medications)? (e) If parental alcoholism or substance abuse exists, how much and in what way does it contribute to the youth's runaway behaviour? Does the parent acknowledge the substance abuse as a problem? Is the parent willing to seek help? (f) What is the status and quality of the parent's relationship: are they married? Duration and stability of their relationship? Frequency and intensity of marital arguments? General affectional level? Quality of sexual relationship? Parental communication styles and skills? Problem solving abilities and strategies? Methods for coping with stress? (g) How, and in what way, does the parental relationship seem to affect the youth? (h) How much are the parents aware of the youth's perception of the problems which contributed to the runaway behaviour? (i) In the judgement of the interviewer, how much are the parents a part of the problem? (j) Do the parents acknowledge any responsibility for existing problems? (k) What are the parent's feelings toward the youth (both current feelings, and the predominant ones they usually have)? (l) Are the parents willing to be involved in change efforts? Will they make a commitment for personal change, rather than expecting all change to be on the youth's part? In the judgement of the interviewer, are the parents capable of effective participation in change efforts? (m) Will it be workable to have parents and youth living in the same household during the early treatment or intervention efforts? (n) What is the youth's general relationship with her/his siblings? (o) Are there patterns of sibling interaction which contributed to the runaway behaviour? (p) What assets and resources does the family have which may assist in change efforts?

IIIa. Intervention strategies (long-term therapy)

The *purpose* of this component is to resolve the individual and/or family problems which appear directly linked to the runaway behaviour. The *desired outcome* is, initially, the resolution of both intra- and interpersonal problems within the family, sufficient to establish family stability and to promote positive growth in family members; and then to help family members learn skills for preventing and resolving problems that may arise. The *responsible parties* include the youth, the parents, other family members, and the agency providing long-term therapy. (*Note*: the desired outcome is not always achievable, and it is critical that therapists acknowledge this fact. Encouraging a youth with unrealistic hopes of parental or family change not only destroys therapist credibility, but the lack of change may be interpreted by even high-functioning adolescents as an indication of personal inadequacy or failure.)

The *important issues* to be considered include: (a) Is there agreement between therapist and clients as to the primary issues and goals of therapy? (b) If alcohol or drug abuse exist, is concurrent treatment for the substance abuse underway or imminent? (c) What combination of individual and family therapy is likely to prove most productive? (d) Is there a need for inpatient treatment of any family member? (e) Can parent(s) and youth live together while treatment is ongoing? If not, what criteria will determine when, or if, the youth returns home?

Caution: far too many adolescent "treatment programmes" (broadly defined) still attempt to "treat" youth in near-isolation from their families. This can result in predictable, but too often unforeseen, consequences. Good treatment staff typically listen to a youth (which may be a novel experience for some adolescents); convey to the youth a sense of caring; provide role models of appropriate adult behaviour; honestly attempt to understand the youth's feelings, ideas and concerns (again, possibly a new experience); try to show the youth more effective communication and problem solving skills; and help the youth understand that positive alternatives are indeed available. If the youth is then thrust back into a dysfunctional family environment which remains virtually unchanged, the contrast can be actually traumatic. Tentative attempts by a youth to use new-learned communication or problem solving skills may backfire and make things worse at home. The youth is then put into a more difficult, possibly more painful situation, and also gets the unfortunate message that highly touted skills do not work in the real world.

If parents cannot, or will not, make critical changes, the therapist has basically two options: help the youth find a different residence, or help the youth learn to cope with an unpleasant (but time-limited) situation. This latter alternative involves several factors: acknowledging the dysfunctional (and unchangeable) aspects of the youth's dilemma; identifying and teaching coping strategies to help the youth "survive"; teaching skills appropriate for extra-familial contexts; and helping the youth differentiate "normal" and dysfunctional aspects of the family situation.

IIIb. Intervention strategies (interpersonal skills education and/or training)
The *purpose* of this component is to provide remedial education or training for identified areas of skill deficit (and, where appropriate, provide such training to improve existing skills). These skill areas should be ones which can substantially enhance the quality of family interaction (e.g. parent education, communication skills, assertiveness training, marital enrichment). The *desired outcome* would be a significant improvement in client functioning which decreases the probability of runaway behaviour, and which increases the general "quality" of family interactions. The *responsible parties* would be the client(s) directly involved, and the agency accepting referral for education/training. (*Note*: it seems entirely possible that in some situations a judicious referral for education or skill training may be a far more beneficial use of a client's time than equivalent time spent in therapy.)

The *important issues* to be considered in this regard include: (a) Are there existing knowledge or skill deficits (adolescent or parent) in any major areas such as:
social skills; communication skills; problem solving skills; assertiveness; human
sexuality; personal hygiene; parent education/training; building self-esteem;
drug/alcohol education, etc. (b) Would education or skill training in any of
these areas substantially reduce the likelihood of running away, reduce intrafamilial stress, improve relationships within the family, or improve functioning
in social interactions? (c) Are there existing training programmes in your area
to which clients could be referred? (d) How could education or training efforts
be incorporated into ongoing therapy? (e) Would the potential gains resulting
from the education/training be substantial enough to justify the time and money
necessary to complete it?

IIIc. Intervention strategies (support services)

The *purpose* of this component is to identify any critical needs or environmental
stress factors which could seriously disrupt family functioning, and/or have a
major adverse impact on therapy if the needs are not addressed. Having identified these needs, the therapist would then help the family locate or develop the
resources for meeting them. The *desired outcome* would be early identification of
major needs and problems (or potential problems), alleviation or prevention of
major problems by timely intervention, and maintenance of family stability and
functioning by reducing or eliminating disruptive environmental stress factors.
The *responsible parties* would include the family, the therapist and the agency
accepting the request for assistance. (*Note*: attempts at clinical therapeutic interventions may seem almost meaningless to a family overwhelmed by major stress
factors such as unemployment, serious illness, eviction notices, parental
imprisonment, etc. To a family in situations like these, assistance in resolving a
situational crisis may prove far more valuable than any amount of individual or
family therapy.)

The *important issues* to be considered include: (a) How knowledgeable are
you, as a human services professional, about the types of support services available (and lacking) in your local area, and the procedures for accessing such
services? (b) Does the family have serious problems which threaten family functioning, or which may interfere with therapeutic progress? If so, in what general
areas (e.g. unemployment, financial problems, alcohol abuse, illness, legal problems, etc.)? (c) How effective are current family strategies for coping with
these problems? (d) Does the family have other resources that might help
resolve a particular problem? (e) Which agencies might assist the family in
resolving their problems? How do you make a referral to those agencies? (f) Are
family members intellectually and emotionally capable, at this time, of successfully negotiating bureaucratic mazes and paperwork? If not, what might be
done to assist them? (g) If there are no "formal" agency resources available,
are there "informal" resources which could help the family through a crisis

(e.g. relatives, churches, volunteer organizations)? How would such resources be accessed or activated?

CONCLUSION

Effective intervention with runaways requires a clear comprehension that the word "runaway" is only a shorthand way of representing multiple types, classes or categories of youth. Trying to understand runaways or provide assistance to runaway youth and their families will be much more difficult for those who continue to misperceive runaways as a homogenous group. The intervention strategies advocated in this chapter are intended to provide individualized "treatment plans" which deal with the common needs of all youth, but take into account the uniqueness of each youth, each family and the circumstances which contributed to the runaway behaviour. This combination of common needs and unique circumstances provides an optimum blend for effective intervention, and seems appropriate for use by professionals of any service agency and any theoretical persuasion.

REFERENCES

Adams, G.R. and Munro, G. (1979). Portrait of the North American runaway: A critical review. *Journal of Youth and Adolescence* **8** (3), 359–373.

Adams, G.R. (1980). Runaway youth projects: comments on care programs for runaways and throwaways. *Journal of Adolescence* **3**, 321–334.

Adams, G.R., Gullotta, T. and Clancy M.A. (1985). Homeless adolescents: a descriptive study of similarities and differences between runaways and throwaways. *Adolescence* **20** (79), 715–724.

Ambrosino, L. (1971*a*). Runaways. *Teacher Education* **60** (9): 26–28.

Ambrosino, L. (1971*b*). *Runaways*, Boston: Beacon Press.

Baizerman, M., Thompson, M.J. and Stafford-White. (1979). Adolescent prostitution. *Children Today* **8**, 20–24.

Balser, B. (1939). A behavior problem – runaways. *Psychiatric Quarterly* **13**, 539–557.

Bartollas, C. (1975). Runaways at the training institution in central Ohio. *Canadian Journal of Criminology and Corrections* **17**, 221–235.

Bassis, E. (1973). Characteristics of adolescent runaways in a community residential treatment center. Unpublished doctoral dissertation. United States International University, 73–11433 33/11–B:5505.

Beyer, M. (1974). Psychosocial problems of adolescent runaways. Unpublished doctoral dissertation, Yale University, 74–25718 35/05–B:2420.

Blood, L. and D'Angelo, R. (1974). A progress research report on values issues in conflict between runaways and their parents. *Journal of Marriage and the Family* August, 486–491.

Bock, R. and English, A. (1973). Got me on the run: a study of runaways. Cambridge: The Sanctuary.

Boyer, D. and James, J. (1981). Easy money: adolescent involvement in prostitution. In *Women and the law: The interdisciplinary perspective*, Weisberg, K. (Ed.). Cambridge: Schuckman.

Brandon, J. (1974). The relationship of runaways behaviour in adolescence to the individual's perceptions of self, the environment, and parental antecedents. Unpublished doctoral dissertation, University of Maryland, 75–17712 36/02:B–646.

Brennan, T. (1980). Mapping the diversity among runaways: a descriptive multivariate analysis of selected social psychological background conditions. *Journal of Family Issues* **1** (2), 189–209.

Brennan, T., Huizinga, D. and Elliott, D.S. (1978). *The social psychology of runaways.* Boston: D.C. Heath & Co.

Chapman, C. (1976). *America's runaways.* New York: Morrow.

Community Health and Welfare Council of Hennepin County, Minneapolis, Minnesota (1972). *Follow-up study of runaway youth served by The Bridge*, U.S. Department of Health, Education and Welfare, Washington, D.C.

D'Angelo, R. (1972). *Families of sand: a report concerning the flight of adolescents from their families.* National Directory of Runaway Centers/National Youth Alternatives Project, 1830 Connecticut Ave., N.W., Washington, D.C. 20009.

Davis, N.J. (1971). The prostitute: developing a deviant identity. In *Studies in the sociology of sex*, Henslin, J. (Ed.). New York: Appleton-Century Crofts.

Edelbrock, C. (1980). Running away from home: Incidence and correlates among children and youth referred for mental health services. *Journal of Family Issues* **1** (2), 210–228.

Elenewski, R. (1974). Runaway youth: a study of personality factors and the locus-of-control dimension in adolescent runaways. Unpublished doctoral dissertation, University of Miami, 74–23393 35/04–A: 1975.

Goldberg, M. (1972). Runaway American. *Mental Hygiene* **56** (1), 13–21.

Goldmeier, J. and Dean, R. (1973). The runaway: person, problem, or situation. *Crime and Delinquency* **19**, 539–544.

Gordon, J.S. (Ed.) (1981). *Reaching troubled youth: runaways and community mental health. Symposium papers.* DHHS–ADM–81–955. Washington, D.C., National Youth Work Alliance.

Gothberg, L. (1947). A comparison of the personality of runaway girls with a control group as expressed in the themes of Murray's Thematic Apperception Test. *American Journal on Mental Deficiency* **51**, 627–731.

Gottlieb, D., and Chafetz, J.S. (1977). Dynamics of familial generational conflict and reconciliation. *Youth and Society* **9**, 213–224.

Gullota, T.P. (1978). Runaway: reality or myth. *Adolescence* **13**, 543–50.

Hildebrand, J. (1963). Why runaways leave home. *Journal of Criminal Law, Criminology and Police Science* **54** (2), 211–216.

Hildebrand, J. (1968). Reasons for runaways. *Crime and Delinquency* **14**, 42–48.

James, J. and Vitaliano, P.O. (1979). *Modeling the drift towards sex role deviance.* Unpublished manuscript, University of Washington.

Jenkins, R. and Stahle, G. (1972). The runaway reaction: a case study. *Journal of the American Academy of Child Psychiatry* **11**, 294–313.

Justice, B. and Duncan, D.F. (1976). Running away: an epidemic problem of adolescence. *Adolescence* **11**, 365–372.

Leventhal, T. (1963). Control problems in runaway children. *Archives of General Psychiatry* **9** (2), 122–128.

Leventhal, T. (1964). Inner control deficiencies in runaway children. *Achives of General Psychiatry* **11**, 170–176.

Libertoff, K. (1976). Runaway children and social network interaction. Paper presented at the meetings of the American Psychological Association, Washington, D.C.

Libertoff, K. (1980). The runaway child in America. *Journal of Family Issues* **8**, 91–102.

Marecek, J. (1979). Psychological and behavioral status of children born to adolescent mothers. Paper presented at the annual meeting of the American Psychological Association, New York.

Maulfair, V. (1974). A study of selected personality characteristics of non-runaway delinquent, non-runaway, and runaway youths in Missoula, Montana. Unpublished doctoral dissertation, University of Montana, 75–00091 35/07A:4717.

Nye, F.I. and Edelbrock, C. (1980). Some social characteristics of runaways. *Journal of Family Issues* **1** (2), 146–150.

Olson, L., Liebow, E., Mannino, F.V. and Shore, M.F. (1980). Runaway children twelve years later: a follow-up. *Journal of Family Issues* **1**, 165–188.

Opinion Research Corporation (1976). *National statistical survey on runaway youth* (HEW–105–75–2105). Princeton, New Jersey: Opinion Research Corporation, North Harrison Street.

Orten, J.D. and Soll, S.K. (1980). Runaway children and their families: a treatment typology. *Journal of Family Issues* **1** (2), 249–261.

Ostensen, K.W. (1981). The runaway crisis: Is family therapy the answer? *American Journal of Family Therapy* **9** (3), 3–12.

Outland, G. (1938). The home situation as a direct cause of boy transiency. *Journal of Juvenile Research* **22**, 33–43.

Perlman, S.B. (1980). Pregnancy and parenting among runaway girls. *Journal of Family Issues* **1**, 262–272.

Pittell, S.M. (1968). The current status of the Haight-Ashbury hippie community: September, 1968. Haight-Ashbury Research Project, San Francisco (mimeo).

Porter, G. (1970). Runaways: a million bad trips. *Newsweek* 26(October), 67–68.

Raphael, M. and Wolf, J. (1974). *Runaways: America's lost youth*. New York: Drake Publishers.

Reimer, M. (1940). Runaway children. *American Journal of Orthopsychiatry* **10**, 522–527.

Roberts, A.R. (1982). Stress and coping patterns among adolescent runaways. *Journal of Social Service Research* **5** (1–2), 15–27.

Robey, A., Rosenwald, R.J., Snell, J. and Lee, R. (1964). The runaway girl: a reaction to family stress. *American Journal of Orthopsychiatry* **10**, 752–767.

Robins, L.N. and O'Neal, P. (1959). The adult prognosis for runaway children. *American Journal of Orthopsychiatry* **29**, 752–767.

Shellow, R., Schamp, J., Liebow, E. and Unger, E. (1967). Suburban runaways of the 1960s. *Monograph of the Society for Research in Child Development* **1**, 165–188.

Skinner, M. and Nutt, A. (1944). Adolescents away from home. *Annals of the American Academy of Political and Social Science* **236**, 51–59.

Sullivan, K. and Sullivan, A. (1980). Adolescent-parent separation. *Developmental Psychology* **16**, 93–99.

Tobias, J. (1970). The affluent suburban male delinquent. *Crime and Delinquency* **16** (3), 273–279.

U.S. News and World Report (1973). Runaways: rising U.S. worry. September 3, 34.

Van Houten, T. and Golembiewski, G. (1978). *Adolescent life stress as a predictor of alcohol abuse and/or runaway behavior*. Washington, D.C.: Youth Alternatives Project, 1346 Connecticut Avenue.

Walker, K. (1976). Suburban runaway youth at the 1970s. Paper presented at the meeting of the American Psychological Association, Washington, D.C.

Wattenberg, W. (1956). Boys who run away from home. *Journal of Educational Psychology*
    47, 335–343.
Wein, B. (1970). *The runaway generation*. New York: McKay.
Wilgosh, L. and Paitick, D. (1974). Juvenile offenders grouped according to type of
    delinquent behaviour and their parents; intelligence achievement and family inter-
    action. *Canadian Journal of Criminology and Corrections* **16**, 68–76.
Wodarski, J.S. and Ammons, P.W. (1981). Comprehensive treatment of runaway
    children and their parents. *Family Therapy* **8** (3), 229–240.
Wolk, S. and Brandon, J. (1977). Runaway adolescents' perceptions of parents and self.
    Adolescence **12**, 175–188.
Young, R. L., Godfrey, W., Matthews, B. and Adams, G.R. (1983). Runaways: a
    review of negative consequences. *Family Relations* **32**, 275–281.
Young, T.M. and Pappenfort, D.M. (1977). *Secure detention of juveniles and alternatives to its
    use: national evaluation program, phase one, summary report*. Washington, D.C., Depart-
    ment of Justice.

19. Working with troubled adolescents: a conclusion

JOHN COLEMAN

In drawing this book to a conclusion I intend to explore three major themes which, I believe, run through many of the contributions. The psychology of adolescence, the impact of theory and the context and rationale for treatment are especially important themes because looked at in combination they reflect the history, the limitations and the future direction of intervention with troubled young people. Reading these chapters has left me with a sense of optimism. This particular field of therapeutic endeavour is alive and well. Innovation is occurring, professionals are questioning their practice and, perhaps most important, theoretical developments are opening up avenues for the exploration of new approaches to treatment. These are all positive and encouraging signs, and render all the more significant the issues raised for debate by the authors of this Handbook.

PSYCHOLOGY OF ADOLESCENCE

The first major theme running through a large number of contributions is that of the psychology of adolescence, and the effect this has on the appropriateness of various interventions. Adolescence as a stage in human development has very particular characteristics, which create important constraints on treatment strategies. These constraints need to be clearly understood if the choice of

strategy is to prove worthwhile. For example, a number of writers draw attention to the developmental tasks of both adolescent and parent in relation to
separation and autonomy, noting how difficulties surrounding the disengagement process can distort or hinder treatment programmes.

Berkowitz in Chapter 2 underlines the fact that without at least some degree
of severance of the infantile emotional ties, the young person is likely to find the
making of new and appropriate relationships outside the family extremely problematic. He makes the point that resistance to this disengagement can come not
only from the adolescent, with his or her fear of true individuation, but from the
parents as well, who may struggle in a variety of ways to ''hold their adolescent
close, to possess their child, and to prevent individuation''. As Berkowitz says,
unless the parents can see the young person as a real object, an individual
separate and distinct from them, then the essential developmental tasks will
prove most difficult for the teenager.

This point is taken up by a number of contributors, in particular by Fulmer
and Medalie in Chapter 3, and by Kerfoot in Chapter 13. Fulmer and Medalie
draw attention to the concept of the family as a system, and to the inevitable
repercussions on all members of that system when changes occur in any one of
them. Thus when the young person seeks to separate from the family, by
leaving home or by becoming more emotionally independent within the home,
this will inevitably bring changes in the parental relationship. Thus adults,
having less opportunity to take the parenting role, will be forced towards an
intensification of the husband or wife role. These changes may be positive, but
clearly they will not necessarily be so, and even if the outcome is a better or
closer relationship between man and woman, there are likely to be substantial
readjustment problems on the way.

These developmental issues raise important questions for the consideration
of individual or family therapy with adolescents. In Chapter 13 Kerfoot points
out the risks of family work, precisely because of the overriding importance of
the separation/autonomy problem. As Kerfoot says, the young person may be
quite unable to make use of family therapy because it represents a demand for
co-operation with adults, and becomes just one more, perhaps rather subtle,
form of parental control. Alternatively the young person may be so caught up in
the infantile regressive phase of adolescence that he or she simply becomes an
echo of the parents' views and attitudes. Clearly in any consideration of the
relative merits of individual and family work with teenagers some attention
needs to be paid to the current state of the young person *vis-à-vis* separation and
individuation.

All workers in this field need to bear in mind that certain features of
adolescent behaviour – for example, ambivalence, negativism, resistance to
authority and so on – may hinder attempts to involve teenagers in any form of
adult-directed treatment. Such characteristics of adolescent behaviour are of

course commonplace, but they are especially important where they come to be used "in the service of resistance". In such situations the therapist has to work not only with the presenting problem but with adolescence itself if growth and change are to be achieved.

It may at times be necessary to use specialized techniques to get round such problems, especially with the younger age group. This is something which is noted by a number of authors, and it links with the more general point that the level of maturity is a critical factor in deciding upon treatment alternatives. McAdam, in her discussion of cognitive behaviour therapy (Chapter 9), underlines the importance of this factor in her work. Thus for example the generation of alternative ideas, the ability to perceive cognitive distortion, and the perception and differentiation of the young person's own mental constructs from those of others all depend upon the adolescent's move from concrete to formal operational thinking. If this has not occurred then the teenager will not be able to make much use of such a technique. Other writers have stressed similar points. Lindsay, in Chapter 8, notes that a typical "social skills package", designed for adults, is not always appropriate for young people, and needs to be at the very least set within a particular context in order for adolescents to be able to make use of it.

As Lindsay points out, young people, especially those with difficulties, are likely to find a group of strangers daunting, and to be inhibited and anxious if plunged into a group setting organized and designed by adults. It was for this reason that Lindsay designed his social skills training approach for use in a youth club setting, so that the teenagers could have unstructured time getting to know each other before embarking on the training, as well as having a setting for practising the skills learned. Other writers draw our attention to the fact that adolescence is a period of very rapid maturation in both cognitive and social skills. As the young person reaches increasing levels of maturity so new treatment options become available. It is essential to bear this in mind, not only in order to ensure that alternatives will not be missed, but also so that the therapist does not fail as a result of making unrealistic demands.

Another important developmental issue, of special relevance to adolescents, has to do with the setting of limits, and the importance of boundaries. Both Steinberg (Chapter 6) and Holmes (Chapter 7) discuss group work in a hospital setting where, not surprisingly, boundaries and limits are of considerable significance. Holmes outlines three levels of containment, ranging from the physical, i.e. the therapy room, or the hospital front door, to rules and regulations, and finally to emotional containment, i.e. the young person's own internalized defences and controls. These different levels of containment operate in a variety of ways within a treatment setting but, as Holmes points out, it is the therapist's responsibility to utilize the boundaries so as to reduce anxiety and to free young people sufficiently in order that their own inner resources can be used creatively in the treatment process. Steinberg also draws attention to the role of the adult in setting limits. As he says, "the adolescent needs a safe base in terms of his or her relationships in order to conduct social and personal experiments which at some level are charged with dangerous feelings". The adult therefore has at least three tasks: to provide such a setting, to provide continual definitions (in the form of feedback) of what the limits are, and to provide a living demonstration of survival in the face of continuous attempts to transgress those limits.

Kerslake in Chapter 5 discusses a similar point in the context of group work in an I.T. setting. He describes one aspect of leadership in such a group as that of an "enlightened autocrat". As he says, the aim of the leader should not be to collect arbitrary power, but to provide a clearly defined framework that will be to the group members' benefit. Rules should be as few as possible to maintain the boundaries of the group, and any that cannot be defined and explained should be discarded. Kerslake makes an important point here when he states that a common fault of social workers in groups is to try and achieve a democratic style of leadership too soon. Many adults attempt to share decision-making in order to provide for young people a genuine sense of "ownership". Yet adolescents need exceptional maturity to cope with such responsibilities. However much they may give the contrary impression, young people require first and foremost a defined structure in order for them to feel safe and secure, and to be confident that their own impulses will be controlled. This is why limit setting in treatment is so fundamental to success. Poorly defined limits increase anxiety and lead to more and more acting out. Clearly defined limits, paradoxically, act as a liberating force, allowing the teenager the space and security to work on the problems which brought him or her to the treatment setting in the first place.

It is by considering dimensions such as these that we can see how an awareness of the psychology of adolescence is critical in selecting or developing therapeutic techniques. The process of disengagement, the parental role, issues of cognitive maturity, relationships with authority, structure and containment – all these are factors which will play a part in determining not only the success but the appropriateness of various interventions. Without this background knowledge adults are bound to be severely limited in the opportunities they have for rewarding work with young people.

THEORIES AND METHODS

A second major theme running through the book has to do with the impact of theory, and its interaction with methods of intervention. As I pointed out in Chapter 1, theory has a variety of roles to play. Not only does the practitioner's theoretical background influence to a large extent his or her choice of treatment, but theory alerts us to especial areas of vulnerability, points up possibilities for new treatment strategies, and provides a framework within which to make sense of particular problems, disorders or disabilities.

One excellent example of this latter point may be found in Will (Chapter 15). Here the author uses systems theory to understand the problem of incest. Thus asking the question "What function does incest serve for the family?", although at first sight a rather strange way of looking at such a situation, forces the enquirer to consider the roles of all members of the family, especially those of the spouse and the other siblings. This perspective sheds a quite different light on what at first might appear to be, for example, a problem solely of the sexual abuse of the daughter by the father. As Will indicates, a systems approach alerts us to a range of anxieties, defences and shared myths within the family, all of which contribute to an environment in which incest becomes possible. Incest is thus seen as a manifestation of extensive psychopathology concerning the family as a system rather than within one member of that family.

Brown (Chapter 10) provides a further illustration of the same point, only from a different angle. This author uses a behavioural approach to explain violent behaviour in the classroom to the teachers involved. Brown and his co-workers demonstrated that violence on the part of the young people was closely related to certain interpersonal behaviours of the teachers themselves, and his analysis of the pattern of interaction facilitated a marked reduction in aggressive outbursts by teenagers. Here Brown relied upon a behavioural analysis to throw some light on apparently spontaneous and unpredictable actions, and with the help of his theoretical framework was able to ameliorate the situation.

In the best of circumstances theoretical developments inform, encourage and stimulate new approaches to treatment. The growth of systems theory and its application to family therapy is one such example of this trend; another is the use of learning theory by behaviour therapists. A third area currently of considerable interest is that of social cognition. Two papers in this book – those of McAdam (Chapter 9) and Buss and Enright (Chapter 11) – provide us with a good sense of the way in which theories of cognitive development applied to the social arena are influencing practitioners. McAdam outlines a relatively new approach – what has become known as cognitive behaviour therapy. In describing this she shows how Piaget's notion of formal operational thought has been integral to the creation by the therapist of strategies which the young person may use in order to deal with such things as cognitive errors. Elkind's theory relating to adolescent egocentrism is also important here. McAdam makes it clear that the very concept of egocentrism in adolescence, with its associated ideas of the personal fable and the imaginary audience, has been fundamental to the development of cognitive behaviour therapy, and that ideas about the types of skills needed by young people to deal with interpersonal problems have followed on from ideas about the cognitive deficits to be expected as part of adolescent development.

Buss and Enright (Chapter 11) draw not only upon Piaget and Elkind, but also upon Erikson and Selman. As these authors point out, formal operations *per se* may not be sufficient for identity formation. The young person needs social perspective-taking abilities as well as abstract intellectual skills if he or she is to develop a coherent and realistic sense of self. Yet even these capacities may be hindered by identity confusion, the situation described by Erikson and explained by Elkind as being the result of an inability to distinguish between what you think about yourself and what others think about you. Buss and Enright describe the development of cognitive strategies which enable adolescents to improve their level of ego identity and avoid the sorts of confusion outlined by the theorists. This work is still in an early stage. It links closely with the development of social skills training (see Chapter 8) and has wide implications for a variety of intervention strategies. Most important it is an excellent example of the way in which theory and intervention should be working together.

Of course not all practitioners espouse any one particular theory. Indeed in many situations it would clearly be inappropriate to do so. This fact is reflected in a number of chapters where authors, in describing their work with particular groups of young people, underline the necessity for an eclectic approach, and stress the need for flexible methods of working. Garralda and Ainsworth (Chapter 12) do just this in their chapter on the psychotic adolescent. As they say, the treatment of this group of young people raises exceptionally difficult questions, and one has to accept that almost all treatment methods – drugs, family work, behavioural programmes and so on – may have their place. Garralda and Ainsworth take the view that hospitalized adolescents will need different approaches at different times. At one moment they may require basic physical care, at another the opportunity for social interaction, and at another individual counselling or psychotherapy.

In discussing the importance of flexibility, Will's chapter describing work with the resistant family (Chapter 4) should not be overlooked. In this a vivid example is given of how it is possible, starting from an orthodox theoretical viewpoint, to encompass a variety of treatment strategies. Thus in suggesting ways of dealing with the resistant family Will uses insights from psychoanalysis, systems theory, behaviour therapy and cognitive behaviour therapy, demonstrating that in certain circumstances eclecticism can be a strength rather than a weakness. Throughout this Handbook theory has been used in a variety of ways. Most striking, perhaps, is the lack of evangelical fervour. Even where authors use theory to develop or underpin new approaches they are still able to draw upon ideas deriving from alternative viewpoints. Ideological purity seems no longer to be at a premium, and it is encouraging to note a refreshing freedom on the part of the practitioners represented here to make use of theory rather than to be bound into a straitjacket by its limitations.

THE CONTEXT AND RATIONALE FOR TREATMENT

Motivation and the justification for treatment or intervention is the third theme which re-occurs throughout this book. Bryant-Waugh and Bates (Chapter 14) bring their chapter to a close with these words: "For many professionals working with troubled adolescents, those with eating disorders are particularly difficult and frustrating. Many, especially those with anorexia nervosa, are resistant to treatment attempts, and those offering help may often feel discouraged and uncertain when faced with consistently poor results." Thus Bryant-Waugh and Bates draw attention to the difficulties which arise when young people themselves reject treatment. This may be because they are defensive, it may be because treatment is associated with parents, control and authority, or it may be because teenagers believe that therapy is neither necessary nor relevant to their particular situation. How practitioners work with those who reject what they have to offer is a question which will have troubled almost all in this field, since apart from anything else it forces upon adults the necessity to justify their work, and to provide a rationale for what they do. This may be easy when dealing with the obsessive compulsive disorders, but it certainly is not so simple when faced with a girl who believes she is "just very slim", or with the teenage mother, the young offender, the runaway, the truant or the disruptive adolescent in school, where problems may be as much social as personal.

Steinberg (Chapter 6) faced such a problem in a hospital setting where the rationale for the introduction of group work was far from obvious. Yet, as he points out: "Small group activities happened anyway, and were an influential part of the unit's social environment. Therefore we [decided we] would organize ways of seeing what went on in them and examining what we found". Having taken the plunge, and reorganized the treatment environment in this way, Steinberg was then faced with problems of motivation, not only from young people but from staff as well. Questions such as: "What is the point of it? Why are we doing it? What are we getting out of it? What are *they* getting out of it?" were frequently asked, forcing the practitioners on the defensive in having to "justify" the intervention. Perhaps the biggest single issue here is whether intervention can be effective if motivation is lacking, and because for adolescents motivation is so closely tied up with autonomy, the context in which intervention takes place must always be a major factor for consideration.

Badger (Chapter 16), Jones (Chapter 17) and Adams and Adams (Chapter 18) all raise questions around this theme. In these chapters the client groups described would be unlikely to be seeking treatment of their own volition. Thus, although as Adams and Adams say, running away is both an adolescent and a family problem, this does not necessarily mean that the young person will be wanting help. After all, is running away a problem? How is a "problem" to be defined, and indeed, where does the "problem" lie? For runaway young people the problem is most likely to be seen to lie in the home, while for the parents the problem is rarely perceived in this light. In such situations adolescent motivation for help, even of the non-directive counselling variety, is likely to be questionable at best. Badger's work too is influenced by very similar considerations. Who is to say that teenage mothers need intervention? How can motivation be maximised, and how can the adults involved be sure that attendance at a training programme represents an autonomous decision to take part, rather than child-like compliance with "what adults think best"? Perhaps most interesting of all is the problem of defining the optimal point of intervention – a question critical to all preventative mental health programmes. Badger's conclusion is that motivation is highest at the birth of the first baby. As she says: "What a young mother wants and hopes for in her infant, that she may have missed, can serve to motivate and mobilize her at a turning point in her life".

Badger, and others working in this particular field, are fortunate perhaps to have such an obvious life event so clearly associated with motivational change. Those who work with other groups of socially disadvantaged young people are not so fortunate. For them it will always be an uphill struggle to provide intervention programmes which are acceptable and justifiable to young people. As Jones (Chapter 17) points out in his discussion of recent work with young offenders, "it is not possible to force someone to receive help". If adolescent motivation is absent, then intervention will fail, however much the adult world may believe it necessary. It is for this reason, as Jones makes clear, that elements of justice and welfare need to be kept separate, and that intervention is shown to be paying attention to the needs of adolescents as well as to the needs of society.

Unless we bear this in mind, and unless we acknowledge the necessity to utilize adolescent autonomy and individuation as an aid rather than a hindrance to the development of a satisfactory rationale for intervention, we will be unlikely to provide the context for growth and change.

Some final questions

The three themes discussed here clearly do not tackle every issue, nor do they provide a complete picture of the current state of work with troubled adolescents. Some chapters raise important questions which have not yet been mentioned. For example Kerslake (Chapter 5), among others, refers to the qualities necessary in those who act as group leaders, and who work with young people in such settings. In particular he points out the importance of being able to use self-disclosure, honesty and humour, and of providing good role-modelling if group work is to be successful. The personal style and degree of preparation necessary for involvement in work with adolescents are all too often perceived as secondary to the more obvious concerns of family dynamics, teenage behaviour, intervention strategies and so on. Yet as a number of authors make clear this is a factor which should not be ignored, and while it is understandable that practitioners pay less attention to questions relating to their own personal skills and abilities, Kerslake's discussion may encourage others to take note of these important issues.

Will's outline of his work with the incestuous and sexually abusive family (Chapter 15) draws to our attention a further question of considerable significance – the interaction between intervention strategy and public policy. Jones (Chapter 17) and Adams and Adams (Chapter 18) write about related issues. Will's point is particularly telling, since he had experience of treating sexual abuse in two countries which have different policies, and therefore use the legal system in a different manner. In his view one country – Canada – provides a markedly better setting for the treatment of this particular problem, facilitating more effective intervention which is less damaging to the family as a whole. Will's point is a specific one, relating to sexual abuse, but it does raise very much broader issues, for in considering intervention we are all too often culture-bound, or inhibited by the daunting prospect of initiating any change in public policy.

Finally Steinberg (Chapter 6), Brown (Chapter 10) and Badger (Chapter 16) all underline the key role of evaluation, again a subject which is frequently ignored or side-stepped, even in the best treatment programmes. In the course of these discussions a number of questions are raised about evaluation, in particular the relation between method of treatment and ease of evaluation, and the difficulty of reconciling different evaluative criteria. As far as the former is concerned Brown's chapter emphasizes how much easier it is to evaluate behaviourally oriented programmes. Yet clearly some forms of treatment lend themselves more readily to evaluation than others, particularly if evaluation is based on observable behaviour change, reduction in symptomatology or other "measurable" criteria. This issue is further compounded by the fact that the different individuals involved with any one young person will themselves have a variety of expectations of the treatment outcome. Parents, teachers, social workers, young people themselves will see therapy or intervention from different perspectives, wanting different things from the helping process. To incorporate all such viewpoints in an evaluation exercise will almost certainly be impossible. Thus while we all agree that evaluation is important, we frequently falter when faced with the inevitable limitations of most evaluation procedures.

Readers will be aware that there is a very substantial literature on evaluation, in which problems such as these are examined in great detail. Nonetheless it is no bad thing to bring this volume to a conclusion by mentioning both the necessity for and the limitations of evaluation. Most of the time decisions about intervention and treatment are primarily based on commitment and faith. They are very rarely based on clear evidence concerning the comparative effectiveness of different therapeutic approaches. Furthermore there is little doubt that we could make greater attempts to assess the impact of our work, but we fail to do so for a variety of reasons, not all of which are to do with the practical difficulties of evaluation.

It is my hope that this Handbook stimulates and encourages those who dip into it. The three themes which I have discussed and the questions surrounding evaluation, public policy and the personal qualities of the therapist will all repay further consideration. Work with troubled adolescents is a growing, changing and demanding field. Practitioners need to know as much as possible about what others are doing, and it is the intention of this book, and indeed of the *Journal of Adolescence*, to provide the opportunity for just that type of communication.

Subject Index